Electromechanical
Energy Conversion

A BLAISDELL BOOK IN THE PURE AND APPLIED SCIENCES

CONSULTING EDITOR
William Huggins
Johns Hopkins University

Electromechanical Energy Conversion

C. R. CHAPMAN

Bradley University

BLAISDELL PUBLISHING COMPANY

A Division of Ginn and Company

NEW YORK · TORONTO · LONDON

TO MY WIFE
Ann
AND TO OUR CHILDREN
Sue, Sally, Charles, Kathy, and Greg.

Preface

THE STUDY of electromechanical energy conversion is especially challenging because it involves the wedding of two linear disciplines to produce nonlinear offspring. Even when all electric, magnetic, and mechanical components are linearized, electromechanical energy conversion systems often lead to nonlinear differential equations. This potential for nonlinearities, of a type much more basic than the nonlinearity arising from saturation effects, has been almost completely obscured in the conventional textbooks on electric machines. Indeed, the conventional coverage has tended to emphasize a welter of details at the expense of principles, and so has declined in importance and in student interest.

Recently there have appeared new and imaginative treatments in this area, each excellent, but, unfortunately, requiring a rather special arrangement of the undergraduate curriculum before they can be used.

The present text, in a one-semester presentation, integrates many of these newer ideas with the most useful of the conventional concepts, at a level suitable for the undergraduate student. It can serve either as an introduction to more advanced study, or as a terminal course. As background, it requires a reasonable mastery of linear circuit theory, and some knowledge of magnetic circuits (the latter is covered briefly in the appendix).

In order to focus attention on the energy conversion process itself, many simplifications and idealizations have been used. Magnetic saturation, winding resistance, leakage flux, and friction are generally ignored. Although nonlinear equations arise frequently, the solutions are not pursued to the point of distraction. The analysis of interconnected machines is introduced, but the details are left to courses in feedback theory and servomechanisms.

Chapter 1 serves as an introduction and a review of mechanical systems, emphasizing electrical analogs and applying to mechanical systems some of the circuit concepts (transfer function, free response, phasor analysis) that the student has already studied in circuits courses. It also develops in some

vii

detail a system of reference directions for mechanical systems that is consistent with commonly-used electrical polarity conventions.

Chapter 2 introduces the energy conversion process from both the field-energy and the varying-circuit-parameter points of view, stresses the nonlinear nature of the problem, and uses a number of simple translational and rotational devices as illustrations.

Chapters 3, 4, 5, and 6 provide brief, concise treatments of the principal types of rotating machines from the rotating-field and torque-angle point of view. Although this approach has limited analytical power, the rotating field is an invaluable help in visualization for the beginner. The rotating magnetic field is emphasized as a genuine unifying concept for all machine types, with the conventional equivalent circuits, circle diagrams, etc., developed from the field concepts as a secondary consideration. Special topics are included near the end of each of these chapters, in such a way that they can be omitted if desired.

Chapter 7 introduces analysis of the generalized machine from the varying-circuit-parameter point of view, and gives several examples of its modification to fit special conditions. Only the simplest transformations of reference frames are introduced, with the thought that this area, if it is to be covered adequately, will require additional study. However, it is made clear that matrix methods are suitable for the more complicated situations where rotating-field theory becomes cumbersome.

Attention has been given throughout to the development and explanation of a consistent set of reference directions for mechanical as well as electrical quantities, a topic that seems especially troublesome to students. A special effort has been made to provide an ample number of simple problems, for problems in this area tend to become long and complicated even in their wording. Problems found at the end of a section should be worked before proceeding to the next section, for many ideas that might have been presented in the text are developed in these problem sets instead. No attempt has been made to provide an encyclopedic coverage, or to consider all possible methods of analysis in each situation. In fact, a major effort has been made to exclude material that does not contribute to the central theme.

This text has been classroom tested, in the form of notes, and the author has found it to be at a level that challenges the abilities of students who are just mastering linear circuit analysis. In supplementary experimental work using the educational generalized machines by Westinghouse, the students seem adequately prepared for the numerous unusual operating modes of these devices.

The author is indebted to Dean Emeritus R. E. Gibbs of the College of Engineering at Bradley University, to Dean M. G. Abegg, and to Phil Weinberg, Head of the Electrical Engineering Department, for their continuing encouragement and help. Several colleagues, R. L. Gonzales, W. M. Hammond, B. P. Lathi, J. L. Jones, D. R. Schertz, D. L. Markley, and T. L. Stewart, have contributed through many informal discussions. Thanks also goes to several faithful typists, Lori Kelly, Tess Stone, Evelyn Kahrs, and Virginia Parrett; and to James Hardin, William Mustain, Robert Thompson, William Ferry, and Thomas Freeburg, students who assisted in proofreading and problem checking. And a special word needs to be said for my wife, Ann, and my children, with whom I agree that family life is more important than textbooks, and who have conspired with me to delay completion of this one for at least a year.

C. ROBERT CHAPMAN
Peoria, Illinois

Contents

Electromechanical
Energy Conversion

Symbols and Abbreviations

IN SOME CASES, the same symbol is used to represent two different quantities, or two different symbols are used for the same quantity; the correct selection will be obvious from the context. Numbers following symbol descriptions give the text location where the symbol is first defined or extensively used. Symbols appearing briefly during a development, and not used again, may not be listed.

Abbreviations are based on the 1961 recommendations of the Commission on Symbols, Units, and Nomenclature (SUN Commission) of the International Union of Pure and Applied Physics, and are distinguished chiefly by their use of capital letters to abbreviate units named for persons.

Subscripts are listed separately in most cases, to avoid an excessively long list.

$\mathbf{a}_r$	unit radius vector for cylindrical coordinates. (3.4)
$\mathbf{a}_z$	unit axial vector for cylindrical coordinates. (3.8, 6.4)
A	*abbreviation;* ampere.
A	area. Unit, m².
ac	*abbreviation;* alternating current.
B	magnetic flux density; may represent axial magnitude of airgap field. Unit, Wb/m².
B	magnetic flux density vector; also axial space phasor representing airgap field. Unit, Wb/m². (3.4, 4.1)
$\mathscr{B}$	Airgap field distributed sinusoidally in both time and space. Unit, Wb/m². (3.5)
C	capacitance. Unit, F.
C	*abbreviation;* coulomb.
[*C*]	connection matrix. (7.9)
c	servomotor constant; ratio of magnitude of control voltage to magnitude of reference voltage. (5.12)

1

cps	*abbreviation;* cycles per second.
d	spacing when system is de-energized.
dc	*abbreviation;* direct current.
d-q	*abbreviation;* direct and quadrature (axes).
D	friction or damping coefficient; ratio of force to velocity. Unit, N-s/m. (1.3)
D_θ	rotational friction or damping coefficient; ratio of torque to angular velocity. Unit, N-m-s/rad. (1.9)
e, E	voltage of ideal voltage source. The symbol v is also used. Unit, V.
e	base of natural logarithms; always appears with an exponent.
$\mathbf{E}$	electric field intensity or voltage gradient. Unit, V/m.
$f, f(t), F$	force. Unit, N. (1.3, 1.4, 2.3)
F	magnetomotive force, mmf. Unit, ampere turns. (4.6, A.2)
F	*abbreviation;* farad.
g	length of air gap, along direction of magnetic flux. Unit, m.
G	conductance. Unit, mho. (1.4)
H	*abbreviation;* henry.
H	magnetic field strength; may represent magnitude of air gap field. Unit, ampere-turns/m.
$\mathbf{H}$	magnetic field strength vector; also axial space phasor representing air gap field. (3.4, 4.1)
$\mathscr{H}$	Air gap field distributed sinusoidally in both time and space. (3.5)
$i, i(t), I$	current. Unit, A.
$\mathbf{I}$	phasor representation of current varying cosinusoidally with time.
$\mathbf{I}_r'$	induction motor rotor current, expressed in equivalent stator terms. (5.6)
$\mathbf{I}_0$	induction motor stator current at no load. (5.6)
j	imaginary unit number, $j = \sqrt{-1}$.
J	moment of inertia. Ratio of torque to angular acceleration. Unit, N-m-s/rad. (1.9)
J	*abbreviation;* joule.
K	spring constant. Ratio of force to resulting displacement. Unit, N/m. (1.3)
K_θ	torsional spring constant. Ratio of torque to resulting angular displacement. Unit, N-m/rad. (1.9)
K_b, K_h	torque constants for rotating machines. (3.3)
k, k', k''	induction motor torque constants (5.3); dc machine constants (6.10, 6.11).
K_v	voltage generation constant for rotating machine. (4.2)

K_d, K_q	direct and quadrature axis torque constants. (4.5)
kW	*abbreviation;* kilowatt.
l, $\mathbf{l}$	length, usually of a conductor. Bold face used when it is desired to emphasize the vector nature of the length. Unit, m.
L, L_{11}, L_{22}	self inductance. Unit, H or V-s/A.
L_0	quiescent or average inductance.
L_{er}	leakage inductance of rotor circuit. (5.6, 7.4)
L_{er}'	equivalent L_{er}, expressed in stator terms. (5.6)
M	mass. Unit, kG. (1.3)
M, M_{12}	mutual inductance. M_{12} refers to voltage induced into winding 1 by changing current in winding 2. (2.9, 7.2)
M_0	magnitude of variable mutual inductance. (2.9)
M_r	motional inductance between rotor brush axes. (7.6)
mmf	*abbreviation;* magnetomotive force. (3.8, A.2)
n	number of phases. (4.2)
N	number of turns on a winding.
N	*abbreviation;* newton, unit of force.
p	differential operator, $p = d/dt$.
p, $p(t)$	instantaneous power. Unit, W. (1.7)
P	average power. Unit, W.
q, $q(t)$, Q	charge. Unit, C.
r	radius. Unit, m.
rad	*abbreviation;* radian.
R	resistance. Unit, ohm. The symbol Ω is not used for ohm in this text.
$\mathscr{R}$	magnetic reluctance. (2.7, A.2)
Re	real part (of a complex number).
R_r'	equivalent rotor resistance, expressed in stator terms. (5.6)
s	operator in Laplace transforms; exponent in exponential solution of form Ae^{st}.
s	slip, in induction motor theory. (5.2)
s	*abbreviation;* second.
s_m	slip for maximum torque (5.3, 5.5)
t	time. Unit, s.
$T(t)$	instantaneous torque. Unit, N-m (1.9, 2.8)
T, T_{av}	average torque. Unit, N-m. (2.8)
u, $u(t)$, U	velocity. Unit, m/s. (1.4)
$U(t)$	unit step function.
v, $v(t)$, V	voltage. Unit, V.
V	*abbreviation;* volt.
V	volume. Unit, m³. (2.7)
$\mathbf{V}$	phasor representation of cosinusoidally-varying voltage.

V_{ao}	initial armature voltage for self-excited dc generator. (6.11)
V_0	voltage induced into rotor of induction motor when rotor is stationary. (5.2)
V_r	component of synchronous machine stator voltage, induced by rotor field B_r. (4.3)
V_r	voltage induced into rotor of induction motor by total revolving air gap field. (5.2)
V_t	total or terminal voltage.
w	energy density of magnetic or electric field. Unit, J/m³. (2.5)
W	*abbreviation;* watt.
W	energy. Unit, J. (2.2)
W_e	electric energy; energy input to device from electrical terminals. (2.2)
W_f	energy stored in electric or magnetic field. (2.2)
W_f'	coenergy. (2.6)
W_m	mechanical energy; energy input to device from mechanical terminals. (2.2)
Wb	*abbreviation;* weber.
$x, x(t), X$	distance. Unit, m. (1.3)
x_0	distance between ends of spring when no force is applied. (1.3)
X_L, X_c	inductive and capacitive reactance. Unit, ohms.
X_m	magnetizing reactance for induction motor. (5.6)
X_s	synchronous reactance. (4.3)
Y	admittance. Unit, mho.
$Z(p)$	operational impedance.
Z	complex impedance to sinusoidal ac.

Greek Symbols

α, β, γ	phase angles
δ	torque angle, a constant or slowly-varying angular displacement, usually between two rotating magnetic fields. (2.8, 3.3)
Δ	increment (2.4); value of determinant (7.11).
∂	partial derivative symbol
ε	permittivity (2.3)
ε_0	permittivity of free space, $\varepsilon_0 = 8.85 \times 10^{-12}$ C²/N-m. (2.3)
ϕ	magnetic flux (A.1); also phase angle.
λ	magnetic flux linkage; $\lambda = Li = N\phi = \int v \, dt$. Unit, linkage, Wb-turns, V-s. (2.7, 7.2, A.1)
θ	angular position, measured from specified reference. Unit, radians or degrees. (1.9)
θ_r	angular position of rotor axis. (2.8)
θ_0	angular position of coilside on rotating machine. (3.6, 3.8, 6.4)

θ'	power factor angle; phase angle by which voltage leads current. (4.2)
ω	electrical radian frequency. Applies to voltage or current. Unit, rad/s.
Ω, $\Omega(t)$	mechanical angular velocity. Applies to a rotating shaft. Unit, rad/s. (1.9)
ω_b	electrical frequency of brush voltage or current.
Ω_b	mechanical angular velocity of rotating brush mount. (6.4)
μ	magnetic permeability. Unit, H/m.
μ_0	Magnetic permeability of free space; $\mu_0 = 4\pi \times 10^{-7}$ H/m. (2.5, A.1)
μ_r	relative magnetic permeability; $\mu_r = \mu/\mu_0$. (A.1)

Subscripts

Subscripts frequently appear in pairs; for example, i_{bq} reads *current in quadrature-axis brushes* and B_{sm} reads *maximum value of flux density from stator*. The standard *double subscript reference direction notation* is also used for variables, and is described in Sections 1.5 and 1.6.

a	armature (6.8)
av, avg	average
b	brush (6.4)
b	backward-rotating (component). (5.8)
c	central coil, midway between brushes on a commutated rotor winding. (6.4)
c	compensating winding. (6.9)
c	control winding. (7.8)
d	direct axis. (4.5, 7.5)
e	electrical, as distinguished from mechanical.
f	electric or magnetic field.
f	shunt field winding on dc machine stator. (6.8)
f	forward-rotating (component). (5.8)
L	load. (7.11)
m	mechanical, as distinguished from electrical.
m	maximum value, usually of sinusoidally-varying quantity.
n	original variable in matrix transformation ($n = a, b, c, \ldots$). (7.9)
o	quiescent value. (2.4, 6.13)
o	initial value.
q	quadrature axis. (4.5, 7.5)
r	rotor.
s	stator.

s	synchronous.
s	series field of dc machine. (6.11)
ss	steady-state. (6.13)
t	total, terminal.
t	transpose (of matrix). (7.9)
θ	rotational, as distinguished from translational.
η	new variable (eta) in matrix transformation ($\eta = 1, 2, 3, \ldots$). (7.9)
1	small incremental variation (2.4); also used in numbered sequences.
2	second harmonic component (2.8); also used in numbered sequences.
	(*prime*) rotor variable expressed in stator terms (5.6); second identical system (7.7); θ' represents power factor angle. Also other minor uses.

CHAPTER ONE

Mechanical and Electrical Analogs

1.1 Introduction

Mechanical systems that can be represented by linear, lumped elements are subject to a form of dynamic analysis that is directly analogous to that commonly employed in electrical systems. The study of these analogies requires a review of both electrical and mechanical theory, and so provides a good introduction to electromechanical system theory.

1.2 The Meaning of "Lumped" Mechanical Elements

In electrical theory, lumped-parameter analysis can be used when the time of signal propagation through an element is short compared with the period of the signal. Otherwise, distributed-parameter or "long-line" analysis, using partial differential equations, is required. This same criterion applies to mechanical elements.

As an example, consider a long helical spring suspended from the ceiling. If the lower end of the spring is pulled downward, a traveling wave of elongation can be observed moving upward, and it is not until this wave reaches the ceiling that the applied force is felt at the upper end of the spring. If a short, stiff spring is substituted, however, the force is transmitted very rapidly, and to a good approximation it can be said that a force applied at one end is felt at the other end immediately. This occurs because the mass of the spring has negligible effect compared with that of its stiffness, and is analogous to continuity of current in an electrical element. In a lumped electrical element, the current flowing into one terminal is identical with the current flowing out from the other terminal; in a lumped mechanical element, the force applied at one end is felt immediately at the other end.

1.3 The Mechanical Elements

The linear lumped mechanical parameters are stiffness, friction, and mass. These are shown in Figure 1.3 along with their equations and symbols, and are discussed further in the subsections that follow.

Stiffness. The stiffness K is often called the "spring constant." For the spring to be linear, it must be possible to compress as well as to stretch it. If it is desired to let x represent the distance between the ends of the spring, then the equation becomes

$$f = K(x - x_0),$$

where x_0 is the distance between the ends of the spring, when it is at rest (i.e., contains no stored energy).

Friction. The friction constant D implies that a proportional relationship exists between force and velocity. Truly linear friction is seldom encountered; more often, the frictional force is nearly independent of velocity or varies as some higher power of velocity, rather than being proportional to it. In some cases these effects average out to produce approximately linear friction over the range of interest, and in other cases, such as electrical indicating instruments, considerable pains are taken to design damping mechanisms that are closely linear.

Mass. A force can be associated with a mass only when acceleration is taking place, and this acceleration is measured between the mass and a fixed reference frame, rather than between two points on the element. As a reminder of this, the mechanical "earth" symbol is incorporated into the representation for a mass.*

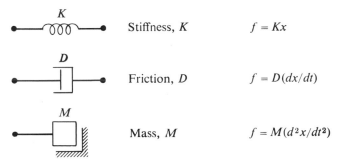

Stiffness, K $f = Kx$

Friction, D $f = D(dx/dt)$

Mass, M $f = M(d^2x/dt^2)$

FIGURE 1.3. Lumped, linear mechanical elements. The force through the element is represented by f and the relative displacement of the ends of the element from their rest position is represented by x.

* Problems inserted between sections are intended to enhance the understanding of the material just read, and should be worked before proceeding further. Advanced problems are to be found at the end of each chapter.

PROBLEM 1.3.1. Modify the equations in Figure 1.3 so that the variables are force, f, and velocity, u, instead of f and x. Note that $u = dx/dt$.

1.4 Analogous Mechanical and Electrical Elements

Two systems are said to be analogous when the mathematical equations that describe the systems are identical in form, differing only in the symbols used. The quantities represented by corresponding symbols are then said to be analogous quantities.

Often what appears to be an analogy in a simple case will fail as the situation becomes more involved. Suppose it were decided to identify stiffness with resistance, giving the analogous equations

$$f = Kx, \qquad v = Ri.$$

Here force and voltage are analogous, as are displacement and current. Upon proceeding to friction, it is possible to write

$$f = D \frac{dx}{dt} ; \qquad v = L \frac{di}{dt}.$$

Here damping is analogous to inductance and the analogy still holds. But no electrical parameter exists that is analogous to mass in the expression

$$f = M \frac{d^2x}{dt^2},$$

if the f-v and x-i correspondence is also to be maintained. Thus, this is not a valid analogous system.

A system of analogs that is valid and is widely used is shown in Table 1.4.

TABLE 1.4

The Force–Current (f-i) Analogy

Mechanical Quantity	Electrical Quantity
Force, f	Current, i
Velocity, u	Voltage, v
Displacement, x	Flux linkage, λ
Compliance, $1/K$	Inductance, L
Frictional damping, D	Conductance, G
Mass, M	Capacitance, C

Example 1.4. A mass of M kilograms is subjected to a force $f(t) = F_m \sin \omega t \, U(t)$, where $U(t)$ is the unit step function. Determine the expressions for the velocity u and the position x as functions of time, if the initial conditions are $u(0+) = 0$ and $x(0+) = 0$.

Solution. From $f = M(du/dt)$, $u = \dfrac{1}{M}\displaystyle\int f\, dt = f/Mp$, where $p = (d/dt)$. Thus,

$$u = -\frac{F_m}{\omega M}\cos \omega t + k, \qquad t > 0.$$

To evaluate the constant of integration, k, the initial condition $u(0+) = 0$ is used.

$$u(0+) = 0 = -\frac{F_m}{\omega M} + k$$

$$k = \frac{F_m}{\omega M}.$$

Thus,

$$u(t) = \frac{F_m}{\omega M}(1 - \cos \omega t).$$

The force and velocity variations are sketched in Figure 1.4.

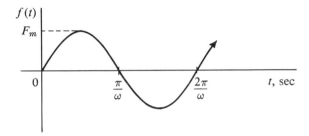

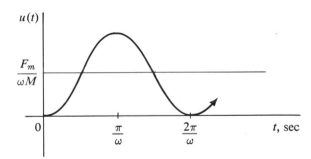

FIGURE 1.4. Force and velocity waveforms for Example 1.4.

This problem may also be solved by reference to the analogous electric circuit element, which is a capacitor of value $C = M$. For this analogous element, $i(t) = I_m \sin \omega t\, U(t)$ and

$$v(t) = \frac{1}{C}\int i\, dt = \frac{1}{Cp}\, i, \qquad t > 0.$$

After calculations analogous to those above, there results

$$v(t) = \frac{I_m}{\omega C} (1 - \cos \omega t).$$

The magnitude of the alternating portion of this response could also be found from $V_m = I_m X_c$, where $X_c = 1/\omega C$, the capacitive reactance. The analogous quantity, $1/\omega M$, is the mechanical reactance (or impedance) for the mass.

PROBLEM 1.4.1. Show mathematically that the quantities in Table 1.4 are valid analogs.

PROBLEM 1.4.2. A certain spring has an initial length of 0.4 meter and a constant $K = 200$ N/m (newtons per meter). It is subjected to a force $f(t) = 50(1 - e^{-0.1t})$ N. Find the numerical expressions for u and x, and sketch them as a function of time. *Answer:* $x = 0.25(1 - e^{-0.1t})$; $u = 0.025e^{-0.1t}$.

PROBLEM 1.4.3. A certain dashpot moves at 1 mm/s·when subjected to a constant force of 5 N. Evaluate the damping constant D, and find the total travel when it is subjected to a force $f(t) = 50e^{-0.1t}$. *Answer:* $D = 5 \times 10^3$ N-m/s; $x = 0.1$ m.

PROBLEM 1.4.4. A force $f(t) = 5 \cos 2t$ is applied to a certain mechanical element. Determine the steady-state equation for the velocity if the element is (a) a dashpot having $D = \frac{1}{2}$; (b) a spring with $K = \frac{1}{2}$; (c) a mass of $M = \frac{1}{2}$. *Answer:* (a) $u_s = 10 \cos 2t$; (b) $u_s = -20 \sin 2t$; (c) $u_s = 5 \sin 2t$.

PROBLEM 1.4.5. For each of the elements in Problem 1.4.4, define and evaluate numerically a quantity analogous to the complex (phasor) impedance **Z**. *Answer:* (a) 2.0; (b) $j4$; (c) $-j$.

1.5   Analogous Circuit Laws

For an analogy to apply to interconnected systems of elements, the laws regarding interconnected elements must also give analogous results. Figure 1.5.1(a) shows a junction between several mechanical elements, all of which are constrained to vertical displacement only. Each element may exert a force on the junction, which is itself considered ideal (no friction or mass). Any net force on the ideal junction would (according to the equations of Figure 1.3) produce infinite velocity and acceleration, and since these are never observed it must be concluded that the sum of the forces on a node is zero. This relationship, known formally as D'Alemberts's principle, is analogous to Kirchhoff's current law, illustrated in Figure 1.5.1(b).

The analog for Kirchhoff's voltage law is illustrated in Figure 1.5.2. A statement of the analogy is that the relative velocity between two given points in a mechanical system equals the (vector) sum of the relative velocities

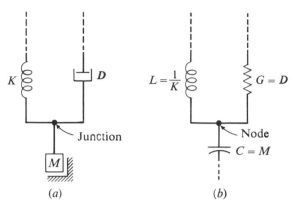

FIGURE 1.5.1. Mechanical and electrical analogies at connection points. (*a*) D'Alembert's principle at a mechanical junction, $\Sigma f = 0$ at junction. (*b*) Kirchhoff's current law at an electrical node, $\Sigma i = 0$ at node.

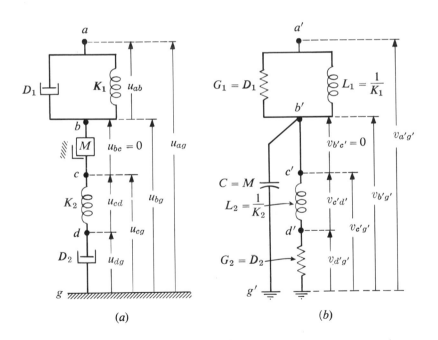

FIGURE 1.5.2. Illustration of the mechanical analogy to Kirchhoff's voltage law. (*a*) Mechanical system; $\Sigma u = 0$. (*b*) Analogous electrical system; $\Sigma v = 0$.

between any series of locations interconnecting the two given points. (In Figure 1.5.2, the situation is simplified considerably by using a mechanical system where only vertical motion is permitted.)

The system of Figure 1.5.2 contains no sources, so initial energy storage must be provided in the form of initial velocity of the mass, or of a compressed (or stretched) spring. Then, the system will undergo damped oscillations until it comes to rest. The relationships between the velocities are obvious; for example, $u_{cd} + u_{dg} = u_{cg}$. Alternatively, $u_{cd} + u_{dg} + u_{gc} = 0$.

Of particular interest is the relationship between the mass M and its analog, the capacitor. The relative velocity between junctions b and c is zero, because they are rigidly interconnected. This corresponds to the short circuit that holds the voltage $v_{b'c'}$ to zero. The capacitor itself is shown connected to ground, since the acceleration of a mass is always measured relative to a fixed reference frame, which in this case is the earth.

The force in each member corresponds to the current through the analogous circuit element. The force at one terminal of a spring or dashpot is identical with the force at the other end, but this is not so with the mass. For a mass, the force at one terminal differs from the force at the other terminal by the force of acceleration acting on the mass. This is provided for in the electrical analog by the way the capacitor is connected. The force at mechanical junction b corresponds to the total current passing electrical node b'. The current $i_{b'c'}$ corresponds to the force passed on to the spring K_2, and the capacitor current $i_{b'g'}$ represents the force applied to acceleration of the mass.

The method for constructing the electrical analog should by this time be obvious. An electrical node is made to correspond with each mechanical junction, and appropriate analogous circuit elements from Table 1.4 are connected in place. <u>Care must be taken that each capacitor representing a mass is properly connected to ground.</u>

Example 1.5. In the mechanical system of Figure 1.5.2, let the upper junction a be rigidly connected to the earth, so that node a cannot move ($u_{ag} = 0$). Write the characteristic equation which will give the free modes of oscillation for the system.

Solution. In the electrical analog [Figure 1.5.2(b)] the constraint corresponding to $u_{ag} = 0$ is $v_{a'g'} = 0$, or a short circuit between node a' and the ground. After elimination of node c' as identical to node b', there remain only the two nodes b' and d' in addition to the reference node g'. Node equations can then be written by inspection, giving

$$\left(G_1 + \frac{1}{L_1 p} + Cp + \frac{1}{L_2 p} \right) v_{b'g'} - \frac{1}{L_2 p} v_{d'g'} = 0$$

$$-\frac{1}{L_2 p} v_{b'g'} + \left(\frac{1}{L_2 p} + G_2 \right) v_{d'g'} = 0. \qquad \left[p \equiv \frac{d}{dt} \right]$$

Upon transformation and solution by some suitable method, there results the characteristic equation

$$s^3 CG_2 + s^2(G_1 G_2 + C/L_2) + s(G_1/L_2 + G_2/L_1 + G_2/L_2) + 1/L_1 L_2 = 0,$$

where s is the exponent in the exponential solution Ae^{st}. This is a third-order characteristic equation, so that there will be three modes of free response, consisting either of three exponential components (overdamped case) or of one exponential plus a damped oscillation (underdamped case).

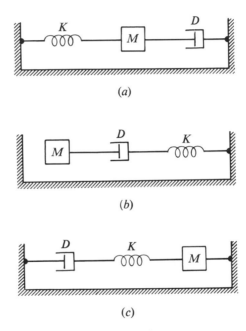

(a)

(b)

(c)

FIGURE P1.5.2.

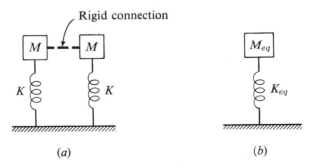

Rigid connection

(a)

(b)

FIGURE P1.5.3.

PROBLEM 1.5.1. Suppose that in Figure 1.5.2(*b*) the capacitor connection is moved from terminal *b′* to terminal *c′*. What corresponding change would be required in Figure 1.5.2(*a*) for it to remain an exact analog?

PROBLEM 1.5.2. Sketch the electrical analogs for the mechanical systems of Figure P1.5.2, which are all constrained to one direction of motion. Neglect gravity.

PROBLEM 1.5.3. The two identical systems of Figure P1.5.3(*a*) are to be joined by a rigid connection and represented by the single equivalent system of Figure P1.5.3(*b*). Determine the values of M_{eq} and K_{eq}, by reference to the appropriate *f-i* analog. *Answer:* $M_{eq} = 2M$; $K_{eq} = 2K$.

1.6 Reference Polarities for Mechanical Elements

To this point, the troublesome matter of reference directions has been entirely bypassed. If force is analogous to current, which direction is a "positive" force in the actual mechanical system? Which direction is a positive velocity? These questions are examined in this section.

Analogous mechanical and electrical elements are depicted in Figure 1.6.1, with a set of reference directions marked. For the electrical element, $v = v_{x'y'} = v_{x'} - v_{y'}$, and is read "the voltage at node *x′* with respect to the voltage at node *y′*," or "the voltage drop from node *x′* to node *y′*." For example, if node *x′* is at 2 volts and node *y′* is at 5 volts, $v_{x'y'} = -3$ volts. The current reference arrow marking $i = i_{x'y'}$ signifies the (conventional) electric current direction, and is numerically positive when positive charges are moving from *x′* to *y′* through the element. These electrical polarity conventions are usually referred to as the *load convention*, because the electric power to a circuit element, given by $p = vi$, is numerically positive when the circuit element is an electrical load absorbing energy from the circuit. The load convention is widely used in electric circuit theory, and it is assumed that the student is familiar with it.

The *velocity polarity convention*, as marked on the mechanical element in Figure 1.6.1, is interpreted in exactly the same way as was the analogous

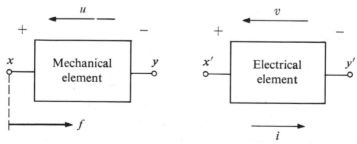

FIGURE 1.6.1. For discussion of reference directions.

electrical polarity convention. That is, $u = u_{xy} = u_x - u_y$, and is read "the velocity of junction x with respect to the velocity of junction y." Velocities are taken with respect to the direction of the reference arrow. Thus, if junction x is moving in the reference direction (to the left) at 2 meters per second, and junction y is moving to the left at 5 meters per second, $u_{xy} = -3$ meters per second. This means that junction y is "catching up" with junction x, and the element is decreasing in length. The junction at the head of the velocity reference arrow is referred to as the *positive mechanical terminal.*

The reference direction for force is assigned opposite to that for velocity, so that the markings on the mechanical and electrical elements will be consistent. The *reference direction for force* is interpreted to mean that *the element itself exerts a force on its own "positive" terminal* (x) *in the arrow direction for force when f is numerically positive.* This is conventionally called the "force of reaction" at junction x.

When f and u are both positive, the mechanical element is absorbing power, and so conforms to the load convention. As an illustration, a spring is shown in Figure 1.6.2 in a condition where both f and u are positive. The spring is stretching out, and it must have been stretched past its rest position (x_0) in order to exert a force in the reference direction (to the right) on its own positive terminal. For the position sketched in Figure 1.6.2, the mechanical power, as given by $p = uf$, is also numerically positive, indicating that energy is being absorbed by the element. This is analogous to electrical power, given by $p = vi$, which (using the load convention) is numerically positive when energy is being absorbed by the electrical element.

There is always room for a good deal of confusion when specifying reference directions for forces in mechanical systems. The mechanical element of Figure

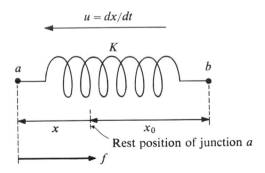

FIGURE 1.6.2. Reference directions on a spring. For the configuration shown, the spring is being stretched past its rest position so that u and f are both numerically positive. The mechanical power given by $p = uf$ is also numerically positive, indicating that energy is being absorbed by the element (load convention).

1.6.2 has three other forces associated with it, all equal in magnitude and differing only in sign. For example, there is the externally applied force at terminal *a*, which is positive to the left; the use of this force corresponds to the *source convention* for marking electrical elements. Also, there are two forces at the *b* terminal. By routinely specifying a certain one of these four forces, the need to distinguish between applied and reaction forces is eliminated. A similar problem was a cause of difficulty a generation ago in many treatments of electrical theory, where it was felt necessary to designate "applied" and "back" voltages by different conventions.

It is important to note that the advantages of this system of polarity marking are lost unless all mechanical polarities are taken with reference to the same set of reference directions. An example of the sort of difficulty that may be encountered is illustrated by the mechanical system of Figure 1.6.3(*a*). If u_1 is numerically positive, junction *a* is moving upward and u_2, as marked, must be numerically negative. That is, $u_1 = -u_2$. In the electrical analog of Figure 1.6.3(*b*), which appears to be topologically identical, $v_1 = v_2$ and both rise and fall together. The proper way to represent the mechanical system is given in Figure 1.6.3(*c*), where only one earth reference is shown. The difficulty arises because electric circuits are not affected by their configuration in space, whereas mechanical systems are. It can be avoided if the polarities of all mechanical elements are referred to the same set of reference directions, as in Figure 1.6.3(*c*).

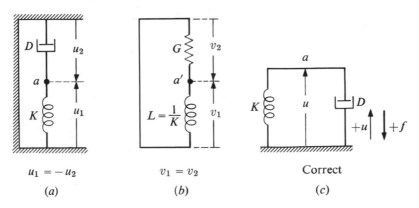

$$u_1 = -u_2 \qquad\qquad v_1 = v_2 \qquad\qquad \text{Correct}$$

(*a*)   (*b*)   (*c*)

FIGURE 1.6.3. Illustration of a possible source of confusion in assigning reference polarities to analogous systems.

PROBLEM 1.6.1. Make a sketch similar to Figure 1.6.2, but for a mass, showing the circumstances under which both *f* and *u* are numerically positive. Is the mass accelerating or decelerating? *Answer:* Accelerating.

PROBLEM 1.6.2. Repeat Problem 1.6.1, for a dashpot, *D*.

1.7 Mechanical Sources

The *force source* is an idealized model of a device such as pneumatic piston or a torque wrench, where the force is independent of velocity, position, or acceleration. The force source may be connected between the earth and a mechanical junction, or between two mechanical junctions. Its electrical analog is a current source.

Analogous to a voltage source is the *velocity source*. This is a device that establishes the velocity (or position) of a junction independently of the force required to do so. Velocity sources often use cams or levers, as in the timing and valve mechanism for an automotive engine. A velocity source may be connected between a junction and the earth, or between two junctions.

It is desirable to review the polarity conventions for electrical sources before proceeding further. Figure 1.7.1 depicts the four possibilities for

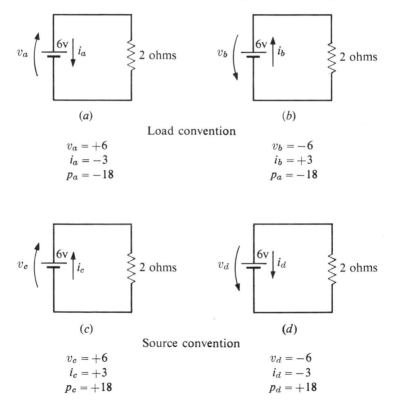

(a)

Load convention

$$v_a = +6$$
$$i_a = -3$$
$$p_a = -18$$

(b)

$$v_b = -6$$
$$i_b = +3$$
$$p_a = -18$$

(c)

Source convention

$$v_c = +6$$
$$i_c = +3$$
$$p_c = +18$$

(d)

$$v_d = -6$$
$$i_d = -3$$
$$p_d = +18$$

FIGURE 1.7.1. Comparison of four possible ways of marking reference polarities on a source. Long bar of battery is by convention positive.

marking the polarities of a six-volt battery connected to a resistive load. The markings in (*a*) and (*b*) are according to the load convention, and give negative power for the battery as it delivers energy to the circuit. The markings in (*c*) and (*d*) are for the source convention, and give positive power for the battery under the same condition of operation. Passive circuit elements such as resistors and inductors are commonly marked according to the load convention; if they were marked according to the source convention, it would be necessary to write the terminal relationships as $v = -iR$ and $v = -L\,di/dt$.

The polarities of electrical sources are sometimes specified according to the source convention and sometimes according to the load convention. In the formal procedure for writing mesh or node equations, the source convention is ordinarily used, and the summation of voltage sources equated to the summation of drops. In many cases involving electromechanical energy conversion, however, energy sources and loads are initially indistinguishable and it becomes desirable to use only one convention for all elements. In this text, the load convention is adopted in such cases.

In Figure 1.7.2 a velocity source and a force source are shown; both are marked according to the load convention references. The interpretation of the *velocity source* is that if *u* is numerically positive, terminal *a* is forced to move upward with respect to terminal *b*. A positive *force source* signifies that the source exerts a force in the reference direction for force (downward) on its own positive terminal (terminal *a*), tending to pull the terminals together. Whenever either element is actually acting as a source (delivering energy to the mechanical system), the power for that element, given by $p = uf$, is numerically negative. If it is desired to reverse the polarity of a mechanical

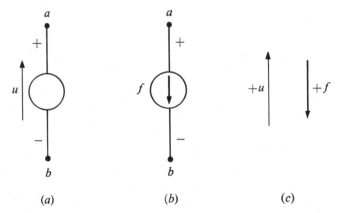

(*a*)   (*b*)   (*c*)

FIGURE 1.7.2. Ideal mechanical sources marked by load convention. If it is desired to indicate a reversal of source polarity, the symbol itself should not be changed, but instead, the sign of the functional expression for *u* or *f* should be reversed. (*a*) velocity source; (*b*) force source; (*c*) reference directions for load convention.

source, the symbol itself should not be changed, but instead, the sign of the functional expression for u or f should be reversed.

Practical mechanical sources, like practical electrical sources, are never ideal. Practical mechanical sources may be represented by ideal sources plus an appropriate combination of passive K, D, or M elements, in a manner analogous to that used in representing electrical sources by Thevenin's or Norton's equivalents.

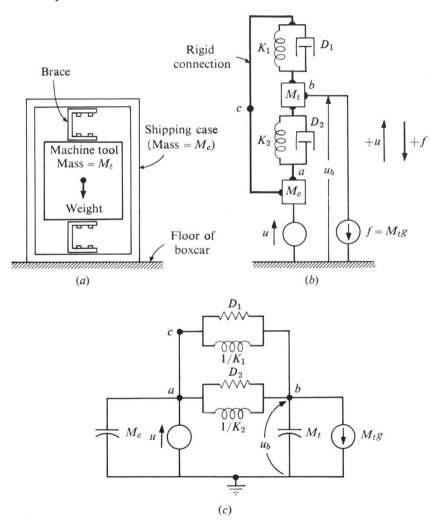

FIGURE 1.8. System for Example 1.8. (*a*) machine tool in shipping case; (*b*) mechanical model; (*c*) electrical analog.

1.8 Example. A heavy machine tool is to be mounted in a crate that is to be bolted to the floor of a boxcar for shipment. The mountings, which will restrict vibration to the vertical direction only, contain both springs and damping. The general layout is as in Figure 1.8(*a*).

It is decided that the floor of the boxcar should not be taken as the earth reference, but instead should be represented as a velocity source which will joggle the crate up and down in the manner characteristic of railroads. The mechanical model of the actual assembly is shown in Figure 1.8(*b*), where it is noted that the box is represented as a rigid connection between top and bottom mountings, and the force of gravity is represented as a force source between the machine tool and earth.

The student should show that the analogous electrical network can be arranged as in Figure 1.8(*c*). From inspection of the electric analog, several comments can be made:

1. The mass of the case has no effect on the performance of the system, since it is shunted by an ideal voltage source.

2. The force of gravity is represented by a constant force (current) source from node *b* to ground. This shows that the force of gravity has no effect on the oscillations of the system.

3. The current i_{ca} represents the force that the upper mounting must withstand. This can be reduced by using a weaker spring at K_1.

4. The analogs of the two mountings are electrically in parallel and can be combined into a single equivalent. Thus it makes no difference if the lower mount is made heavier and the upper one weaker. In fact, the upper mount could be eliminated entirely if not needed to prevent tipping.

The observations that conclude the preceding example are typical of the sort that a person experienced in electric circuit analysis can make from an analogous electric circuit. A person experienced in mechanical system analysis would probably attack the problem directly without resort to the analog; a common alternate approach is through the use of free-body diagrams.

PROBLEM 1.8.1. In each of the battery circuits of Figure 1.7.1, the 2 ohm resistor is replaced by a current source that charges the battery at 3 A. Modify the *v*, *i*, and *p* polarities for each of the four cases.

PROBLEM 1.8.2. For each of the mechanical systems of Figure P1.8.2, $K = 3$, $M = 1$, and $D = 2$. Compute the natural (source-free) modes of response if the source is (*a*) a velocity source; (*b*) a force source.

$$\text{Answer: for case (1), } (a)Ae^{-t}\cos(\sqrt{2}t + \phi); (b) Be^{-2t}.$$

PROBLEM 1.8.3. A storage battery is customarily represented by an ideal voltage source in series with the internal resistance of the battery. Describe in detail a mechanical analog for this, including the effect analogous to voltage regulation (the drop in terminal voltage as load is increased).

PROBLEM 1.8.4. For the electrical network of Figure P1.8.4, draw an analogous mechanical system, using the *f-i* analog. Select an appropriate node to correspond to earth, and identify all analogous quantities and nodes.

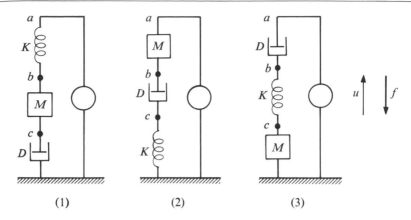

FIGURE P1.8.2.

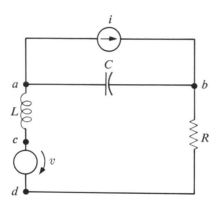

FIGURE P1.8.4.

PROBLEM 1.8.5. For the shipping case example of Figure 1.8, let $D_1 = D_2$ and $K_1 = K_2$. (a) Find the undamped natural frequency of oscillation in terms of K_1 and M. (b) Find the value of $D_1 = D_2$ for critical damping. *Answer:* (a) $\sqrt{2K_1/M_t}$; (b) $\sqrt{2M_tK_1}$.

1.9 Rotational Systems

The equations describing rotational systems are exactly analogous to those describing translational systems, and electrical analogs can be constructed in the same manner. The rotational and translational analogies are tabulated in Table 1.9.

TABLE 1.9

Analogous Rotational and Translational Qualities

	Rotational system	Translational analog
Torque	T (N-m)	f
Angular velocity	Ω (rad/s)	u
Angular position	θ (rad)	x
Torsional stiffness	K_θ (N-m/rad)	K
Torsional friction	D_θ (N-m/rad/s)	D
Moment of inertia	J (N-m/rad/s²)	M

The reference polarities for rotational elements are illustrated in Figure 1.9.1, using a friction clutch as an example. The procedure for assigning polarities is as follows:

1. The positive reference direction for angular velocity (Ω) is selected arbitrarily and marked on the clutch plates. The velocity of interest, to be used in the expression $T = D_\theta\Omega$, is the difference between the plate velocities.

2. By using the right-hand rule as in vectors, the arrow direction of Ω is transferred to the symbolic representation. This establishes a "positive" end of the shaft (end b, in this example). Thus, $\Omega = \Omega_b - \Omega_a = \Omega_{ba}$.

3. A positive reference direction for torque (T) is assigned on the symbolic diagram, opposite to that for the angular velocity.

4. Again using the right-hand rule, the arrow direction of T is transferred back to the pictorial sketch. The torque is the same throughout the element, whereas the angular velocity is not.

The pictorial sketch is not needed, and the same symbolic representations will serve for both translational and rotational systems, as can be seen by reference to Figure 1.6.1. When Ω is numerically positive, the "positive" end

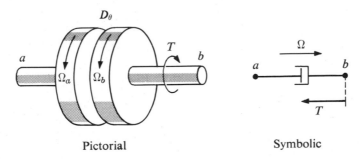

Pictorial   Symbolic

FIGURE 1.9.1. Polarity conventions in rotational systems.

of the shaft (end b in the illustration) is rotating in the reference direction (for Ω) with respect to the other end. When T is numerically positive, the element is exerting a torque on its own "positive" end in the reference direction for torque. When both variables are actually in their positive reference directions, the element is absorbing energy.

Example 1.9. Figure 1.9.2(a) shows a motor driving a load having friction and inertia. The positive reference for velocity has been chosen arbitrarily, and both elements marked for torque according to the load convention. It is obvious that both elements cannot be loads at the same instant, so either T_m or T_L must be numerically negative. This is illustrated in the analogous electric circuit of Figure 1.9.2(b), where the current equilibrium equation is $i_m + i_L = 0$. When the motor is actually acting as a motor and delivering power to the shaft, T_m is numerically negative and T_L is numerically positive.

The analogous electrical solution for v proceeds as follows:

$$i_m + i_L = 0$$

$$i_m = -(G + Cp)v$$

$$v/i_m = -(1/C)/(p + G/C).$$

Now let the motor produce a constant torque, T_m, in the positive direction for torque, with the shaft initially at rest. This corresponds to $i_m = I_m$ in the positive direction for the analogous current source. The voltage response is then of the form

$$v = K_1 e^{-\frac{G}{C}t} + K_2.$$

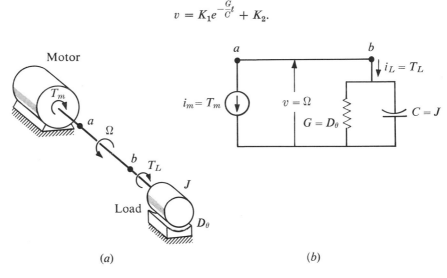

(a)   (b)

FIGURE 1.9.2. Rotational system and electrical analog for Example 1.9.

At $t = 0$, $v = 0$, so that $K_1 = -K_2$. As $t \to \infty$, $K_1 e^{-\frac{G}{C}t} \to 0$ and the steady-state voltage is

$$v_s = K_2 = -I_m/G.$$

Thus,

$$v = \frac{I_m}{G} (e^{-\frac{G}{C}t} - 1).$$

The mechanical solution is, then,

$$\Omega = \frac{T_m}{D} (e^{-\frac{D}{M}t} - 1).$$

It is noted that this solution indicates that the shaft will turn in the $-\Omega$ direction. This follows because the motor torque T_m was chosen positive. The solution also shows that if T_m is numerically negative, Ω is numerically positive.

PROBLEM 1.9.1. Write the expressions relating torque and angular velocity for each of the three rotational elements. Also explain the analogs of Kirchhoff's laws for rotational systems.

PROBLEM 1.9.2. Make pictorial sketches similar to Figure 1.9.1 for a torsional spring and for a rotating mass (moment of inertia), and go through the steps for assigning reference polarities for each. Note that the positive reference for angular velocity also applies for angular acceleration and for angular position.

PROBLEM 1.9.3. Develop electrical analogs for the rotational systems of Figure P1.9.3. Tell what mechanical quantity is analogous to each voltage and current.

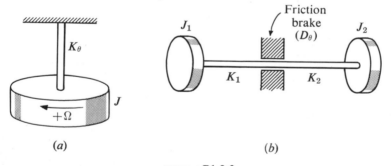

(a)   (b)

FIGURE P1.9.3.

1.10   The Force–Voltage (f-v) Analogy

A somewhat limited analogy can be constructed using voltage as the analog of force, and current as the analog of velocity. This analogy applies only to planar mechanical systems, and actually depends on the idea of electrical duality rather than on a true mathematical analogy. When restricted to planar

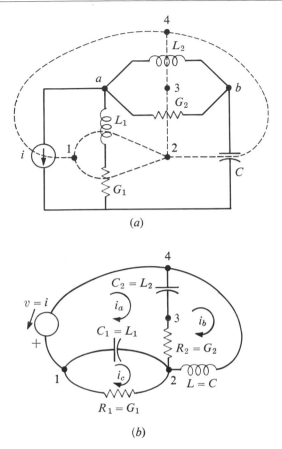

(a)

(b)

FIGURE 1.10. Conversion of a network to its electrical dual. (a) Original network showing procedure. (b) Electrical dual of network in (a).

networks (where duals exist), however, the *f-v* analogy is valid. It leads to mesh rather than node equations.*

As a result of the easy, natural correspondence between junctions and nodes in the force–current analogy, it is usually simpler to construct the *f-i* analog first, as already described in previous sections, and then construct the electrical dual to obtain the force–voltage analog. Dual electrical equations are produced by replacing nodes by meshes, v by i, i by v, G by R, L by C, and C by L, where the new quantities have identical numerical values with the old ones.

---

* See Reference 1.1 for a discussion of topology. References are found at the end of each chapter.

A graphical method for constructing an electrical dual consists of the following steps, and is illustrated in Figure 1.10.

1. Place a node inside of each mesh of the original network, and one additional node outside the network.
2. Connect the nodes with one (and only one) line drawn through each circuit element. This forms the graph of the dual network.
3. Wherever the dual graph crosses an element of the original network, insert into it the dual of that element.
4. Mesh currents are duals of node voltages. To get proper source polarities, assign (arbitrarily) a positive direction for mesh currents. Then, since (in this example) the current source i tends to drive node a more negative, the dual voltage source v is directed to make i_a increase in its negative direction.

The analogous mechanical equations are then obtained by substituting the appropriate analogous quantities into the mesh equations for the dual network.

PROBLEM 1.10.1. Construct a table, similar to that of Table 1.4, illustrating the force–voltage analogy and the torque–voltage analogy.

PROBLEM 1.10.2. Construct the electrical dual for the circuit of Figure P1.8.4.

PROBLEM 1.10.3. Construct the *f-v* analog for the system of Figure 1.5.2.

1.11 Analogs and Analog Computers

The study of analogous circuits is a fascinating topic in its own right. For example, mutual coupling is used to represent gears, and can also represent lever action that is limited to small angles.* The student who has operated an electrical analog computer, however, will recognize that the analogous electric circuits described in this chapter are not actually used in solving problems on the analog computer, where all system variables are represented by voltages, and none at all by currents. The principal purpose of discussing analogs in this introductory chapter has been to help the student to feel at ease with the relatively simple mechanical systems that will be involved in the electromechanical energy conversion processes discussed in the remainder of this book.

Advanced Problems

1.1 A mass of 0.5 kg is at rest 200 meters above the earth's surface. (*a*) What force in newtons is required to hold it there? (*b*) Determine and sketch the equations of

* Reference 1.2; also Reference 1.3 for a more advanced and comprehensive treatment.

acceleration, velocity, and distance above the earth's surface if a force $f(t) = 4.9 (1 - e^{-0.1t})$ is applied to the mass in an upward direction. Include the effect of gravity.

1.2   A force $f(t) = 5 \sin 2t U(t)$ is applied to a mass of $M = 3$ which is initially at rest. (*a*) Determine and sketch the complete velocity response. (*b*) Determine and sketch the complete position (x) response.

1.3   Draw the electrical analog for the mechanical system shown in Figure P1.3. The system is constrained to vertical motion only. To what mechanical quantity is each current and voltage analogous? Neglect gravity.

1.4   Draw the electrical analog for the mechanical system shown in Figure P1.4. The system is constrained to vertical motion only. To what mechanical quantity is each current and voltage analogous? Neglect gravity.

1.5   For each of the mechanical systems of Figure P1.8.2, determine the mechanical driving point impedance as a function of the sinusoidal source frequency, ω.

1.6   For the mechanical system of Figure P1.8.2(2), determine the transfer function relating the velocity at junction c to the applied force f.

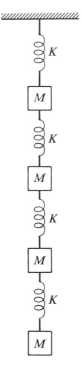

FIGURE P1.3.

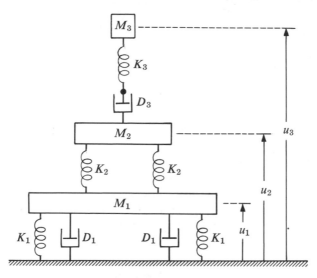

FIGURE P1.4.

1.7 The system of Figure P1.8.2(2) is initially at rest, when a step of force $f = 2U(t)$ is applied by a force source. Determine the complete equation for (a) the velocity at junction b; (b) the force at junction b. (c) Which way (up or down) is each of these quantities at the initial instant $t = 0+$?

1.8 The system of Figure P1.8.2(1) is initially at rest, when a step of velocity $u = 10U(t)$ is applied by a velocity source. Determine the complete equation for (a) the velocity at junction b; (b) the force at junction b. (c) Which way is each of these quantities at the initial instant?

1.9 Repeat Problem 1.8 for the system of Figure P1.8.2(3).

1.10 Repeat Problem 1.8.3 except that Norton's equivalent circuit is to be used for the battery.

1.11 A certain force source consists of a pneumatic cylinder in which a constant pressure is maintained regardless of the position or velocity of the piston. However, the piston has finite mass, and also encounters appreciable friction (assumed linear) as it rubs against the walls of the cylinder. Draw a mechanical equivalent for the source, using an ideal source plus additional elements as required. Determine the mechanical time constant of the system (in terms of D, K, and M) and explain the physical significance of the mechanical time constant.

1.12 In the system of Figure P1.4, a velocity source u is connected between masses M_1 and M_2. Draw the analogous electric circuit, and evaluate the transfer function relating the force in D_3 to the source velocity u.

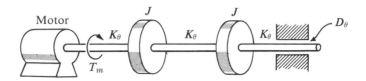

1.13   Develop the *f-i* electrical analog for the system of Figure P1.13.

1.14   The electrical analog of Figure 1.9.2(*b*) is changed so that the source is a step voltage source, $v = VU(t)$. (*a*) What is the corresponding change in the actual system of Figure 1.9.2(*a*)? (*b*) Solve the modified system for shaft torque $T_L(t)$. Interpret the impulse function that arises. (*c*) The shaft in the modified system is now made sufficiently flexible so that it must be represented as a torsional spring. If damping is reduced to a negligible amount, what shaft speed (expressed in terms of J and K) is to be avoided?

1.15   An air compressor is mounted on a heavy platform which is supported by springs, as shown in Figure P1.15. The compressor has an internal vertically-mounted piston of mass M_p, that moves up and down. At a certain speed the assembly vibrates excessively, and an external vibration damper, M_d and K_d has been added to correct this. (*a*) Draw a mechanical model of the compressor, including its internal piston. The total mass of compressor, piston, and platform is M. Note that the source is *not* connected directly to earth. Is the source to be represented as a force source or as a velocity source? (*b*) Draw the *f-i* analogous circuit and show that the damper can effectively "short out" the oscillations at a particular frequency.

1.16   Construct *f-v* analogs for the systems of Problem 1.5.2.

1.17   Construct the *f-v* analog for the system of Problem 1.3 (Figure P1.3).

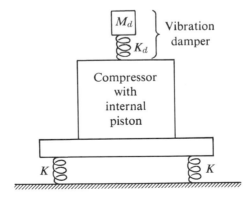

FIGURE P1.15.

1.18 Construct the *f-v* analog for the system of Problem 1.12 (Figure P1.4).

1.19 Construct the *f-v* analog for the system of Figure 1.8.

REFERENCES

1.1 E. A. GUILLEMIN. *Introductory Circuit Theory*. New York: John Wiley and Sons, Inc., 1953.

1.2 D. K. CHENG. *Analysis of Linear Systems*, Chapter 4. Reading, Mass.: Addison-Wesley, 1959.

1.3 I. M. HOROWITZ. *Synthesis of Feedback Systems*, Chapter 1. New York: Academic Press, 1963.

CHAPTER TWO

Electromechanical Energy Conversion

2.1 The Nonlinear Nature of the Problem

Electromechanical energy conversion systems may give rise to nonlinear differential equations, even when the individual components are themselves electrically linear and mechanically linear. Nonlinearities may arise in even the simplest systems, although they can sometimes be avoided by applying suitable constraints. This tendency toward nonlinearity lies at the heart of many of the special difficulties encountered in the analysis of electromechanical systems.

The simple electromechanical energy conversion device of Figure 2.1 provides an illustration of nonlinearity. It consists of a parallel-plate capacitor with one movable plate. When voltage is applied, the capacitor becomes charged and a force of attraction appears between the plates. This force is available to do work if the movable plate is allowed to move through a distance.

When the plate moves, however, the value of the capacitance changes, thus rendering the electric circuit nonlinear. As the plate moves, the magnitude of the force also changes, but in a manner that cannot be represented by a combination of linear mechanical elements (K, D, and M). Thus, the mechanical circuit is also rendered nonlinear.

If the capacitor plates are pulled apart by an externally applied force, mechanical work is done on the electric field. This work is partly stored in the field and partly transferred to the electric circuit via induction, as will be seen in detail later.

The presence of the electric field is essential to the energy conversion process. Without the field, there is no force, and therefore, no possibility of

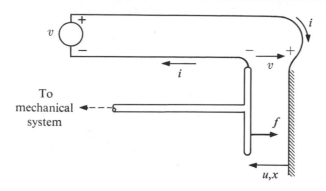

FIGURE 2.1. A simple electromechanical energy converter.

energy conversion. The quantitative development that follows is based on a consideration of the energy stored in the field.

2.2   The Energy Balance Equation. Polarities

The energy balance is illustrated symbolically in Figure 2.2. The electrical and mechanical systems are both considered as sources capable of supplying energy, through an idealized conversion process, to an electric or magnetic field. The conversion is depicted as completely reversible, all losses being assigned to either the electrical system (as resistance) or to the mechanical system (as friction). The energy balance equation corresponding to Figure 2.2 is

$$dW_e + dW_m = dW_f, \qquad (2.2.1)$$

where dW_e is an increment of electric energy entering the field, dW_m is an increment of mechanical energy entering the field, and dW_f is the resulting incremental increase in field energy.

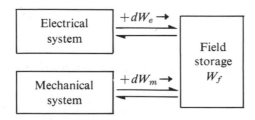

FIGURE 2.2. Diagram of energy balance.

In the assignment of positive reference directions, the conversion device with its field is considered as a "load" from both its electrical and its mechanical terminals. This is illustrated in Figure 2.1, where v and i are marked on the device as for an electrical load, and f and u (or x) are marked as for a mechanical load. The reference direction for u was chosen so that the movable plate would be the positive mechanical terminal. The corresponding direction for f is interpreted to mean that the force is numerically positive when the element itself (i.e., the field) exerts a force to the right on the movable plate.

When v, i, f, and u are all numerically positive, energy is being delivered to the field both from the electrical system and from the mechanical system. There is, however, no special relationship between the reference polarities for the electrical quantities and those for the mechanical quantities.

Upon returning to the basic energy balance, Equation (2.2.1), it is seen that should the stored field energy be held constant, as is often the case in rotating machines, then $dW_e + dW_m = 0$ and one term or the other must be numerically negative. If the positive term is dW_e, electric energy is entering the device and it is acting as a motor. If dW_m is positive, mechanical energy is entering and it is a generator.

2.3 Calculation of Electromechanical Force

In the simple parallel-plate capacitor of Figure 2.1, a formula for the electromechanical force can be developed readily from field considerations and will perhaps be recognized* in the form

$$f = \tfrac{1}{2}v^2 \frac{\varepsilon A}{x^2}, \qquad (2.3.1)$$

where v is the voltage across the capacitor, A is the plate area, x is the spacing, and ε is the permittivity (for free space $\varepsilon_0 = 8.85 \times 10^{-12}$ C²/N-m²), and fringing of the field is neglected.

In more complicated configurations, however, the electromechanical force is difficult to calculate directly, and the following procedure is to be used.

The basic energy balance equation (2.2.1) is

$$dW_e + dW_m = dW_f.$$

By substitution of appropriate values, this becomes

$$vi\, dt + f\, dx = d(\tfrac{1}{2}Cv^2). \qquad (2.3.2)$$

In this case it is desired to eliminate i. Since C is a variable, the substitution must be

$$i = \frac{dq}{dt} = \frac{d}{dt}(Cv) = C\frac{dv}{dt} + v\frac{dC}{dt}. \qquad (2.3.3)$$

* For example, Reference 2.1, Chapter 33.

The term $C\, dv/dt$ is the familiar result for a fixed capacitor, whereas the term $v\, dC/dt$ is the current resulting from physical motion of the movable plate and is zero for a fixed capacitor.

By substituting Equation (2.3.3) into Equation (2.3.2), and expanding the right-hand term of Equation (2.3.2) as well, there results

$$vC\, dv + v^2\, dC + f\, dx = Cv\, dv + \tfrac{1}{2}v^2\, dC$$

$$f\, dx = -\tfrac{1}{2}v^2\, dC$$

$$f = -\tfrac{1}{2}v^2\,\frac{dC}{dx}. \tag{2.3.4}$$

Several comments may be made about this result:

1. It agrees with Equation (2.3.1), when appropriate substitutions are made for the capacitance of the parallel-plate capacitor. Equation (2.3.4) is, however, a general result applying to any configuration.

2. The quantity dC/dx is negative for the parallel-plate capacitor since the capacitance decreases as the plates are separated. Thus, the force is numerically positive, tending (in Figure 2.1) to close the gap.

3. The force at any instant depends on the square of the voltage, but in no way on how the voltage is varying, nor on its polarity.

4. The presence of the term dC/dx shows that the capacitance *must* vary with motion, re-emphasizing the potential nonlinearity of electromechanical energy conversion.

Further insight into the energy conversion process can be gained by a more careful examination of one of the steps in the derivation of the force equation (2.3.4). This step, repeated below, is

$$\overbrace{Cv\, dv}^{dW_e} + \overbrace{v^2\, dC}^{dW_m} + \overbrace{f\, dx}^{dW_f} = Cv\, dv + \tfrac{1}{2}v^2\, dC. \tag{2.3.5}$$

If the movable plate of the capacitor is held fixed, $dC = dx = 0$ and the energy balance becomes

$$\overbrace{Cv\, dv}^{dW_e} + \overbrace{0}^{dW_m} + \overbrace{0}^{dW_f} = Cv\, dv + 0.$$

Thus, the first term on the left represents electrical energy which passes directly from the voltage source to field storage and does not depend on the presence of incremental motion.

If the term $Cv\, dv$ is canceled from both sides of Equation (2.3.5), there results an equation each of whose terms represents energy transfer caused by motion:

$$v^2\, dC + f\, dx = \tfrac{1}{2}v^2\, dC.$$

From this it is obvious that the electrical source contributes exactly twice the energy that the mechanical source contributes, plus the amount $Cv\,dv$ which was shown to be transferred in the absence of motion. Also, the electrical contribution, $v^2\,dC$, and the mechanical contribution, $f\,dx$, must be opposite in sign, since dC and dx are necessarily opposite in sign (see reference directions on Figure 2.1).

Example 2.3.1. The parallel-plate capacitor of Figure 2.1 is connected to a 100-V dc source, and the plates are allowed to move together by $\Delta x = -10^{-3}$ m. The resulting capacitance change is $\Delta C = 10^{-8}$ F. Find f, ΔW_e, ΔW_m, and ΔW_f.
Solution. Approximately, $f = -\frac{1}{2}v^2(\Delta C/\Delta x) = -\frac{1}{2}(100)^2(10^{-8})/(-10^{-3}) = +0.05$ N. The positive sign indicates a force on the "positive" mechanical terminal (the movable plate) in the positive f direction (to close the gap).
    Since the voltage is held fixed by the source, the term $Cv\,dv = 0$. Then,

$$\Delta W_e = v^2\,\Delta C = (100)^2(10^{-8}) = 10^{-4}\,\text{J};$$

$$\Delta W_m = f\,\Delta x = (+0.05)(-10^{-3}) = -5 \times 10^{-5}\,\text{J};$$

$$\Delta W_f = \tfrac{1}{2}v^2\,\Delta C = +5 \times 10^{-5}\,\text{J}.$$

Thus, the electrical source contributes 10^{-4} J, half of which goes to doing mechanical work (ΔW_m is negative) and the other half of which goes into electric field storage. This distribution, often called the "50–50 rule," will always hold for constant-voltage nonsaturating systems.

Example 2.3.2. In Figure 2.3(a), the capacitive energy converter of Figure 2.1 is shown coupled to a simple mechanical system consisting of a mass and a spring. With the system deenergized, the spacing between the plates is d. It is desired to find the mechanical behavior of the system when the voltage $v(t)$ is applied.
    The electrical analog of the mechanical portion of the system is shown in Figure 2.3(b). The current i' is analogous to the electromechanical force f, and the voltage v' is analogous to the velocity u of the movable plate. The current i_c corresponds to the force of acceleration applied to the mass, and the current i_L is analogous to the force transmitted to the spring. The current i' and the voltage v' are shown oppositely directed because the reference directions for the energy converter were originally chosen according to the load convention.
    From Kirchhoff's current law,

$$i_L + i_c + i' = 0$$

and by analogy,

$$f_k + f_m + f = 0,$$

where

$$f = -\tfrac{1}{2}v^2\frac{dC}{dx}.$$

Thus, the equation of the system is

$$\frac{K}{p}u + Mpu = \tfrac{1}{2}v^2\frac{dC}{dx}.$$

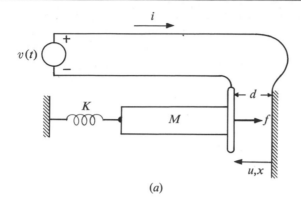

(a)

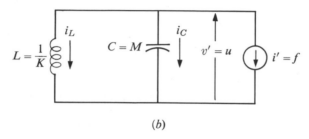

(b)

FIGURE 2.3. (a) Electromechanical system for Example 2.3.2. (b) Electrical analog for mechanical portion of system.

Here the voltage v represents an ideal source. Also, dC/dx can be evaluated, since for the parallel-plate capacitor

$$C = \frac{A\varepsilon_0}{x}, \quad \frac{dC}{dx} = -\frac{A\varepsilon_0}{x^2}, \quad \text{and so} \quad f = +\frac{A\varepsilon_0 v^2}{2x^2}.$$

The equation of the system can be rewritten in terms of x and v, taking care that the constant of integration is not omitted in writing the term involving the spring:

$$K(x - d) + Mp^2x + \frac{A\varepsilon_0 v^2}{2x^2} = 0.$$

This equation is nonlinear because of the presence (after multiplying through by $2x^2$ to clear the denominator) of terms containing x^3, x^2, and x^2px. It can be solved readily on a digital computer using incremental steps, or manually by the same method, or on an analog computer equipped with function multipliers.

It is important to note that solutions of nonlinear differential equations are usually numerical solutions rather than symbolic expressions. Each change in the numerical value of a parameter, or of an initial condition, will yield a different solution. In the example above, if d is initially too small, the application of a voltage may cause the plates to move together until they touch, whereas a different initial spacing would permit oscillations. Also, the frequency of the oscillations will be affected by the magnitude of the applied voltage as well as by K and M.

PROBLEM 2.3.1. In Figure 2.1, let $x = 0$ when the two plates are in contact. The surface area is A and the permittivity of the dielectric is ε_0. Compute and sketch the variation of capacitance with time if x is caused to vary according to (a) $x = 3e^{2t}$; (b) $x = 10 + 5 \cos 2t$. *Answer:* (a) $(A\varepsilon_0/3)e^{-2t}$; (b) $A\varepsilon_0(0.1 - 0.05 \cos 2t + 0.025 \cos^2 2t - \cdots)$.

PROBLEM 2.3.2. A voltage $v(t)$ is applied to the capacitor of Figure 2.1. Compute and sketch the time variation of the current, $i(t)$, if (a) $v(t) = 10$ and $x(t) = 0.1e^{-t}$; (b) $v(t) = 10 \sin 3t$ and $x(t) = 10e^{2t}$. (c) In each case, does the element act as an electrical load or as an electrical source? *Answer;* (a) $i = 100A\varepsilon_0 e^t$, load; (b) $i = A\varepsilon_0 e^{-2t}(3 \cos 3t - 2 \sin 3t)$.

PROBLEM 2.3.3. A voltage $v(t) = 2t$ is applied to the capacitor of Figure 2.1, and at the same time the plates are moved so the capacitance varies according to $C(t) = (3 - 0.4t)$. (a) Sketch the variation of $v(t)$, $C(t)$, and $i(t)$ over a 5-s interval. (b) Calculate and sketch the electric energy entering the capacitor terminals during the 5-s interval. (c) Calculate the energy stored in the capacitor field at the end of the 5-s interval, and explain any difference with the result in (b). *Answer:* (a) $i = 6 - 1.6t$; (b) Electric energy input at $t = 5$, $W_e(5) = 16.7$ J; (c) Stored field energy at $t = 5$, $W_f(5) = 50$ J.

PROBLEM 2.3.4. The device of Figure 2.1 is found to have a capacitance $C = 0.1$ F when $x = 0.2$ m. It is then charged to 100 V, and with the electric circuit disconnected the spacing is changed according to $x(t) = 0.2e^{-2t}$. Calculate (a) $v(t)$; (b) $W_f(t)$, the stored field energy; (c) $W_m(t)$, the mechanical energy input; (d) $f(t)$, the mechanical force exerted by the field, using the result of part (c). *Answer:* (a) $v = 100e^{-2t}$; (b) $W_f = 500e^{-2t}$; (c) $W_m = 500(e^{-2t} - 1)$; (d) $f = 2500$, constant.

PROBLEM 2.3.5. For the device of Problem 2.3.4, calculate $f(t)$ using Equation (2.3.4). *Answer:* $f = 2500$ N.

PROBLEM 2.3.6. In Example 2.3.1, the source voltage is not held constant but increases by $\Delta v = 0.5$ V. It is known that $C = 10^{-6}$ F initially. Determine f, ΔW_e, ΔW_m, and ΔW_f. Does the 50–50 rule hold in this case? *Answer:* $f = +0.05$; $\Delta W_e = 1.5 \times 10^{-4}$; $\Delta W_m = -0.5 \times 10^{-4}$; $\Delta W_f = 10^{-4}$ J. No.

PROBLEM 2.3.7. In Problem 2.3.6, the change takes place in a time increment $\Delta t = 10^{-4}$ sec. Calculate (a) the current; (b) the velocity of the mechanical shaft. *Answer:* (a) 1.5×10^{-2} A; (b) -10 m/s.

PROBLEM 2.3.8. The parallel-plate capacitor of Figure 2.1 is connected to a 100-V dc source. At a particular instant the current is -0.2 A and the force is 0.10 N.

For that instant calculate: (a) dC/dt; (b) P_e (electric power input); (c) P_f (power input to the field); (d) P_m (mechanical power input); (e) u (mechanical velocity). *Answer:* (a) -2×10^{-3} F/s; (b) -20 W; (c) -10 W; (d) 10 W; (e) 100 m/s.

2.4 Linearization by Small-Signal Assumptions

Many inherently nonlinear situations can be linearized if the variables are limited to relatively small excursions about fixed quiescent values. This process will be illustrated using the system of Figure 2.3, whose equation was derived in the previous section, and is

$$K(x - d) + Mp^2x + \frac{A\varepsilon_0 v^2}{2x^2} = 0, \qquad (2.4.1)$$

where v is the source variable and x is the response. It is now assumed that the applied voltage v consists of a relatively large dc component V_0 and a relatively small varying component v_1. Similarly, the resulting variations of x are assumed to be small excursions, of magnitude x_1, about an average or quiescent position X_0. Thus,

$$v = V_0 + v_1, \qquad V_0 \gg v_1$$
$$x = X_0 + x_1, \qquad X_0 \gg x_1. \qquad (2.4.2)$$

The varying components v_1 and x_1 may be sinusoidal, but need not be; the only restriction is on their magnitude.

The linearizing expressions of Equation (2.4.2) are now substituted into the original equation, giving

$$K(X_0 - d + x_1) + Mp^2x_1 + \frac{A\varepsilon_0(V_0 + v_1)^2}{2(X_0 + x_1)^2} = 0. \qquad (2.4.3)$$

When the squaring operations are performed on the right-hand term of Equation (2.4.3), certain approximations can be made, and it is these approximations that accomplish the linearization. The numerator of the right-hand term is expanded first, giving

$$(V_0 + v_1)^2 = V_0^2 + 2V_0v_1 + v_1^2 \cong V_0^2 + 2V_0v_1.$$

Since v_1 is restricted to a small value, v_1^2 is negligible and can be dropped. The denominator term will be handled in a slightly different manner, using the first two terms of the infinite series approximation, $1/(1 + a) \cong (1 - a)$.

$$\frac{1}{(X_0 + x_1)^2} \cong \frac{1}{X_0^2 + 2X_0x_1} = \frac{1}{X_0^2}\left[\frac{1}{1 + \dfrac{2x_1}{X_0}}\right] \cong \frac{1}{X_0^2} - \frac{2x_1}{X_0^3}.$$

With these approximations, Equation (2.4.3) becomes

$$K(X_0 - d + x_1) + Mp^2x_1 + \frac{A\varepsilon_0}{2}[V_0^2 + 2V_0v_1]\left[\frac{1}{X_0^2} - \frac{2x_1}{X_0^3}\right] = 0.$$

The term involving the product v_1x_1 is infinitesimal and can be discarded, leaving

$$K(X_0 - d + x_1) + Mp^2x_1 + \frac{A\varepsilon_0}{2}\left[\frac{V_0^2}{X_0^2} - \frac{2V_0^2x_1}{X_0^3} + \frac{2V_0v_1}{X_0^2}\right] = 0.$$

This equation is essentially two separate equations, one involving only quiescent (steady-state) quantities and the other involving only incrementally varying quantities, as shown below.

$$K(X_0 - d) + \frac{A\varepsilon_0}{2}\frac{V_0^2}{X_0^2} = 0 \qquad \text{(Quiescent).} \quad (2.4.4)$$

$$Kx_1 + Mp^2x_1 - \frac{A\varepsilon_0V_0^2}{X_0^3}x_1 + \frac{A\varepsilon_0V_0}{X_0^2}v_1 = 0 \qquad \text{(Variable).} \quad (2.4.5)$$

The variable equation will be considered first. It can be readily rearranged and transformed to give the linear transfer function

$$\frac{X_1(s)}{V_1(s)} = -\frac{A\varepsilon_0V_0/X_0^2M}{s^2 + \left(\dfrac{K}{M} - \dfrac{A\varepsilon_0V_0^2}{X_0^3M}\right)}. \qquad (2.4.6)$$

This function is of the form $-k/(s^2 + \omega^2)$, which indicates that the time-domain response to a small step of voltage will be a continuing sinusoidal oscillation. There is no decay because neither resistance nor friction was included in the problem.

If the dc voltage level V_0 is increased sufficiently, the bracketed denominator term of Equation (2.4.6) becomes zero, yielding the form $-k/s^2$. This corresponds in the time domain to a negative ramp, which will result in the capacitor plates moving quickly together and touching. Actually, the ramp does not describe the motion accurately, for the small-signal linearization assumption has been violated. The increase in V_0 has decreased the spacing between the capacitor plates, reducing the quiescent value of X_0 to such a small value that the condition $X_0 \gg x_1$ no longer holds. Nevertheless, the result indicates correctly that the system becomes unstable if V_0 is made too large.

Further information about the stability of the system can be derived from the quiescent equation, Equation (2.4.4), which can be written as

$$K(X_0 - d) = -F_0, \qquad (2.4.7)$$

where $F_0 = A\varepsilon_0V_0^2/2X_0^2$, the quiescent electromechanical force. From Equation (2.4.7) the quiescent operating points can be found graphically.

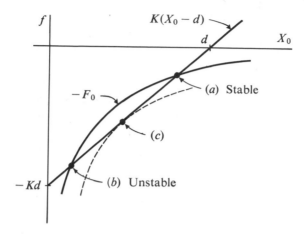

FIGURE 2.4. Graphical determination of equilibrium conditions.

The left-hand term represents the spring force, which varies linearly with quiescent position X_0, and gives the straight-line graph in Figure 2.4. The right-hand term of Equation (2.4.7) is the quiescent electromechanical force, and varies hyperbolically with X_0. The intersection of these two curves yields the equilibrium positions.

Of the two equilibrium points shown in Figure 2.4, only that at (a) is stable. If the spacing is at any point between (a) and (b), the magnitude of the spring force will exceed that of the electromechanical force and the spacing will increase to point (a). If the spacing is made less than (b), the larger electromechanical force will pull the plates together. Thus, the equilibrium at (b) is unstable and will be upset by any small random disturbance.

If V_0 is increased, the $-F_0$ curve moves toward its limiting position, shown as the dashed curve in Figure 2.4. Here, the two equilibrium points have coalesced at (c). For larger values of V_0, there is no stable quiescent point.

In this example, linearization by small-signal analysis gave the linear transfer function $X_1(s)/V_1(s)$. Several other system functions could be derived for this example, including the electrical impedance $V_1(s)/I_1(s)$ and the transfer function $F_1(s)/V_1(s)$, where f_1 is the variable component of the electromechanical force. As an alternative, the voltage variation could be eliminated ($v = V_0$) and a small mechanical force or displacement applied to the movable capacitor plate. Within the limits of the linearization assumption, all of the techniques of linear system analysis can be applied.

PROBLEM 2.4.1. Apply small-signal linearization to the equation $2v^2/x + px = 10$, to obtain the transform network function $X_1(s)/V_1(s)$. *Answer:* $-(4V_0/X_0)/[s - (2V_0^2/X_0^2)]$, an unstable situation.

2.5 The Quantity $\partial W_f/\partial x$

The force developed by an electromechanical energy conversion device is related in a simple and important way to the quantity $\partial W_f/\partial x$, the rate of change of stored field energy with respect to mechanical displacement. This idea will be developed in terms of the magnetic field energy converter of Figure 2.5.1, for which the force equation can be shown, by methods analogous to those of Section 2.3, to be (see Problem 2.5.2)

$$f = -\tfrac{1}{2}i^2 \frac{dL}{dx}. \tag{2.5.1}$$

This expression is to be related to the quantity $\partial W_f/\partial x$. The magnetic field energy is $\tfrac{1}{2}Li^2$, so

$$\frac{\partial W_f}{\partial x} = \frac{\partial}{\partial x}(\tfrac{1}{2}Li^2) = Li\frac{\partial i}{\partial x} + \tfrac{1}{2}i^2\frac{\partial L}{\partial x}. \tag{2.5.2}$$

Now let it be assumed that the magnetizing coil is supplied from an independent current source, so that $\partial i/\partial x = 0$. Then from Equations (2.5.1) and (2.5.2),

$$\frac{\partial W_f}{\partial x} = +\tfrac{1}{2}i^2\frac{\partial L}{\partial x} = -f \qquad \text{(current constrained)}. \tag{2.5.3}$$

Suppose, instead, that the magnetizing coil is supplied from a voltage source. A voltage source constrains flux linkages, since $v = d\lambda/dt$. Therefore, Equation (2.5.2) is rewritten in terms of linkages, by the substitution $i = \lambda/L$:

$$\frac{\partial W_f}{\partial x} = \frac{\partial}{\partial x}\left(\frac{\lambda^2}{2L}\right) = -\frac{1}{2}\frac{\lambda^2}{L^2}\frac{\partial L}{\partial x} + \frac{\lambda}{L}\frac{\partial \lambda}{\partial x}.$$

Since $\partial \lambda/\partial x = 0$, because of the voltage source,

$$\frac{\partial W_f}{\partial x} = -\frac{\lambda^2}{2L^2}\frac{\partial L}{\partial x} = -\tfrac{1}{2}i^2\frac{\partial L}{\partial x},$$

and comparing this with Equation (2.5.1), it is seen that

$$\frac{\partial W_f}{\partial x} = +f \qquad \text{(voltage constrained)}. \tag{2.5.4}$$

Comparison of Equations (2.5.3) and (2.5.4) raises a question about the difference of signs. It might at first be thought that the different constraints (current and voltage sources) lead to opposite directions of forces, but this is incorrect. The proper interpretation is that with a positive incremental change

(a)

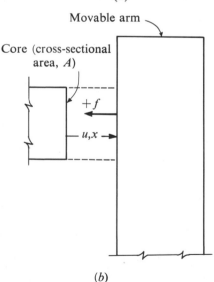

Movable arm

Core (cross-sectional
area, A)

$+f$

u, x

(b)

FIGURE 2.5.1. Magnetic energy converter. (a) Photograph of electromagnetic relay, showing winding (black) and magnetic circuit. Cylindrical iron core extends through coil. Movable arm (right) normally carries contacts which have been removed in this view. (Photo by Bradley University Audio-Visual Dept.) (b) Detail of air gap. Magnetic field is assumed to be uniform as it crosses the gap, and to be confined within the volume indicated by the dashed lines.

in x, energy leaves the field in the first case and enters it in the second case. The force is always the same way. Examples 2.5.1 and 2.5.2, at the end of this section, illustrate this idea further.

The use of $\partial W_f/\partial x$ to determine force is much more general than is indicated above. More advanced analysis (see Section 2.6) shows these three important extensions.

1. The method applies not only when current or voltage is constrained, but whenever current or voltage is the independent variable, regardless of the nature of the source or connections. Thus, Equation (2.5.3) applies if W_f is expressed in terms of current or mmf, whereas Equation (2.5.4) applies if W_f is expressed in terms of voltage, flux, or flux linkages.

2. The method applies regardless of the number of electrical or mechanical connections. For example, it applies to a rotating machine having several electrical windings, where W_f is the energy in the net field resulting from all of the windings.

3. The method applies in systems where physical motion is impossible. It is assumed that an incremental displacement takes place, so that $\partial W_f/\partial x$ can exist. This is called a *virtual* displacement.

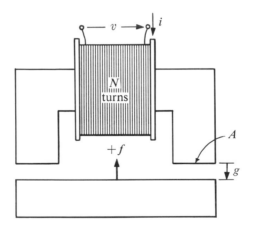

FIGURE 2.5.2. Electromagnet for Examples 2.5.1 and 2.5.2.

Example 2.5.1. Current, the independent variable. Find the lifting force, as a function of the gap length g, for the electromagnet shown in Figure 2.5.2. The current is considered constant, field fringing is to be neglected, and the iron parts are considered to have zero reluctance.

The stored field energy is found by

$$W_f = \int_V w \, dV,$$

where w is field energy density [$w = \frac{1}{2} B \cdot H = \frac{1}{2} \mu_0 H^2 = \frac{1}{2} B^2 / \mu_0$], V is total volume of the airgap, and μ_0, the magnetic permeability of space, is $\mu_0 = 4\pi \times 10^{-7}$.

In this case, the integration is simple to perform, for B and H are assumed to be colinear and uniform throughout the air-gap space.

$$W_f = wV = (\tfrac{1}{2} \mu_0 H^2)(2gA) \text{ for both gaps together.}$$

By substituting $H = \dfrac{\text{mmf}}{2g} = \dfrac{Ni}{2g}$ *,

$$W_f = (\tfrac{1}{2} \mu_0) \left(\frac{N^2 i^2}{4g^2} \right) (2gA) = \tfrac{1}{4} \mu_0 N^2 i^2 A \, \frac{1}{g}. \qquad (2.5.5)$$

Since W_f is expressed as a function of current, Equation (2.5.3) is used.

$$f = -\frac{\partial W_f}{\partial g} = +(\tfrac{1}{4} \mu_0 N^2 i^2 A) \frac{1}{g^2}. \qquad (2.5.6)$$

The force calculated is the total force from both gaps, since the total energy in both gaps was considered. Each gap could have been solved separately and the forces added. The force is numerically positive, in a direction to pull the bar upward and close the gaps. As the gaps close, Equation (2.5.5) shows that the field energy W_f stored in the gaps *increases*. This is characteristic of situations where the current is constrained.

Example 2.5.2. Voltage, the independent variable. A simple example of a voltage constraint is provided when the magnetic flux linkage in Example 2.5.1 is held constant ($d\lambda = 0$), regardless of spacing. This might be accomplished by making rapid adjustments of the coil current. However, the flux linkage is to be constant, so that the coil voltage is

$$v = \frac{d\lambda}{dt} = 0$$

Thus, if the coil terminals were short circuited, and if the coil resistance were negligibly small, the shorted coil would automatically carry the current needed to hold the flux linkage constant. This condition is actually observed in experiments with low-temperature superconducting coils, and will be assumed to exist in this illustrative example.

With constant flux linkage, the magnetic flux across the air gap remains constant, regardless of spacing. Then B, H, and the field energy density w all remain constant. The energy stored in the air-gap field, expressed in terms of flux density B, is

$$W_f = wV = \left(\frac{B^2}{2\mu_0} \right) (2gA). \qquad (2.5.7)$$

The flux density B (rather than H) is the preferred variable because there is present a voltage source which constrains the time variation of the magnetic flux. This distinction will not affect the results, however, as long as the assumption of a nonsaturating magnetic material insures that B and H are proportional.

* Refer to Appendix for discussion of magnetic circuits.

With a voltage source, the force expression to use is Equation (2.5.4), and

$$f = + \frac{\partial W_f}{\partial g} = +B^2 A/\mu_0. \tag{2.5.8}$$

This force is positive, in a direction to close the gaps, just as in the previous example. As the gaps close, however, Equation (2.5.7) shows that the stored field energy *decreases*. This is characteristic of situations where the voltage is constrained.

PROBLEM 2.5.1. Show that the inductance of a coil can be expressed in terms of the magnetic reluctance as $L = N^2/\mathscr{R}$ (see Appendix).

PROBLEM 2.5.2. The magnetic solenoid of Figure P2.5.2 has an inductance that is a function of plunger position x. It is energized from a current source $i(t)$. Start with the energy balance equation, Equation (2.2.1), and derive the force expression of Equation (2.5.1). This is essentially the dual of the derivation of Equation (2.3.4) for the capacitive energy converter.

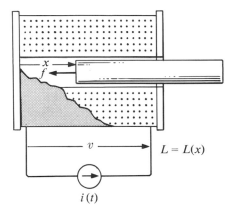

FIGURE P2.5.2.

PROBLEM 2.5.3. For the magnetic relay device of Figure 2.5.1, calculate (*a*) the magnetic reluctance; (*b*) the inductance of the coil as a function of x; (*c*) the magnetic force f as a function of x. *Answer:* (*a*) $\mathscr{R} = x/\mu_0 A$; (*b*) $L = N^2\mu_0 A/x$; (*c*) $f = +i^2 N^2 \mu_0\, A/2x^2$.

PROBLEM 2.5.4. For the magnetic relay of Figure 2.5.1, an incremental increase of gap length, $\Delta x = 0.01$ m, causes a corresponding change in inductance $\Delta L = -0.05$ H. (*a*) If the current is held constant at $i = 2.0$ A, find f, ΔW_e, ΔW_m, and ΔW_f. (*b*) If the change takes place in $\Delta t = 10^{-3}$ s, find v and u. *Answer:* (*a*) $f = 10$; $\Delta W_e = -0.2$; $\Delta W_m = 0.1$; $\Delta W_f = -0.1$ J. (*b*) $v = -100$; $u = 10$ m/s.

PROBLEM 2.5.5. For the magnetic relay of Figure 2.5.1, assume current is the independent circuit variable. Calculate (*a*) H in the air gap; (*b*) the energy W_f

stored in the air gap; (c) the force by $\pm \partial W_f / \partial x$. *Answer:* (a) $H = Ni/x$; (b)
(b) $W_f = \mu_0 N^2 i^2 A / 2x$; (c) $f = +\mu_0 N^2 i^2 A / 2x^2$.

PROBLEM 2.5.6. For the magnetic relay of Figure 2.5.1, the voltage is taken as the independent circuit variable. (a) Express the linkages λ in terms of the source voltage. (b) Express the stored field energy W_f in terms of λ. (c) Calculate the force by $\pm \partial W_f / \partial x$. *Answer:* (a) $\lambda = \int v \, dt$; (b) $W_f = \lambda^2 x / 2\mu_0 N^2 A$; (c) $f = +\lambda^2 / 2\mu_0 N^2 A^2$, independent of x.

PROBLEM 2.5.7. A magnetic relay carries a constant current of $i = 2.0$ A. At a particular instant the voltage at its terminals is -50 V and the magnetic force is $+0.10$ N. For that instant calculate (a) dL/dt; (b) P_e (electric power); (c) P_f (power input to field); (d) P_m (mechanical power input); (e) u. *Answer:* (a) -25 H/s; (b) -100 W; (c) -50 W; (d) 50 W; (e) 500 m/s.

PROBLEM 2.5.8. For a capacitive energy converter, derive the relationship between the quantity $\partial W_f / \partial x$ and the force f, for (a) voltage the independent variable; (b) current the independent variable. This derivation is the dual of that of Section 2.5. *Answer:* (a) $f = -\partial W_f / \partial x$; (b) $f = +\partial W_f / \partial x$.

PROBLEM 2.5.9. Use the $\pm \partial W_f / \partial x$ concept to calculate the force from the capacitive device of Figure P2.1. Note that the energy density in an electric field is $w = \frac{1}{2}\mathbf{D} \cdot \mathbf{E}$. *Answer:* $f = +\varepsilon_0 v^2 b / g$.

2.6 Saturable Materials and Coenergy

In addition to the nonlinearities inherent in the energy conversion process, nonlinear magnetic or dielectric materials may introduce further complications. Figure 2.6.1 shows the magnetization characteristic typical of saturable ferrous magnetic material. (Hysteresis will also be present, but is not shown.)

The power input to the magnetizing coil is

$$p = vi = i \, d\lambda/dt,$$

and the energy stored in the field for a certain linkage λ_1 is

$$W_f = \int_0^{t_1} p \, dt = \int_0^{\lambda_1} i \, d\lambda.$$

This integration is performed with respect to the ordinate variable λ, so the shaded area to the left of the curve corresponds to the stored field energy W_f. It is useful at this point to define the area *under* the curve as the *coenergy*, symbolized as W_f'. Thus

$$W_f' = \int_0^{i_1} \lambda \, di \quad \text{(coenergy)}$$

$$W_f = \int_0^{\lambda_1} i \, d\lambda \quad \text{(energy)}.$$

These two integrations imply that in defining coenergy, λ is regarded as a function of i, whereas in defining energy, i is considered to be a function of λ. Thus, the coenergy might be expected to be useful for cases where current is the independent variable, whereas the energy would be more useful in problems where voltage or linkages are given as independent variables.

Now let it be assumed that an electromechanical device such as that of Figure 2.5.1 is constructed of a saturable ferrous material. With the air gap closed, the saturation curve retains the shape of the magnetic material, but as the gap opens, two changes take place.

1. The curve moves downward, as shown at x_1 or x_2 in Figure 2.6.2, because with the increasing magnetic reluctance, there is less flux linkage for a given current.

2. The curve tends to straighten out, approaching in shape the linear characteristic of the air gap.

When a change takes place in the state of the device, λ and i change from their initial values to new values, the change taking place along a path that depends on the system constraints. Consider a case where the gap is closed, and the corresponding operating values (Figure 2.6.2) are λ_A and i_A. If now the gap is pulled open, so that $x = x_1$, a new operating point such as B, B', or B'' will be reached. The path as marked to point B is for a constant current

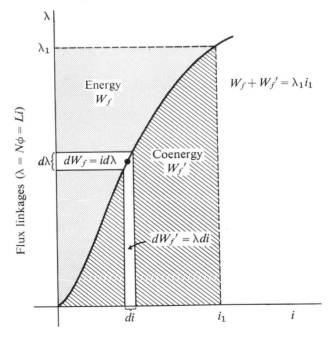

FIGURE 2.6.1. Graph illustrating magnetic saturation curve, energy, and coenergy.

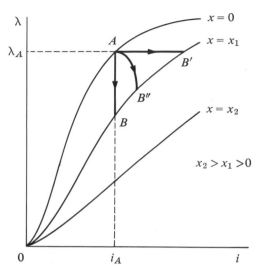

FIGURE 2.6.2. Operating paths when air gap is forced open. Path AB is for constant current, path AB' is for constant linkage, and path AB'' is a general path without special constraints.

constraint, that to B' is for constant linkages (ideal short circuit), and that to B'' is for a general case. The mechanical energy put into the system in the process is equal to the area enclosed by the operating path and the two saturation curves, such as the areas $OABO$ or $OAB'O$. This idea is developed in detail in Figure 2.6.3.

The electromagnetic force will now be determined* for the case of nonlinear magnetic materials, using the concept of the infinitesimally small "virtual displacement." The development starts with the basic energy equation, Equation (2.2.1), rearranged slightly to give

$$dW_m = dW_f - dW_e. \tag{2.6.1}$$

Let it be a condition of the problem that the independent variables are flux linkage λ and spacing x. It is desired to determine the electromechanical force developed, in terms of these variables. In order to keep the chosen variables clearly in mind, let Equation (2.6.1) be rewritten as

$$dW_m = dW_f(\lambda, x) - dW_e(\lambda, x). \tag{2.6.2}$$

Then, the differentials can be expanded as

$$dW_m = \frac{\partial W_f}{\partial \lambda} d\lambda + \frac{\partial W_f}{\partial x} dx - \frac{\partial W_e}{\partial \lambda} d\lambda - \frac{\partial W_e}{\partial x} dx. \tag{2.6.3}$$

* Based on a more general development in Reference 2.2, Chapter 1.

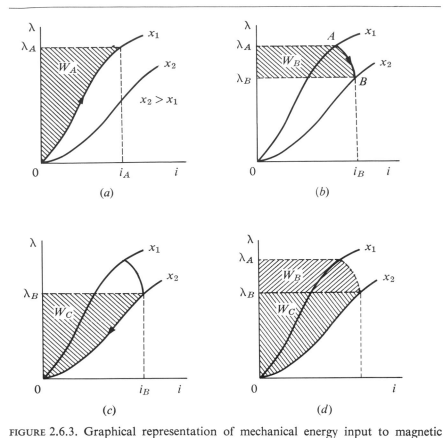

FIGURE 2.6.3. Graphical representation of mechanical energy input to magnetic field energy converter. (*a*) Magnetizing current is increased from zero to i_A. Area to left of magnetization curve is $W_A = \int_0^{\lambda_A} i\,d\lambda$, electric energy stored in magnetic field. (*b*) Air gap is forced open mechanically from x_1 to x_2 along path AB. Area to left of path is $W_B = \int_{\lambda_A}^{\lambda_B} i\,d\lambda$, electric energy entering field during the mechanical motion. In this example, W_B is numerically negative and represents energy leaving the electrical terminals. (*c*) Magnetizing current is reduced to zero, with gap held at x_2. Area to left of magnetization curve is $W_C = \int_{\lambda_B}^0 i\,d\lambda$, representing all remaining field energy returned to electric circuit. (*d*) Composite shows $W_B + W_C$, total field energy leaving electric terminals during entire cycle. (*e*) Resultant of $(W_B + W_C) - W_A$. Since stored field energy is zero at end of cycle, W_M represents mechanical energy input during cycle. Clockwise traverse represents mechanical energy into device (positive), and counterclockwise traverse represents mechanical energy out of device.

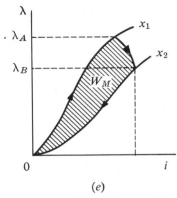

(e)

FIGURE 2.6.3. (*continued*)

In each term of Equation (2.6.3), the partial derivative notation implies that one of the variables, λ or x, is held constant. Thus the fourth term on the right is zero, since $dW_e = vi\, dt = i\, d\lambda$, and

$$\frac{\partial W_e}{\partial x} = \frac{dW_e}{dx}\bigg|_{\lambda\;\text{const}} = \frac{i\, d\lambda}{dx}\bigg|_{\lambda\;\text{const}} = 0.$$

Also, the first and third terms on the right of Equation (2.6.3) sum to zero, since with x constant the mechanical energy increment is zero, and $\partial W_f = \partial W_e$. Equation (2.6.2) then reduces to

$$dW_m = \frac{\partial W_f}{\partial x}\, dx,$$

and since $dW_m = f\, dx$,

$$f = +\frac{\partial W_f(\lambda,\, x)}{\partial x}. \qquad (2.6.4)$$

This result agrees with that of Equation (2.5.4), which was based on a non-saturating magnetic material.

Now consider the condition where the independent variables are current i and spacing x. By starting again with Equation (2.6.1), but this time expressed as functions of i and x,

$$dW_m = dW_f(i,\, x) - dW_e(i,\, x).$$

Upon expanding the differentials and collecting terms,

$$dW_m = \left(\frac{\partial W_f}{\partial i} - \frac{\partial W_e}{\partial i}\right) di + \left(\frac{\partial W_f}{\partial x} - \frac{\partial W_e}{\partial x}\right) dx. \qquad (2.6.5)$$

Since $\partial W_f = \partial W_e$ with x constant, the first term of Equation (2.6.5) is zero.

Since $dW_e = i\,d\lambda$,

$$\frac{\partial W_e}{\partial x} = \frac{dW_e}{dx}\bigg|_{i\,\text{const}} = i\,\frac{\partial\lambda}{\partial x}.\tag{2.6.6}$$

Upon substitution of Equation (2.6.6) into Equation (2.6.5), there results

$$dW_m = f\,dx = \left(\frac{\partial W_f}{\partial x} - i\,\frac{\partial\lambda}{\partial x}\right)dx.\tag{2.6.7}$$

This expression gives the force, but it can be simplified by use of the concept of coenergy. From the definition of coenergy, illustrated in Figure 2.6.1,

$$W_f = i\lambda - W_f',\tag{2.6.8}$$

where $W_f' = \int \lambda\,di$, a function of i and x. Upon taking the partial derivative of Equation (2.6.8),

$$\frac{\partial W_f}{\partial x} = i\,\frac{\partial\lambda}{\partial x} + \lambda\,\frac{\partial i}{\partial x} - \frac{\partial W_f'}{\partial x}.\tag{2.6.9}$$

But $\partial i/\partial x = 0$, for i and x are specified as being independent. Substitution of Equation (2.6.9) into Equation (2.6.7) results in the simpler form

$$f = -\frac{\partial W_f'(i, x)}{\partial x}.\tag{2.6.10}$$

The shape of the magnetic saturation curve is such that the coenergy W_f' is larger than the energy W_f. In a linear situation, the saturation curve is a straight line and $W_f' = W_f$. With this substitution, Equation (2.6.10) is identical with Equation (2.5.3), which was derived for a nonsaturating magnetic material.

The use of magnetic saturation curves to calculate force involves a tedious process. First the curves must be measured or calculated for a series of spacings. Then, W_f or W_f' must be evaluated for each desired condition by graphical integration. Finally, a curve of W_f or W_f' vs. x is drawn for a constant linkage or current, and the slope of this curve ($\partial W_f/\partial x$) taken to give the force. It should be noted that even this effort does not produce the solution to a typical problem, where the variation of x with time might be desired for a particular condition of mechanical loading.

2.7 Induced Voltages and Stored Field Energy in Multiwinding Magnetic Systems

When the field of a magnetic energy converter is disturbed, the associated change in flux linkages will induce a voltage into any coils that are present. If there is only one coil, the voltage induced into that coil is given by

$$v = \frac{d\lambda}{dt} = \frac{d(Li)}{dt} = L\frac{di}{dt} + i\frac{dL}{dt}.\tag{2.7.1}$$

The first term on the right of Equation (2.7.1) is the familiar voltage of self-induction, and the second term arises when the inductance changes because of physical motion. Thus, these two terms are often called, respectively, "induced" and "motional" emf's, or sometimes "transformer" and "speed" voltages. A term involving dL/dt will always appear when energy is being converted.

When a magnetic device has several windings, the flux linkage in any one is a function of the currents in all, and if the magnetic material is linear (nonsaturating), the linkage in winding 1 can be expressed in terms of self- and mutual inductances as*

$$\lambda_1 = L_{11}i_1 + M_{12}i_2 + M_{13}i_3 + \cdots + M_{1n}i_n + \cdots. \qquad (2.7.2a)$$

The voltage induced into winding 1 is given by

$$v_1 = \frac{d\lambda_1}{dt} = L_{11}\frac{di_1}{dt} + i_1\frac{dL_{11}}{dt} + M_{12}\frac{di_2}{dt} + i_2\frac{dM_{12}}{dt} + \cdots. \qquad (2.7.2b)$$

Here, the first two terms on the right are similar to those in Equation (2.7.1), the third is an ordinary voltage of mutual induction, and the fourth is a motional voltage arising from a change in mutual inductance caused by physical motion.

The total *field energy* stored in a magnetic device will be seen to depend only on the currents and inductances at the instant under consideration, and not on past history or rates of change. For example, the field energy in a single-winding device is $\frac{1}{2}Li^2$, and does not depend on di/dt or dL/dt. A function of this type is called a "state function" because its value depends only on the present state of certain variables called the "state variables;" in the example just given, i and L are the state variables.

The field energy stored in an electromechanical device may have entered through the electrical terminals or through the mechanical terminals or through both. Past history does not affect the present value of a state function, so the simplifying assumption can be made that all of the field energy entered through the electrical terminals. Thus, $dW_m = 0$, .and $dW_e = dW_f$. The procedure that follows this assumption is illustrated below in an example involving a two-winding magnetic device.

Example 2.7. In the two-winding magnetic device shown in Figure 2.7, it is assumed that the iron has zero reluctance and that leakage is negligible, so that all of the flux goes all of the way around the magnetic path and across the air gap.

The incremental electrical input is

$$dW_e = v_1i_1\,dt + v_2i_2\,dt.$$

Since $v\,dt = d\lambda$, this becomes

$$dW_e = i_1\,d\lambda_1 + i_2\,d\lambda_2.$$

* Reference 2.3, Chapter 1, gives a detailed development.

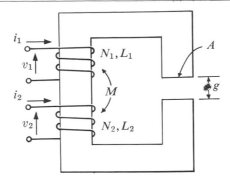

FIGURE 2.7. Two-winding magnetic device.

Substitution of the values of the linkages from Equation (2.7.2) yields

$$dW_e = L_1 i_1\, di_1 + (M i_1\, di_2 + M i_2\, di_1) + L_2 i_2\, di_2 = L_1 i_1\, di_1 + M\, d(i_1 i_2) + L_2 i_2\, di_2.$$

Since $dW_m = 0$ in this example,

$$W_f = W_e = \int dW_e = \tfrac{1}{2} L_1 i_1{}^2 + M i_1 i_2 + \tfrac{1}{2} L_2 i_2{}^2. \tag{2.7.3}$$

This result meets the requirements for a state function, since W_f depends only on the present values of the state variables (current and inductance), and not on their rates of change.

From the energy density point of view of Section 2.5,

$$\text{mmf} = N_1 i_1 + N_2 i_2$$

$$H = \frac{N_1 i_1 + N_2 i_2}{g}$$

$$W_f = wV = (\tfrac{1}{2}\mu_0 H^2)(gA) = \frac{N_1{}^2 i_1{}^2 + 2 N_1 N_2 i_1 i_2 + N_2{}^2 i_2{}^2}{2g}\,\mu_0 A.$$

Since the reluctance of the magnetic path is

$$\mathscr{R} = \frac{g}{\mu_0 A},$$

an alternate form for W_f is

$$W_f = \frac{1}{2}\frac{N_1{}^2}{\mathscr{R}} i_1{}^2 + \frac{N_1 N_2}{\mathscr{R}} i_1 i_2 + \frac{1}{2}\frac{N_2{}^2}{\mathscr{R}} i_2{}^2. \tag{2.7.4}$$

Comparison of Equation (2.7.4) with Equation (2.7.3) shows that

$$L_1 = \frac{N_1{}^2}{\mathscr{R}}; \qquad M = \frac{N_1 N_2}{\mathscr{R}}; \qquad L_2 = \frac{N_2{}^2}{\mathscr{R}}.$$

It is noted that in a nonsaturating magnetic material, the various mmf's can be added in a linear manner by superposition, as also can the H fields. The field energy W_f, however, depends on H^2, and so is not subject to linear combination. That is, the total field energy cannot be determined by adding up the field energies resulting from the various mmf's acting separately.

The ideas developed in this section are drawn upon from time to time in subsequent section and problems relating to various electromechanical devices.

PROBLEM 2.7.1. For the configuration sketched in Figure P2.7.1, the coils are moved such that $M = 0.5 \cos 3t$, while $L_1 = 2$ and $L_2 = 3$ remain constant. For a constant direct current $i = I$, compute $v(t)$. *Answer:* $v = -3I \sin 3t$.

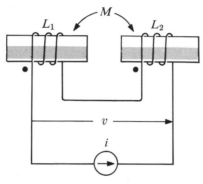

FIGURE P2.7.1.

PROBLEM 2.7.2. Repeat Problem 2.7.1 when $i = I_m \cos 3t$.
Answer: $v = -15I_m \sin 3t - 3I_m \sin 6t$.

PROBLEM 2.7.3. In the magnetic device of Figure 2.7, let $N_1 = N_2$ and $i_1 = i_2$. (a) By what factor does the stored magnetic energy increase if i_2 is doubled, i_1 remaining unchanged? (b) If $i_1 = i_2$, by what factor must both be increased to double the stored field energy? *Answer:* (a) $\frac{9}{4}$; (b) $\sqrt{2}$.

PROBLEM 2.7.4. Develop an equation similar to Equation (2.7.3), for a device having three coils instead of two.

2.8 Rotational Magnetic Systems

Motors and generators are normally rotational rather than translational. Fortunately, all of the expressions already derived hold, if torque (T) and angular displacement (θ) are substituted for force (f) and displacement (x). The two equations of most interest are:

$$T = -\tfrac{1}{2}i^2 \frac{dL}{d\theta}, \qquad (2.8.1)$$

$$T = \pm \frac{\partial W_f}{\partial \theta}. \qquad (2.8.2)$$

The general meaning of these expressions is that an electromagnetic torque can result whenever rotation will produce a changing inductance or a change of stored field energy.

Figure 2.8 depicts a simple rotating machine carrying a single winding on a cylindrical stator (stationary member). The structural parts are of iron, which is assumed for simplification to be nonsaturating and to present negligible reluctance. The rotor (rotating member), also of iron, carries no windings and is shaped in such a way that the inductance of the stator winding will vary with θ_r, and a torque may thus be expected to develop between the two members [by Equation (2.8.1)].

Several comments may be made about the various reference polarities indicated on Figure 2.8.

1. The fixed reference on the stator is placed for convenience along the stator coil axis. The positive current direction in the coil is assigned to produce mmf in the direction of the fixed stator reference axis.

2. The reference direction for θ_r and Ω is such as to make the rotor the "positive" mechanical terminal, with the fixed stator the other mechanical terminal.

3. The reference direction for T is interpreted to mean that when the torque is numerically positive, the device exerts a torque in the reference (clockwise) direction on its own positive terminal (i.e., the rotor).

Variation of inductance with θ_r is also accompanied by an inverse variation of reluctance, since $L = N^2/\mathcal{R}$. The name "reluctance motor" is therefore commonly given to this type of device.

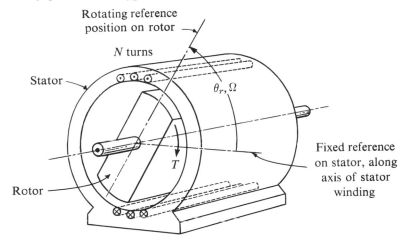

FIGURE 2.8. Simple rotating machine. Stator conductors are connected electrically at ends, top to bottom, to form continuous winding. The axis of the winding is perpendicular to the plane of the winding.

The reluctance motor is one example of the class of machines known as *synchronous* machines which require that the rotor turn exactly in step with the supply frequency if a nonzero average torque is to be produced. This idea is developed analytically in the following example.

Example 2.8. Reluctance Motor. In the device of Figure 2.8, the electromagnetic torque depends on how the stator winding inductance, L, varies with θ_r. It can be seen from inspection that L will be a maximum twice in each revolution, at $\theta_r = 0$ and $\theta_r = \pi$, and will never be zero.

It is possible to shape the rotor such that $L = L_0 + L_2 \cos 2\theta_r$, where $(L_0 - L_2) =$ minimum inductance (at $\theta_r = \pi/2, 3\pi/2$), and $(L_0 + L_2) =$ maximum inductance (at $\theta_r = 0, \pi$). When this value of inductance is used in Equation (2.8.1), the torque becomes

$$T(\theta_r) = +i^2 L_2 \sin 2\theta_r.$$

This expression shows that $T = 0$ when $\theta_r = 0$ or $\theta_r = \pi$, and that if the rotor is moved away from either of these positions, the torque is in a direction to resist the motion. The torque is also zero at $\theta_r = \pi/2$, but this is a point of unstable equilibrium. For any current other than zero, the horizontal position of the rotor is a stable one.

If the coil carries an alternating current, $i = I_m \cos(\omega t + \delta)$, the torque expression becomes $T = I_m^2 \cos^2(\omega t + \delta) L_2 \sin 2\theta_r$, which after trigonometric conversion becomes

$$T(t) = \tfrac{1}{2}I_m^2 L_2 \sin 2\theta_r + \tfrac{1}{2}I_m^2 L_2 \sin 2\theta_r \cos(2\omega t + 2\delta).$$

This shows that if $\theta_r = 0$, $\pi/2$, etc., $T = 0$, but otherwise there will be a constant torque plus a component oscillating at a frequency of 2ω. The constant component will act to return the rotor to its equilibrium position at $\theta_r = 0$ or $\theta_r = \pi$, so the motor is not self-starting. It may be started, however, by driving it externally at a constant angular velocity of Ω rad/s, so that $\theta_r = \Omega t$. With this substitution for θ_r in the torque equation just above,

$$T(t) = \tfrac{1}{2}I_m^2 L_2 \sin 2\Omega t + \tfrac{1}{2}I_m^2 L_2 \sin 2\Omega t \cos(2\omega t + 2\delta)$$

$$= \tfrac{1}{2}I_m^2 L_2 \sin 2\Omega t + \tfrac{1}{2} \cdot \tfrac{1}{2}I_m^2 L_2 [\sin(2\Omega t + 2\omega t + 2\delta) + \sin(2\Omega t - 2\omega t - 2\delta)].$$

Thus the torque contains oscillating components, of frequencies 2Ω, $2(\Omega + \omega)$, and $2(\Omega - \omega)$, and will average to zero over one or more complete revolutions unless $\Omega = \omega$, in which case,

$$T_{av} = -\tfrac{1}{4}I_m^2 L_2 \sin 2\delta.$$

This average torque is seen to have a maximum value when $\delta = 45°$.

If δ is positive, T_{av} is negative, in the direction of advancing θ_r, and the rotor will continue to turn that way once it is brought up to speed by external means. Even though a nonzero average torque is produced, there will still be instantaneous components of frequencies 2Ω and 4Ω, and these may produce mechanical vibrations if the moment of inertia is not sufficiently large.

The angle δ relates the time variation of current to the angular position of the rotor; when $i(t) = I_m$, the rotor is at that instant at $\theta_r = -\delta$. In steady-state operation, δ is constant; if the torque requirement changes, δ adjusts itself (relatively slowly) to a new value; and as δ approaches zero, the electromagnetic torque also approaches zero. For these reasons, δ is often called the "torque angle."

The machine adjusts to varying loads by changing its torque angle. For example, if the external load torque on the rotor shaft is increased until it exceeds the developed torque, the machine starts to slow down. This increases δ until sufficient electromagnetic torque is again developed. As δ exceeds 45°, however, the electromagnetic torque starts to drop off, the motor "pulls out of step" and stops. The equations describing this process will, in general, be nonlinear differential equations.

PROBLEM 2.8.1. Carry through the trigonometric conversions and other missing steps in the development of the reluctance motor example (Section 2.8). Sketch a curve of T_{av} vs. δ for $-\pi < \delta < \pi$, and comment on the significance of: (a) the region where $\delta > \pi/2$. (b) The region where $-\pi/4 < \delta < 0$. *Answer:* Both are regions of generator action.

PROBLEM 2.8.2. Assume that a current source maintains $i = I_m \cos(\omega t + \delta)$ when the reluctance motor is operating at $\Omega = \omega$, and determine the voltage $v(t)$ at the motor terminals. What frequencies does it contain? *Answer:* ω and 3ω.

2.9 A Doubly-Excited Rotating System

The system of Figure 2.9 has two windings, one on the stator (stationary member) and one on the rotor (rotating member). The angle θ_r is measured between the stationary stator winding axis and the rotating rotor winding

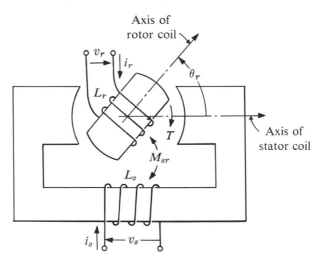

FIGURE 2.9. A doubly-excited rotating system.

axis, and the winding directions shown are such that the mmf's from the two coils add when $\theta_r = 0$ and both currents are positive. The assigned reference directions for θ_r and T indicate that the rotor is considered to be the positive mechanical terminal of the system.

The analysis will be carried out, in this case, in terms of the inductances, which are L_s, L_r, and M_{sr} (or just M). It is obvious that all three will change as θ_r is varied.

It is possible to shape the poles such that

$$L_s = L_{s0} + L_{s2} \cos 2\theta_r \qquad (L_{s0} > L_{s2})$$
$$L_r = L_{r0} + L_{r2} \cos 2\theta_r \qquad (L_{r0} > L_{r2})$$
$$M = M_0 \cos \theta_r.$$

It should be noted from these equations that the self-inductance cannot go negative, whereas the mutual inductance does. Also, the self- and mutual inductances have different periods. The student should study these expressions until he is convinced that they may actually describe the physical situation.

The expression $T = -\partial W_f/\partial \theta_r$ provides a good place to begin the analysis. The field energy is given by Equation (2.7.3), which after appropriate substitution and differentiation yields:

$$T = L_{s2} i_s^2 \sin 2\theta_r + M_0 i_s i_r \sin \theta_r + L_{r2} i_r^2 \sin 2\theta_r. \qquad (2.9.1)$$

Several comments may be made about this equation.

1. No restriction is placed on the way θ_r and the currents may or may not be varying with time.

2. If either current is made zero, the equation reduces to that of the reluctance motor. The first and last terms are, in fact, reluctance torque terms under all circumstances.

3. If L_s and L_r are made constant, only the second term remains. This term, involving mutual inductance, will be seen later to be the most important term in the majority of rotating-machine applications. This term is linear in i_r and i_s, so long as they are not functions of each other, and permits certain rotating machines to operate as linear devices.

PROBLEM 2.9.1.   Derive Equation (2.9.1).

PROBLEM 2.9.2.   Illustrate with a sketch how the physical construction of the device of Figure 2.8 can be modified so that (a) $\partial L_s/\partial \theta_r = 0$; (b) $\partial L_r/\partial \theta_r = 0$ [but $\partial L_s/\partial \theta_r \neq 0$]; (c) $\partial L_s/\partial \theta_r = 0$ and $\partial L_r/\partial \theta_r = 0$.

2.10   The Three Basic Types of Electric Machines

The device of Figure 2.9 forms the basis for the three major types of rotating electric machines. In each of the following cases, reluctance torque is ignored and attention is focused on the mutual inductance term of the torque equation (2.9.1), which thus abridged is

$$T = M_0 i_s i_r \sin \theta_r. \qquad (2.10.1)$$

(*a*) *Synchronous Machine.* If one winding is made to carry a steady direct current and the other an alternating current whose frequency equals the angular velocity of the shaft, a nonzero average torque can be shown to result. This action is similar to the synchronous operation of the reluctance motor, but the torque is much greater and can be adjusted by varying the direct current.

(*b*) *Induction Machine.* If one winding is energized from alternating current, and the second winding is short circuited, the device is called an induction machine. The name arises because the short circuited winding receives energy only by electromagnetic induction, as in a transformer. The analysis is fairly complicated, but it can be shown that this connection will produce a nonzero average torque over a wide range of speed, rather than only at synchronous speed. The induction motor is especially durable because it requires no sliding electrical contacts to provide connections to its rotor.

(*c*) *Commutator Machine.* If one winding carries a steady direct current and the other carries a current that reverses each half-revolution of the rotor, a nonzero average torque will result at all speeds. The reversals are accomplished by a mechanical switch called a commutator (literally, "interchanger") which is attached to the rotor and reverses an applied direct current twice each revolution. Commutator machines produce exceptionally good torque and speed control, but are more costly to build and maintain because of the mechanical complexity of the commutator.

2.11 Circuit vs. Field Analysis

The analysis so far has been partly in terms of circuit parameters (C, L, M, v, i), and partly in terms of field quantities (H, B, ϕ, W_f). Occasionally these two approaches have been interrelated by expressions like $L = N^2 / \mathscr{R}$ or $\lambda = Li = N\phi$.

Ultimately it will be seen that the circuits approach is best for the analysis of very complicated machines or systems of machines, whereas the fields approach can supply a better understanding of the energy processes within an individual machine. In several short chapters, the three major types of machines will be examined with the so-called "rotating field" concept as a central unifying theme. Then, in Chapter 7, the discussion will return to the analysis of the rotating machine as a circuit element.

Advanced Problems

2.1 The special parallel-plate capacitor of Figure P2.1 has three identical plates. The center plate is allowed to move horizontally only. Calculate the force as a function of v and x. Neglect fringing of the field.

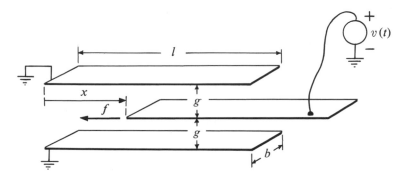

FIGURE P2.1.

2.2 The capacitor of Figure P2.1 is energized by a constant voltage source $v = V_0$. The movable plate is then withdrawn uniformly, such that $u = U_0$. Calculate (a) the battery current $i(t)$; (b) the force $f(t)$ if $x(0+) = 0$.

2.3 The capacitor of Figure P2.1 is energized by a constant voltage $v = V_0$. The center plate has mass M but negligible friction. It is withdrawn until $x = X_0$ and released at $t = 0$. (a) Draw an analogous electric circuit and write a differential equation describing the motion for $t > 0$. (b) Determine the expression for $x(t)$.

2.4 The capacitor of Figure P2.1 is turned until the axis of motion is vertical, with the movable plate of mass M suspended by a spring of stiffness K. The rest position is $x = X_0$. Find the equation for $x(t)$ if $v = V_0 \sin \omega t$.

2.5 For the small-signal linearization example of Section 2.4, determine (a) the electrical driving point admittance $I_1(s)/V_1(s)$; (b) the transfer function $F_1(s)/V_1(s)$. [Hint: Use $q = Cv$ to find $Q_1(s)/V_1(s)$, and take $I_1(s) = sQ_1(s)$.]

2.6 In the small-signal linearization example of Section 2.4, $v = V_0$ and the movable plate (Figure 2.1) is caused to move according to $x = X_0 + x_1$, with $X_0 \gg x_1$. Determine (a) the quiescent equation; (b) the mechanical driving point admittance $F_1(s)/X_1(s)$; (c) the transfer function $I_1(s)/X_1(s)$.

2.7 In the capacitive device of Figure 2.1 the voltage source is rendered nonideal by the insertion of a resistance R in series with $v(t)$. With this modification, derive equations corresponding to Equations (2.4.1), (2.4.6), and (2.4.7).

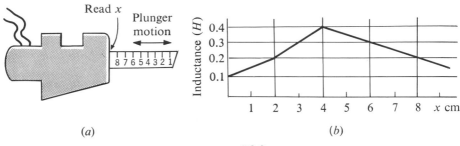

(a)   (b)

FIGURE P2.8.

2.8 The electromechanical device of Figure P2.8(a) has two electrical terminals, and a plunger marked in centimeters. The inductance at the terminals was measured for various plunger positions, with the results shown in the graph of Figure P2.8(b). Plot a graph to scale, showing the force in newtons vs. plunger position, if a steady direct current of 4.0 A flows in the winding. Is the plunger forced in or out?

2.9 The magnetic relay of Figure 2.5.1 has an applied voltage of $v = V_m \cos \omega t$. (a) With the movable arm held at $x = X_0$, calculate the stored field energy as a function of time. (b) Calculate the force by $\pm \partial W_f / \partial x$. (c) Calculate the current.

2.10 In the capacitive device of Figure P2.10, the fixed capacitor has a movable slab of dielectric of relative permitivity $\varepsilon_r = 5.0$. A constant voltage V_0 is applied. (a) With the x direction as specified on the sketch, assign the appropriate reference direction for force and calculate the force by the stored field energy method. (b) Write a differential equation for the system, if $x = 0$ when $f = 0$. (c) Find the complete response $x(t)$ if $x(0+) = 0$.

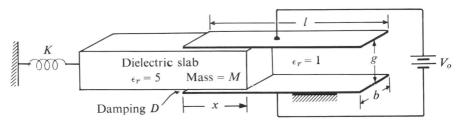

FIGURE P2.10.

2.11 In the device of Figure P2.11, the iron slug of mass M is suspended from the spring K, and at rest $y = Y_0$. (a) Assign a positive reference direction for force, and use the stored energy method to derive an expression for f in terms of the coil current i. (b) Write a differential equation, with v, y, and t as variables, describing the motion of the iron slug.

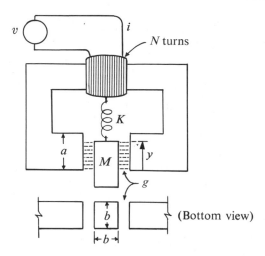

FIGURE P2.11.

2.12 In the magnetic device of Figure 2.5.2, the applied voltage is $v = V_m \cos \omega t$. The winding resistance is considered negligible. The flux is zero at $t = 0$. Calculate the force f, using the energy storage method.

2.13 (a) Two electromagnets have their coils connected in series as shown in Figure P2.13, so that opposing poles are adjacent. Find the force of attraction by the energy storage method. Consider that leakage flux is negligible. (b) Find the force of repulsion if one magnet is turned around, so that like poles are adjacent. Use the energy storage method.

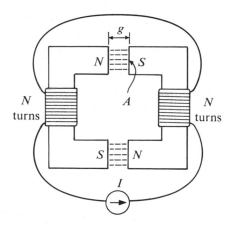

FIGURE P2.13.

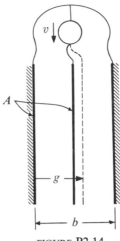

FIGURE P2.14.

2.14 A capacitor is made of three parallel plates, each of area A, as shown in Figure P2.14. The central plate is suspended midway between the others and energized with a voltage v. It may, however, move parallel to itself, into a position such as that shown by the dashed line. Use the stored field energy method to show: (a) that the force on the center plate is zero when it is centrally located (i.e., when $g = b/2$); (b) whether the center plate is forced further to the side or back toward the center, if displaced to the dashed position.

2.15 In the magnetic device of Figure 2.7, $N_1 = 1000$, $N_2 = 2000$, $g = 0.001$ m, and $A = 0.02$ sq. m. Calculate the force of attraction across the air gap if $i_1 = i_2 = 0.10$ A.

2.16 (a) Write a differential equation for the reluctance motor if $i = I_0$ and θ_r is initially held at θ_0, and released at $t = 0$. [$\theta_r(0+) = \theta_0$]. (b) If θ_r is small, the approximation $\sin\theta \cong \theta$ can be used. For small deflections and no damping, show that

$$\theta_r(t) = \theta_0 \cos I_0 \sqrt{\frac{2L_2}{J}}\, t.$$

2.17 Let the reluctance motor be supplied by a voltage source $v = V_m \cos(\omega t - \delta)$. (a) Determine the average torque when the motor is revolving with $\Omega = \omega$. For simplification, assume $L_2 < L_0$ to an extent that any term containing $(L_2/L_0)^2$ is negligible. (b) Determine the current $i(t)$.

2.18 The reluctance motor of Figure P2.18 is so designed that the inductance of the stator coil varies in a sinusoidal manner with θ_r. (a) Write an expression giving $L(\theta_r)$. (b) The rotor is caused to turn at Ω rad/s and a current $i = I_m \cos(\omega t + \delta)$ is caused to flow in the winding. Find the frequencies present in the resulting torque. (c) At what speed will the rotor develop a nonzero average torque? Evaluate this torque.

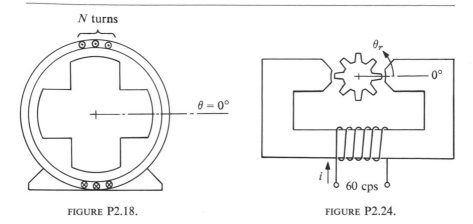

N turns

$\theta = 0°$

θ_r

$0°$

i

60 cps

FIGURE P2.18.

FIGURE P2.24.

2.19 The two windings of the device of Figure 2.9 are connected in series, and an alternating current caused to flow such that $i_s = i_r = I_m \cos (\omega t + \delta)$. Determine, by trigonometric expansions, the rotor speeds at which a nonzero average torque will be produced. Identify reluctance-torque terms and mutual-inductance torque terms.

2.20 The device of Figure 2.9 is modified so that only mutual inductance varies with θ_r (see Problem 2.9.2c). If $i_s = I_s$ and $i_r = I_m \cos (\omega t + \delta)$, determine by trigonometric expansion the speed at which a nonzero average torque is produced, and sketch the instantaneous torque vs. θ_r.

2.21 The device of Figure 2.9 is modified so that $L_s = 0.8$, $L_r = 0.2$, $M = 0.4 \cos \theta_r$. A current $i_s = 10 \cos 100t$ is caused to flow in the stator winding, and the rotor winding left open circuited. Calculate the instantaneous induced voltage v_r when Ω is (a) 0; (b) 40; (c) 100. Let $\theta_r = 0$ when $t = 0$ in each case.

2.22 Show that the induction motor of Problem 2.21 can produce a nonzero average torque if the rotor winding is closed through a 20 ohm resistance when $\Omega = 40$ rad/s.

2.23 The device of Figure 2.9 has $i_s = I_s$, and a steady direct current I_r is impressed on the rotor through a commutator. Let $L_{s2} = L_{r2} = 0$. (a) At what values of θ_r should the commutator reverse the rotor current if maximum average torque is to be produced? (b) Sketch i_r vs. θ_r, paying attention to polarities. (c) Sketch T vs. θ_r.

2.24 The sketch of Figure P2.24 depicts a simple synchronous (reluctance) motor such as might be used in a clock. (a) Write an expression for the inductance of the coil in terms of θ_r, assuming a sinusoidal (or cosinusoidal) variation. (b) At what speed or speeds will the motor develop nonzero average torque? (c) Suppose that the inductance variation in (a) contains higher harmonics, particularly the third harmonic of the assumed sinusoidal variation. In what way, if any, will this affect the production of nonzero average torque?

REFERENCES

2.1   G. H. SHORTLEY and D. E. WILLIAMS. *Elements of Physics*. New Jersey: Prentice-Hall, Inc., 1961.

2.2   D. C. WHITE and H. H. WOODSON. *Electromechanical Energy Conversion*, Chapter 1. New York: John Wiley and Sons, Inc., 1959.

2.3   A. E. FITZGERALD and C. KINGSLEY Jr. *Electric Machinery*, Chapter 1 (2nd Ed.). New York: McGraw-Hill, 1961.

CHAPTER THREE

The Rotating Magnetic Field

3.1 An Elementary Illustrative Example

Because of the importance of the rotating field concept, an elementary illustrative example may prove helpful. In Figure 3.1, the "stator" is physically rotated in the direction shown. The stator carries with it a pair of magnetic poles (either permanent or electromagnetic). The rotor is also magnetized, and tends to follow the rotation of the stator.

If there is no external torque on the rotor shaft, the rotor and stator axes will line up, but if torque is applied, the rotor will tend to drop behind by the angle δ, called the *torque angle*. The torque angle is measured between the axes of two magnetic fields, both of which rotate at the same speed.

It is shown later that it is not necessary to rotate the stator physically to produce a rotating magnetic field. All rotating machines can be analyzed in

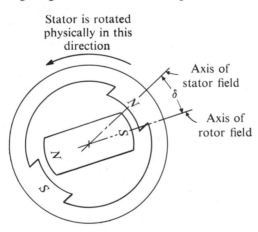

FIGURE 3.1. Illustration of rotating field concept. Stator is rotated physically and pulls rotor along. Torque angle increases as shaft torque increases.

terms of the interaction between rotating fields, which is illustrated most simply by the tendency of magnets to line up with each other.

3.2   The Sinusoidally-Distributed Field in a Uniform Air Gap

In order to simplify the picture as much as possible, a cylindrical machine having uniform air gap, and therefore, zero reluctance torque, will be studied.

The distribution of the magnetic field around the air gap will depend on the distribution of the windings. Figure 3.2.1 shows a machine with a single turn on the stator and none on the rotor. In this example, the rotor serves only to complete the magnetic path.

The resultant air-gap field in Figure 3.2.1 is radial and uniform, as can be shown by considering Ampere's mmf law around a path such as A. The mmf around the path is equal to the current enclosed, and since the iron is considered to have infinite permeability, half of the mmf appears at each of the two places that the path crosses the air gap. This is true regardless of the path; for example, path B encloses the same current as path A, and the mmf across the gaps along path B near the conductor is the same as it is farther away, around path A. Thus, the H (or B) field is uniform around the gap. A path such as C encloses no current, but this does not mean that there is no air-gap field along C. The only requirement is that the H-field integrate to zero around path C.

If the current is caused to flow through a sinusoidally-distributed winding, as in Figure 3.2.2, a cosinusoidally-distributed field can be produced. It can be seen in Figure 3.2.2 that the current enclosed inside path A is greater than that enclosed in path B, so the field in the gap at A is greater than at B. The actual field distribution is not smooth but has small finite jumps at the conductor positions. With many closely spaced conductors, however, a smooth cosinusoidal variation is approached very closely. In the ideal case, the cosinusoidal field intensity H varies with position as $H(\theta) = H_m \cos \theta$, where θ is measured from the coil axis. To find the maximum field intensity H_m, it is necessary to apply Ampere's law around a path that encloses the maximum current. Since the path along the coil axis encloses all of the turns, the maximum value of the air-gap field intensity occurs on the coil axis, and is expressed by $H_m = Ni/2g$, where g is the radial length of the air gap.*

The assumption of a cosinusoidal field distribution leads to considerable simplification in the mathematical analysis. In practice, a uniformly-spaced winding is usually used, but the results are only slightly different from those of a perfect cosinusoidal distribution.

The conductors are actually set in slots, as shown in Figures 3.2.3 and 3.2.4, to provide physical strength and protection. If the air gap is small

---

* N is the total turns in the winding. In some treatments N represents turns "per pole," in which case $H_m = Ni/g$.

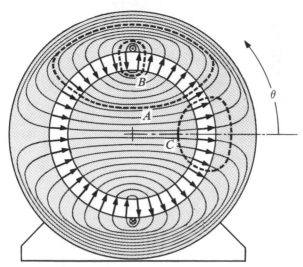

FIGURE 3.2.1. Uniform air-gap field produced by single current-carrying turn on stator. Equal spacing between field arrows indicates uniform field strength.

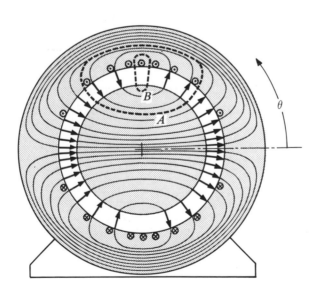

FIGURE 3.2.2. Cosinusoidally varying air-gap field, produced by sinusoidally-distributed winding. Current flows through all coil-sides in series, in relative directions shown.

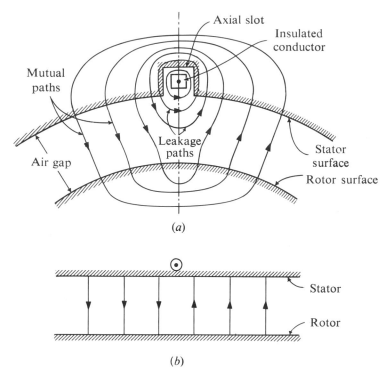

(a)

(b)

FIGURE 3.2.3. (*a*) Detail of magnetic field at air gap. Axial slot would ordinarily contain more than one insulated conductor. (*b*) Parallel approximation to air gap. Gap is assumed very small compared to rotor radius, and leakage field is neglected.

compared with the rotor radius, the rotor and stator surfaces can be approximated by parallel planes. If leakage is neglected, the radial field lines then become parallel.

PROBLEM 3.2.1. Devise a configuration for the conductors, similar to Figure 3.2.2, that will give (*a*) $H(\theta) = H_m \sin \theta$; (*b*) $H(\theta) = H_m \cos 2\theta$.

3.3 An Important Torque Relationship

In this section it is shown that the torque produced by the interaction between two cosinusoidally-distributed fields is proportional to the sine of the angle between the axes of the fields. Figure 3.3 shows a uniform-gap rotating machine with a sinusoidally-distributed winding on the stator and another on the rotor. The rotor is cylindrical and of axial length l (measured into the paper).

The angle θ is measured from the stator coil axis to any general location, and is not to be confused with θ_r used previously.

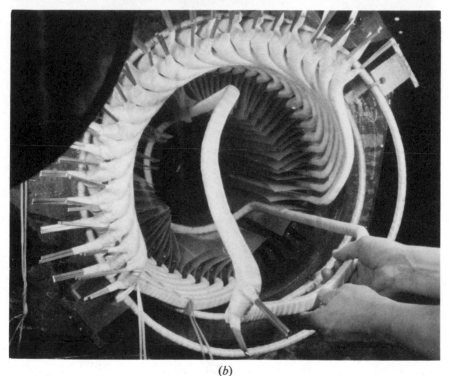

(b)

FIGURE 3.2.4. Photographs of stator construction. (Courtesy of Westinghouse Electric Corporation, Motor and Gearing Division, Buffalo, New York.) (a) Side view of sin le coil, made up of several insulated turns. Front connections are visible as bare copper at left. (b) Coils being assembled into stator of two-pole, 1250 horsepower motor. Axial slots are visible just beyond operator's hands. Stator is assembled from a large number of thin stampings (laminations) which are stacked and clamped together.

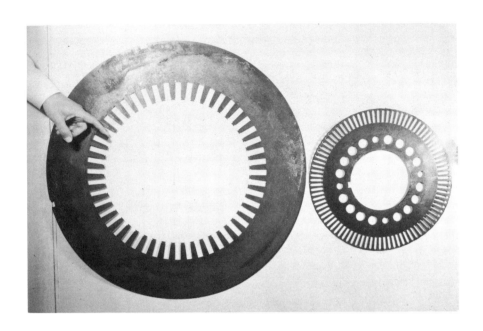

FIGURE 3.2.4. (c) Typical stator and rotor laminations, punched from 0.0185-inch electrical grade sheet steel, thin enough to be bent easily with finger. Laminations are used to reduce losses from induced currents (eddy currents) that would otherwise circulate throughout the iron members; since induced voltages are low, surface contact between laminations blocks these currents without need for additional insulation.

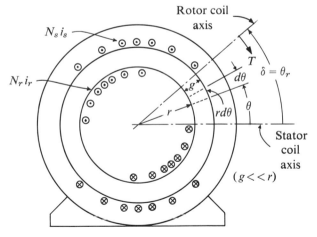

FIGURE 3.3. Cosinusoidally-distributed coils on both stator and rotor. Torque angle δ is between the axes of the two fields, and in this special case is equal to θ_r, the angular position of the rotor coil axis.

The angle δ is the torque angle, measured between the axes of the two fields, and in this special case is the same as θ_r, used previously to measure the angular position of the rotor-coil axis.

Each winding is assumed to produce a sinusoidal distribution of field strength in the air gap, and the fields from the two windings, considered separately, are

$$H_s(\theta) = \frac{N_s i_s}{2g} \cos \theta = \frac{N_s i_s}{2g} \cos (-\theta)$$

$$H_r(\theta) = \frac{N_r i_r}{2g} \cos (\theta - \delta) = \frac{N_r i_r}{2g} \cos (o - \theta). \tag{3.3.1}$$

The reversal of sign of the cosine argument, which does not affect the equation [since $\cos (-\theta) = \cos \theta$], will be helpful in a later section. Equation (3.3.1) shows that $H_s(\theta)$ is a maximum where $\theta = 0$, along the stator coil axis, and $H_r(\theta)$ is a maximum where $\theta = \delta = \theta_r$ (along the rotor coil axis).

Since fields in an air gap are linear, the total field is

$$H_t = H_s + H_r = H_{sm} \cos (-\theta) + H_{rm} \cos (\delta - \theta), \tag{3.3.2}$$

where $\qquad H_{sm} = N_s i_s / 2g \quad \text{and} \quad H_{rm} = N_r i_r / 2g.$

The energy density is $w = \frac{1}{2} H^2 \mu_0$, and is *not* linear in H (because of the squared term); therefore, the stored field energy can be expected to change with δ and a torque can be expected.

To find the total field energy it is necessary to integrate the energy density over the gap volume. Unlike many of the examples considered in Chapter 2, here the energy density is not uniform throughout the air gap, and a formal integration is required. With the assumption that the gap length g in Figure 3.3 is small compared with the rotor radius r, the differential element of volume is $dV = glr\, d\theta$. Thus,

$$W_f = \int_V w\, dV = \int_{\theta=0}^{\theta=2\pi} (\tfrac{1}{2} H_t^2 \mu_0)(glr\, d\theta), \tag{3.3.3}$$

from which, with H_s and H_r (and therefore currents) the independent variables, and after considerable manipulation,

$$T = -\frac{\partial W_f}{\partial \delta} = \mu_0 \pi l r g H_{sm} H_{rm} \sin \delta. \tag{3.3.4}$$

When Equation (3.3.4) is expressed in terms of currents, it becomes

$$T = \frac{\mu_0 \pi l r N_s N_r}{4g} i_s i_r \sin \delta, \tag{3.3.5}$$

showing that a small air gap gives large torque per ampere. Equation (3.3.4) can be written more compactly as

$$T = K_h H_{sm} H_{rm} \sin \delta. \tag{3.3.6}$$

If voltage is taken as the independent circuit variable, B becomes the appropriate field variable and Equation (3.3.4) is rearranged as

$$T = \frac{\pi l r g}{\mu_0} B_{sm} B_{rm} \sin \delta = K_b B_{sm} B_{rm} \sin \delta. \tag{3.3.7}$$

It may be that one winding is energized from a voltage source and the other from a current source. Then the torque equation might best appear in a form such as

$$T = \pi l r g B_{sm} H_{rm} \sin \delta. \tag{3.3.8}$$

Often there may be more than one winding on the stator or on the rotor, in which case H_{sm} represents the total field from all stator currents, and H_{rm} represents the total field from all rotor currents.

The important expressions developed above, describing the tendency of two magnetic fields to align and thereby achieve the position of maximum stored energy (or minimum when the voltage is the independent variable), can serve as the basis for the analysis of all multiply excited rotating machines.*

PROBLEM 3.3.1. Supply the missing steps in the derivations of Equations (3.3.4), (3.3.5), and (3.3.7).

3.4 Phasor Addition of Sinusoidally-Distributed Fields

Phasors are commonly used to add sinusoidal quantities of the same period. The two fields of Figure 3.3 can be expressed as phasors, starting first with the vector (not phasor) expressions developed previously,

$$\begin{aligned}
\mathscr{H}_s(\theta) &= \mathbf{a}_r H_{sm} \cos(-\theta) \\
\mathscr{H}_r(\theta) &= \mathbf{a}_r H_{rm} \cos(\theta_r - \theta).
\end{aligned} \tag{3.4.1}$$

The unit radius vector $\mathbf{a}_r$ is added to emphasize that both fields are radial vector fields in the air gap. The boldface script symbol $\mathscr{H}$ (and later, $\mathscr{B}$) is used specifically to represent a field that is sinusoidally distributed in the air gap. None of these symbols represents phasors, which are introduced below.

The resultant or total air-gap field is the linear vector sum of the two components, or

$$\begin{aligned}
\mathscr{H}_t(\theta) &= \mathscr{H}_s(\theta) + \mathscr{H}_r(\theta) \\
&= \mathbf{a}_r [H_{sm} \cos(-\theta) + H_{rm} \cos(\theta_r - \theta)].
\end{aligned} \tag{3.4.2}$$

* Torque relationships can also be developed from other points of view, including $T = i\partial\lambda/\partial\theta$ and the "*Bli* rule." These are discussed in the Appendix, Section A.6.

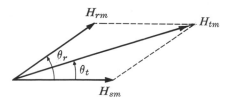

FIGURE 3.4. Phasor addition of sinusoidal fields.

By using the equivalent form $\cos x = \text{Re}\,[e^{jx}]$, where Re indicates "real part of," the total field can be written as

$$\mathcal{H}_t(\theta) = \mathbf{a}_r\,\text{Re}\,[H_{sm}^{\bullet}e^{-j\theta} + H_{rm}e^{j(\theta_r-\theta)}] \tag{3.4.3}$$
$$= \mathbf{a}_r\,\text{Re}\,[(H_{sm}e^{j0} + H_{rm}e^{j\theta_r})e^{-j\theta}].$$

The complex numbers in the inner bracket are now added according to

$$H_{sm}e^{j0} + H_{rm}e^{j\theta_r} = H_{tm}e^{j\theta_t}, \tag{3.4.4}$$

giving

$$\mathcal{H}_t(\theta) = \mathbf{a}_r\,\text{Re}\,[(H_{tm}e^{j\theta_t})e^{-j\theta}] \tag{3.4.5}$$
$$= \mathbf{a}_r H_{tm}\cos(\theta_t - \theta). \tag{3.4.6}$$

Equation (3.4.6) describes a single radial field, of maximum strength H_{tm}, and cosinusoidally distributed in the air gap about an axis lying in the direction $\theta = \theta_t$. The location of the field axis, along which the field has its maximum strength, H_{tm}, was determined from Equation (3.4.6) by setting the argument of the cosine function equal to zero.

The complex addition shown in Equation (3.4.4) is depicted graphically in Figure 3.4, where it is evident that the angle θ_r in the complex plane is equal to the rotor coil angle in Figure 3.3, and the angle θ_t in the complex plane is equal to the angle of the axis of the total field, H_{tm}, in Figure 3.3. Also, the lengths H_{sm}, H_{rm}, and H_{tm} in the complex plane of Figure 3.4 are equal to the maximum (axial) values of the various fields. The complex quantities in Equations (3.4.4) and (3.4.5) are called *space phasors*, and are analogous to the phasors commonly used to represent voltages and currents that vary sinusoidally with time. Space phasors are used to represent quantities distributed sinusoidally in space, in this case a magnetic field distributed around an air gap.

For comparison, the derivation of the *time phasor* of circuit theory is reviewed below. Let a quantity varying sinusoidally in time be given by

$$v(t) = V_m\cos(\omega t + \phi)$$
$$= \text{Re}\,[V_m e^{j(\omega t+\phi)}]$$
$$= \text{Re}\,[(V_m e^{j\phi})e^{j\omega t}].$$

The term $V_m e^{j\phi}$ gives both the phase angle and the magnitude, and is called the *complex amplitude* or *stationary phasor*, designated by the symbol **V**; the term $e^{j\omega t}$ contains the frequency and causes the total complex quantity within the square brackets to become a *rotating time phasor* which rotates once each cycle. Upon returning to the space phasors of Equations (3.4.4) and (3.4.5), it is seen that the term $H_{tm} e^{j\theta_t}$ gives the physical angle θ_t of the (total) field axis, and also gives the axial field magnitude, H_{tm}. The term $e^{-j\theta}$ represents a cosinusoidal space distribution of the field around its axis, just as the term $e^{j\omega t}$ represents the cosinusoidal distribution of a voltage in time.

To summarize, an air-gap field with its axis at some general position $\theta = \alpha$ is expressed by

$$\mathscr{H}(\theta) = \mathbf{a}_r \text{ Re } [H_m e^{j\alpha} e^{-j\theta}], \tag{3.4.7}$$

which contains a complex quantity called a *distributed space phasor* given by

$$\mathbf{H}(\theta) = H_m e^{j\alpha} e^{-j\theta} = H_m e^{j(\alpha-\theta)}, \tag{3.4.8}$$

which in turn contains an *axial space phasor* given by

$$\mathbf{H} = H_m e^{j\alpha}, \tag{3.4.9}$$

sometimes written as $\mathbf{H} = H_m \underline{/\alpha}$. The choice between these various forms depends on how much information it is necessary to express; for most of the applications in subsequent chapters, the simplest form, Equation (3.4.9), is adequate.*

When applied to air-gap magnetic fields, space phasors provide an exceptionally clear and graphic visualization of the field relationships. There is, in fact, an alternative interpretation, that these representations are truly space *vectors*, depicting the maximum value of the field and the direction of its axis in space. It is important, however, that such a field-axis vector not be confused with the actual vector magnetic fields in the air gap, which are always radial regardless of the direction of the field axis. In view of the similarity of the complex phasors of Figure 3.4 to the physical situation in Figure 3.3, it is well to be reminded again that the air-gap fields, as well as their sum, are colinear and radial. The angles of their axes affect the magnitude and axis of the resultant field, but the resultant is always cosinusoidally distributed around the air gap and is always radial at every point in the air gap.

PROBLEM 3.4.1. Two cosinusoidally-distributed fields are given by

$$\mathscr{B}_1(\theta) = \mathbf{a}_r \, 0.5 \cos (-\theta) \quad \text{and} \quad \mathscr{B}_2(\theta) = \mathbf{a}_r \, 0.4 \cos (60° - \theta).$$

* When complex numbers are represented pictorially as phasors, as in Figure 3.4, the symbol placed by the head of the phasor represents the magnitude only, and is therefore not shown in boldface.

(a) Determine the equation for their resultant by phasor methods, expressing it in each of the forms of Equations (3.4.6), (3.4.7), (3.4.8), and (3.4.9). At what value of θ is the resultant field a maximum? (b) Determine the resultant $\mathscr{B}$ at the point in the air gap where $\theta = 270°$. What is the vector direction of $\mathscr{B}$ at this point? *Answer:* (a) $\mathscr{B}_t(\theta) = \mathbf{a}_r\,0.78\cos(26.3° - \theta)$, $\mathscr{B}_t(\theta) = \mathbf{a}_r\,\text{Re}\,[0.78e^{j26.3°}\,e^{-j\theta}]$, $\mathbf{B}_t(\theta) = 0.78e^{j26.3°}\,e^{-j\theta}$, $\mathbf{B}_t = 0.78e^{j26.3°}$, B_m at $\theta = 26.3°$; (b) $\mathscr{B}(270°) = -0.34\,\mathbf{a}_r$, directed upward.

3.5   Representation of the Rotating Magnetic Field

As a simple example of a *rotating* magnetic field, let the rotor coil of Figure 3.3 carry a steady direct current while the stator winding is open-circuited, so that $H_s = 0$. The air-gap field will then be caused entirely by the rotor, and will be similar in appearance to that of Figure 3.2.2 except that the field is now oriented about the axis of the rotor winding.

If the rotor is turned at an angular velocity Ω, the field rotates with it, causing a "traveling wave" of magnetic field to move around the air gap. This situation can be described mathematically by letting the rotor-axis angle θ_r vary with time so that

$$\theta_r = \int_0^t \Omega\,dt + \alpha,$$

where Ω is the angular velocity of the rotor, and the constant angle α has been introduced to provide generality ($\theta_r = \alpha$ when $t = 0$). For a *constant* rotor speed Ω, $\theta_r = \Omega t + \alpha$, and the air-gap field becomes

$$\mathscr{H}(\theta, t) = \mathbf{a}_r H_m \cos(\theta_r - \theta)$$
$$= \mathbf{a}_r H_m \cos(\Omega t + \alpha - \theta) \tag{3.5.1}$$

This last expression is best understood by holding constant first one variable and then another. If time is held constant at t_0, the expression depicts a stationary field cosinusoidally distributed around the fixed axis $\theta = \Omega t_0 + \alpha$. If θ is held constant at θ_0, directing attention to a single location on the air gap, the field there is seen to vary cosinusoidally with time. If neither t nor θ is constrained, the equation describes a cosinusoidally-distributed field which rotates* with time, such that its axis is always at $\theta = \Omega t + \alpha$.

The rotating field of Equation (3.5.1) can also be expressed in complex form as

$$\mathscr{H}(\theta, t) = \mathbf{a}_r\,\text{Re}\,[(H_m e^{j\alpha})e^{j(\Omega t - \theta)}]. \tag{3.5.2}$$

The complex amplitude $H_m e^{j\alpha}$ is an axial space phasor of the type described

---

* There is a philosophical question as to whether the field actually should be said to "rotate." This is analogous to arguing whether ocean waves really move or simply bob up and down. There are certain situations where naive application of the rotating field concept will give incorrect results, but these do not arise in the present discussion.

in Section 3.4, and the remaining factor $e^{j(\Omega t - \theta)}$ will be shown to account for both the rotation and the distribution of the field.

The entire complex quantity in the square brackets of Equation (3.5.2) is termed a *rotating distributed space phasor*, and is of the form

$$\mathbf{H}(\theta, t) = H_m e^{j\alpha} e^{j(\Omega t - \theta)}. \tag{3.5.3}$$

If time is held constant at t_0, this becomes a distributed space phasor,

$$\mathbf{H}(\theta, t_0) = H_m e^{j[(\alpha + \Omega t_0) - \theta]}, \tag{3.5.4}$$

which depicts a stationary air-gap field cosinusoidally distributed around a fixed axis at $\theta = \alpha + \Omega t_0$. If θ is held constant at θ_0, directing attention to a single location on the air gap, the rotating space phasor degenerates into

$$\mathbf{H}(\theta_0, t) = H_m e^{j(\alpha - \theta_0)} e^{j\Omega t}, \tag{3.5.6}$$

which is a simple time phasor rotating in the complex plane and depicting a sinusoidal time variation of field strength in the air gap at the location $\theta = \theta_0$.

When the rotating space phasor is written in the form

$$\mathbf{H}(\theta, t) = H_m e^{j\alpha} e^{-j\theta} e^{j\Omega t}, \tag{3.5.7}$$

with no constraint on t or θ, the function of each exponential factor can be specified. The factor $e^{j\Omega t}$ causes the phasor to rotate, the factor $e^{-j\theta}$ indicates a cosinusoidal field distribution in space, and the factor $e^{j\alpha}$ provides an arbitrary fixed displacement of the axis. The fact that rotation of the space phasor in the complex plane corresponds exactly to physical rotation of the air-gap field axis in the machine is an excellent aid to visualization. The reason for the reversal of sign in the argument of the cosine functions of Equation 3.3.1 [where $(\delta - \theta)$ was substituted for $(\theta - \delta)$] now becomes apparent. Without this reversal, the space phasor would be of the form

$$H_m e^{j(\theta - \Omega t)} = H_m e^{j\theta} e^{-j\Omega t},$$

and the phasor would rotate with time in a direction opposite to that of the physical field axis.

When dealing with interactions between two (or more) fields each of which is known to be cosinusoidally distributed about its axis, and each of which is known to be rotating at the same angular velocity, the complicated expression of Equation (3.5.3) for the rotating space phasor is usually unnecessary. All of the information needed for the determination of the resultant of two such rotating fields, or to find the torque between them, is contained in the much simpler stationary axial phasor of the form

$$\mathbf{H} = H_m e^{j\alpha}, \tag{3.5.8}$$

and this form is adequate for most of the situations encountered in subsequent chapters.

PROBLEM 3.5.1. A certain cosinusoidally-distributed, radial, rotating air-gap field has $B_m = 1.0$ Wb/m², rotates 50 times a second, and has zero value at $\theta = 60°$ when $t = 0$. Write its equation. *Answer*: $\mathcal{B}(\theta, t) = \mathbf{a}_r\, 1.0 \cos(314t + 150° - \theta)$ or $\mathbf{a}_r\, 1.0 \cos(314t - 30° - \theta)$.

PROBLEM 3.5.2. For the air-gap field $\mathcal{H}(\theta, t) = \mathbf{a}_r\, 150 \cos(377t + 40° - \theta)$, write the numerical value of (*a*) the corresponding rotating space phasor; (*b*) the stationary axial phasor; (*c*) the time phasor representing the field variation at $\theta = 120°$; (*d*) the distributed space phasor representing the air-gap field at the instant $t = 0.01$ s.

Answer: (a) $\mathbf{H}(\theta, t) = 150e^{j40°}\, e^{j(377t-\theta)}$;   (b) $\mathbf{H} = 150e^{j40°}$;

     (c) $\mathbf{H}(t) = 150e^{-j80°}e^{j377t}$;   (d) $\mathbf{H}(\theta) = 150e^{-j104°}\, e^{-j\theta}$.

PROBLEM 3.5.3. Two rotating fields are given by

$$\mathcal{B}_1(\theta, t) = \mathbf{a}_r\, \mathrm{Re}\,[1.2e^{j20°}e^{j(50t-\theta)}]$$

$$\mathcal{B}_2(\theta, t) = \mathbf{a}_r\, \mathrm{Re}\,[0.8e^{-j70°}e^{j(50t-\theta)}].$$

Write their resultant in cosine form. *Answer:* $\mathcal{B}_t(\theta, t) = \mathbf{a}_r\, 1.44 \cos(50t - 13.6° - \theta)$.

3.6 A Rotating Field from Stationary Windings

A highly important concept is that a rotating magnetic field can arise without any physical motion of the windings, through the interaction of polyphase currents. A two-phase stator is shown in Figure 3.6.1. The stator

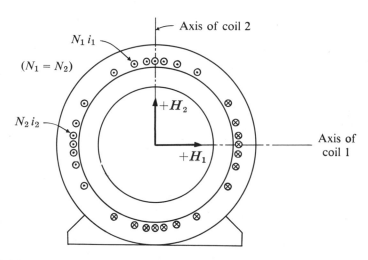

FIGURE 3.6.1. Two-phase stator windings. Coil 1 is identical to that of Figure 3.2.2, and Coil 2 is also identical except that its axis is advanced by 90°. For full distribution of windings, there would be overlap.

is wound with two separate windings whose axes are 90° apart, which carry the balanced currents from a two-phase supply (also 90° apart in time phase) given by:

$$i_1 = I_m \cos \omega t$$
$$i_2 = I_m \cos (\omega t - 90°).$$

(3.6.1)

The fields produced by these coils may be represented, according to Section 3.5, by stationary phasors having angles the same as those of the respective coil axes. The sum of these two phasors will give the resultant field. The axial magnitude of each field is derived from the appropriate current as $H_m = Ni/2g$, and if $N_1 = N_2$, the axial phasors representing the two fields are

$$\mathbf{H}_1(t) = H_{1m}e^{j0°} = \frac{Ni_1}{2g} e^{j0°} = \frac{NI_m}{2g} \cos \omega t \, e^{j0°}$$

(3.6.2)

$$\mathbf{H}_2(t) = H_{2m}e^{j90°} = \frac{Ni_2}{2g} e^{j90°} = \frac{NI_m}{2g} \cos (\omega t - 90°) \, e^{j90°}.$$

The terms $e^{j0°}$ and $e^{j90°}$ give the fixed axes of the two fields, and correspond to $e^{j\alpha}$ in Equation (3.4.9), except that both fields are now produced by alternating currents in stator windings. Both of these fields are time-varying in magnitude, but each is aligned along its respective coil axis and does not rotate. In the complex plane, such nonrotating fields are represented by *reciprocating* phasors, a form not encountered in circuit theory. Their use is justified by the identity

$$\cos \Omega t = \tfrac{1}{2}(e^{j\Omega t} + e^{-j\Omega t}),$$

which represents a phasor reciprocating on the real axis as the superposition of two *counter*-rotating phasors. Thus, any analysis that applies to the counter-rotating components separately also applies to their sum. This idea is used in subsequent developments in Section 5.8.

The fields of the two-phase machine of Figure 3.6.1 are, then, represented as reciprocating phasors in Equations (3.6.2). In view of the 90° angle between the axes, the magnitude of the resultant is readily found by trigonometry:

$$H_T = \sqrt{H_1^2 + H_2^2}$$

$$= \frac{NI_m}{2g} \sqrt{\cos^2 \omega t + \cos^2 (\omega t - 90°)}$$

$$= \frac{NI_m}{2g} \qquad \text{[a constant magnitude]}.$$

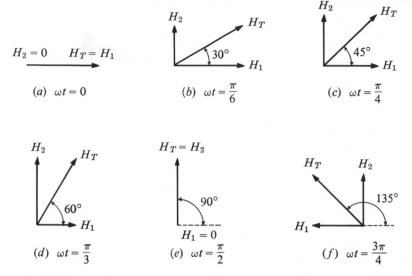

FIGURE 3.6.2. Phasor addition of components to produce uniform rotating field. H_1 and H_2 are "reciprocating phasors" that do not rotate.

The angle of the resultant is

$$\theta_T = \tan^{-1}\frac{H_2}{H_1} = \tan^{-1}\frac{\cos(\omega t - 90°)}{\cos \omega t} = \tan^{-1}\frac{\sin \omega t}{\cos \omega t}$$
$$= \omega t \qquad\qquad \text{[proportional to time]}.$$

Thus, for each cycle of the coil currents, the resultant uniform magnetic field "rotates" once around the air gap, in exactly the same manner that was observed in Section 3.5 when the magnetized rotor was caused to revolve physically. The process is illustrated graphically in Figure 3.6.2 by a series of sketches representing the two reciprocating phasors and their rotating resultant at various instants of time.

PROBLEM 3.6.1. Let each current in Equation (3.6.1) be shifted in time by an angle ϕ. Show analytically that the resulting rotating magnetic field is shifted by the same angle in space.

PROBLEM 3.6.2. What change should be made in the two-phase stator of Figure 3.6.1 so that the resultant field will rotate in the opposite direction? Show quantitative verification.

3.7 Synchronous Operation

It has been shown that torque is produced whenever the rotor and stator field axes are not in line. The production of continuous torque as the rotor turns depends on there being some way to keep the torque angle δ constant as the rotor turns. The ability of a polyphase stator winding to produce a rotating magnetic field is one important solution to this problem. If the rotor is energized with a steady direct current, it will turn in synchronism with a rotating stator field, provided it is first accelerated to this speed (called the "synchronous speed") by some external means. The torque angle δ, measured between the axes of the two rotating fields, will adjust itself to the value required by the torque equation $T = K_h H_s H_r \sin \delta$, and will thereafter remain constant as the two fields rotate together. The electromagnetic torque is therefore uniform, free from the harmonic pulsations often noted in the single-phase devices of Chapter 2. The production of a uniform, nonpulsating torque is one of the outstanding features of polyphase machines.

Torque can also be produced by a machine having polyphase windings on both rotor and stator, and with each energized from a source of different frequency. The rotor field will then rotate with respect to the rotor at a different speed than the stator field rotates with respect to the stator, and the difference must be made up by mechanical rotation of the rotor. The torque angle now is measured between the axes of two rotating fields, and is not directly related to any single coil axis.

When the mechanical speed of a machine must be related in some exact manner to its terminal frequency before a nonzero average torque can be produced, the machine is called a *synchronous machine*.

Example 3.7. A machine has two-phase windings on both rotor and stator. A balanced two-phase voltage of frequency $\omega_s = 40 \, \text{rad/s}$ is applied to the stator terminals, and a balanced two-phase voltage of frequency $\omega_r = 60 \, \text{rad/s}$ is applied to the rotor terminals (through sliding contacts called "slip rings"). At what speed Ω must the rotor be turning to produce a constant torque angle?
Solution. The stator field rotates at $\omega_s = 40$ in the "forward" direction. When the rotor field rotates in the forward direction at $\omega_r = 60$ with respect to the rotor, the rotor must be driven backward at $\Omega = 20$ to produce a constant angle between the two fields.

If the rotor connections are changed so as to cause the rotor field to rotate "backward" at $\omega_r = 60$, then $\Omega = 100$ is required in the forward direction.

PROBLEM 3.7.1. A polyphase stator is energized at ω_s and its polyphase rotor at ω_r. Find a general expression for Ω, the mechanical speed required for a continuous torque to be produced.

3.8 Voltages Induced by Rotating Fields

The air-gap fields have, to this point, been analyzed in terms of the magnetic field intensity, H. For the uniform gap machine, the magnetic flux density B is everywhere proportional to H, according to the relationship $B = \mu_0 H$.

The *H*-field is directly related to the winding current and is the appropriate variable to use when the winding is energized from a current source. If the winding is energized from a voltage source, it is the *B*-field that is more appropriate, for the applied voltage is related to the rotating *B*-field by $v = (\mathbf{u} \times \mathcal{B}) \cdot \mathbf{l}$ (the *Blu* rule; see Appendix, Section A.5). For the same reason, the *B*-field is preferred when the windings are being used for voltage generation. These distinctions are largely academic when the machine has a uniform air gap, but become important for machines with a nonuniform air gap.

As an illustration of the relationship between voltages and rotating fields, the voltage induced into a single turn will be calculated for the uniform-air-gap machine of Figure 3.8.1. It is assumed that there is, in the air gap, a cosinusoidally-distributed field, rotating counterclockwise at uniform angular velocity Ω. This field is produced by windings that are not shown, and is given by

$$\mathcal{B}(\theta, t) = \mathbf{a}_r B_m \cos (\Omega t - \theta). \tag{3.8.1}$$

Thus the field is radial, and has its axis at $\theta = 0$ when $t = 0$. The electric field induced along a conductor at any position θ_0 is given by

$$\mathbf{E} = \mathbf{u} \times \mathcal{B} = \mathbf{a}_z \Omega r B_m \cos (\Omega t - \theta_0), \tag{3.8.2}$$

where $\mathbf{a}_z$ is the unit vector along the cylindrical axis directed out of the paper, r is the mean radius of the air gap ($g \ll r$), and $\mathbf{u}$ is the velocity of the conductor relative to the field ($u = \Omega r$).

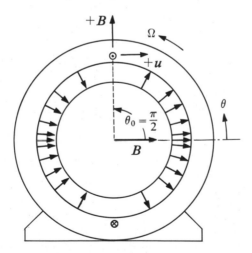

FIGURE 3.8.1.   Reference directions for application of $\mathbf{E} = \mathbf{u} \times \mathbf{B}$ to upper conductor. Rotating **B**-field is produced by windings not shown.

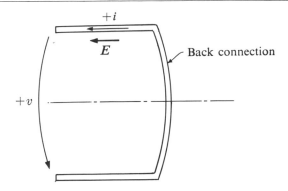

FIGURE 3.8.2. Single coil of Figure 3.8.1 viewed from right side. Front (left) ends of coil are connected to other coils or to exterior terminals; see Figure 3.2.4.

The voltage induced in a single turn (two coil sides, each of length l, connected in series as in Figure 3.8.2) is

$$v = -2 \int_0^l \mathbf{E} \cdot d\mathbf{l} = -2El = -2\Omega r B_m l \cos(\Omega t - \theta_0).$$

Since $\theta_0 = \dfrac{\pi}{2}$ at the coil-side position shown in Figure 3.8.1, the voltage is

$$v = -V_m \sin \Omega t, \qquad (3.8.3)$$

where $V_m = 2\Omega r B_m l$.

The polarity is interpreted in terms of the load convention, with the aid of Figure 3.8.2. If the current reference direction is assigned out of the paper for the upper coil side (an arbitrary designation used throughout this text), then the voltage reference must be taken downward at the terminals to comply with the load convention. The negative sign in Equation (3.8.3) indicates that at time slightly greater than zero the *upper* coil end is numerically positive, which agrees with the conclusion from a direct application of the $\mathbf{u} \times \mathbf{B}$ relationship to Figure 3.8.1.

Figure 3.8.3 shows the same machine with a rudimentary two-phase winding. In accordance with the reasoning above, the rotating field of Equation (3.8.1) will generate the coil voltages

$$v_1 = -V_m \sin \Omega t$$
$$v_2 = V_m \cos \Omega t. \qquad (3.8.4)$$

The rotating phasors representing $\mathbf{V}_1$, $\mathbf{V}_2$, and $\mathbf{B}$ are shown in Figure 3.8.4 for the instant $t = 0$. The same phase relationship will exist if full cosinusoidally-distributed windings are substituted for the rudimentary one-turn

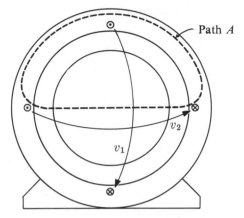

FIGURE 3.8.3. Rudimentary two-phase windings.

windings, for the phasor sum of all of the voltages (connected in series) will contain equal numbers of voltage components that lead and lag that of the central coil. This situation is illustrated in Figure 3.8.5.

The constant relating V_m and B_m for a distributed winding can be determined by carrying the process suggested in Figure 3.8.5 to a limit, giving the result that N sinusoidally-distributed turns will induce $N\pi/4$ times the voltage of a single turn. This derivation is not performed here, but is done by an alternate method in Section 4.2.

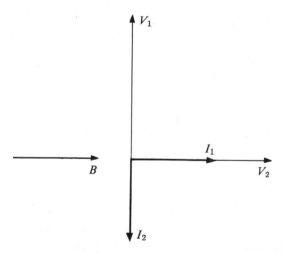

FIGURE 3.8.4. Voltage–current relationships in two-phase winding.

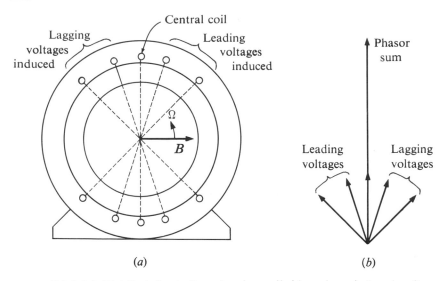

FIGURE 3.8.5. (*a*) Distributed winding showing coil-sides whose induced voltages lead and lag that of central coil. (*b*) Phasor sum of voltages induced into distributed winding of Figure 3.8.5(*a*).

It has been shown that a rotating field will induce balanced sinusoidal voltages into distributed polyphase windings. Conversely, if balanced two-phase voltages are applied from an external source to these distributed windings, the resulting coil currents will produce the identical rotating field $\mathscr{B}$, whose amplitude depends on the amplitude and the frequency of the applied voltage. This concept, that the rotating B-field depends on the applied voltage, is basic to an understanding of the operation of rotating machines that are connected to voltage sources. It is also important to note that the voltages induced by a sinusoidally-distributed rotating field are free from harmonics.

The currents required to produce a given rotating B-field will now be determined. The required B-field [Equation (3.8.1)] is related to the H-field according to $H = B/\mu_0$, so

$$\mathscr{H}(\theta, t) = \mathbf{a}_r \frac{B_m}{\mu_0} \cos (\Omega t - \theta) \tag{3.8.5}$$

Ampere's circuital law, which is $\oint \mathscr{H} \cdot d\mathbf{l} = \text{mmf}$, may be applied around a path such as A in the two-phase machine of Figure 3.8.3, where the winding is now taken to be sinusoidally distributed. The path A must be large enough to enclose all of the turns of the distributed winding. (Some turns of the other phase winding will also be enclosed in the path, but the currents in these enclosed turns will exactly cancel each other.)

Since all of the mmf drop is assumed to occur in the air gaps, the integral around path A need be evaluated only along two radial paths of length g, and the integral becomes

$$\text{mmf} = Ni_1 = 2\int_0^g \frac{B_m}{\mu_0} \cos(\Omega t - \theta_0)\, dg = \frac{2B_m g}{\mu_0} \cos(\Omega t - \theta_0).$$

In this integration, θ_0 is the coordinate at which the path of integration crosses the air gap, so $\theta_0 = 0°$. This, and a similar analysis for i_2, yield

$$Ni_1 = \frac{2gB_m}{\mu_0} \cos \Omega t$$

$$Ni_2 = \frac{2gB_m}{\mu_0} \sin \Omega t.$$

(3.8.6)

These equations agree with Equation (3.6.1), as they should. Comparison of Equation (3.8.6) and Equation (3.8.4) indicates that the voltage leads the current by 90° in each phase winding, as illustrated in Figure 3.8.4. This shows, as might have been expected, that zero average power input is required once the rotating field has been established. Further, the total instantaneous power to both phases always sums to zero even though the power to each phase is an alternating quantity. The proof of this is left as an exercise.

PROBLEM 3.8.1. A cosinusoidally-distributed field rotates at $\Omega = 100$ and induces 50 V ac at the terminals of each of the phases of a polyphase winding. If the field strength is reduced to half, and the speed of rotation changed until the induced voltage is again 50 V ac, what is the new speed of rotation and new frequency of the induced voltage? *Answer:* $\Omega = \omega = 200$.

PROBLEM 3.8.2. A balanced polyphase stator winding is energized from a balanced polyphase source. At a certain condition of operation the voltage applied to each phase winding is 50 V ac at 100 cps. It is now desired to energize the stator from a 60 cps source. What voltage must be applied so that the air gap field will remain unchanged in magnitude? *Answer:* 30 V.

PROBLEM 3.8.3. Carry out a derivation, similar to that of Section 3.8, to find the voltage v_2 in Equation (3.8.4).

PROBLEM 3.8.4. Derive Ni_2 in Equation (3.8.6), starting with Equation (3.8.5).

3.9   Multiple Poles

The magnetic fields considered so far are called "two-pole" fields because of their similarity to the field produced by a bar magnet having one north pole and one south pole.

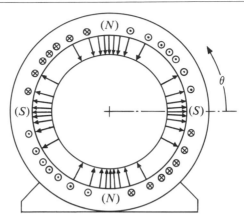

FIGURE 3.9.1. Four-pole air-gap field and cosinusoidally-distributed winding. Current flows through all coil-sides in series, in relative directions shown.

A "four-pole" field is produced by the winding configuration shown in Figure 3.9.1, where the approximate field distribution is also indicated. The same current flows in all conductors, in the direction shown. It is to be noted that the two north poles are diametrically opposite each other, as also are the south poles. The air-gap field produced by such a four-pole, sinusoidally-distributed winding, is given by $\mathscr{H}(\theta) = \mathbf{a}_r H_m \cos 2\theta$.

A four-pole *rotating* field requires twice as many windings as does the two-pole case. Such a winding is shown on the stator of Figure 3.9.2, where

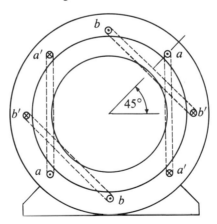

FIGURE 3.9.2. Four-pole, two-phase winding to produce four-pole rotating field. The windings a–a' are a single-turn representation of the distributed winding of Figure 3.9.1. The windings b–b' represent a similar winding displaced by 45° from winding a–a'.

for simplicity each sinusoidally-distributed winding is represented symbolically as a single turn. All of the windings labeled *a-a'* are to be connected (either in series or in parallel) to phase *A* of the two-phase power supply. When so connected, and acting without phase *B*, they produce a four-pole, recipro- cating, *non*rotating field like that of Figure 3.9.1. The addition of the second set of windings, connected to phase *B*, produces the desired four-pole, uniformly-rotating field.

The mechanical synchronous speed of the four-pole machine is exactly half that of the two-pole machine. Multiple-pole machines are used primarily to match mechanical speed requirements with the available or desired electrical frequency.

Advanced Problems

3.1 A commonly-used representation of a machine is the "developed" drawing, where the air gap is "unrolled" and laid along the horizontal axis. Such a drawing, for the uniform-field machine of Figure 3.2.1, is shown in Figure P3.1(*a*), giving the location of the stator conductors as well as a graph of the resulting field strength, plotted in the vertical direction within the air-gap space. Make similar sketches and graphs for (*a*) sinusoidal distribution (Figure 3.2.2); (*b*) four conductors

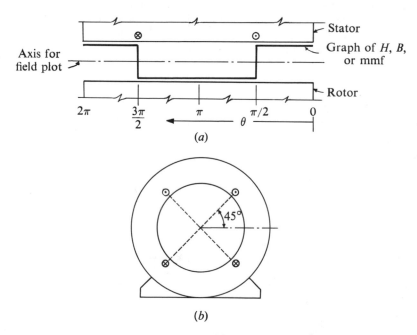

FIGURE P3.1.

spaced as in Figure P3.1(*b*); (*c*) eight conductors equally spaced but with the first at 22.5°; (*d*) a large number of conductors, spaced uniformly, and very close together.

3.2 Find an expression for the torque produced by a uniform-gap machine like Figure 3.2.1, having only a single turn on the rotor as well as on the stator. Let δ be the angle between the two coil axes, and $i_s = i_r = i$.

3.3 Start with Equations (3.6.1) and carry out the subsequent derivation by trigonometric conversions instead of exponentially. Give the answer in trigonometric form similar to Equation (3.5.1).

3.4 Show that *three* coils spaced 120° apart on a stator will produce a rotating field of uniform magnitude when balanced three-phase currents flow in the coils.

3.5 Show analytically that the voltages of Equation (3.8.4) and the currents of Equation (3.8.6) give a total instantaneous two-phase power that is always zero.

3.6 This problem consists of a number of short exercises dealing with multiple-pole windings. (*a*) Compare the field shown in Figure 3.9.1 with that produced in the arrangement of Figure P3.1(*b*). Show that the latter is a two-pole field. (*b*) Make a plot similar to those of Problem 3.1 for the field of Figure 3.9.1. Compare. (*c*) Sketch diagrams similar to Figures 3.9.1 and 3.9.2 for a three-phase, two-pole winding and for a three-phase, four-pole winding. (*d*) Sketch the air-gap distribution of a six-pole field, and express this field analytically in trigonometric form. Show the conductor distribution required to produce this field. (*e*) When connected to a 60 cps source, what are the synchronous speeds in rpm of a two-pole, a four-pole, a six-pole and a *P*-pole machine?

CHAPTER FOUR

Synchronous Machines

4.1 Motor Action and Generator Action

This chapter discusses the common type of large synchronous machine used for power generation and for constant-speed drives. In this type of machine, an example of which is illustrated in Figure 4.1.1, the rotor carries a single winding energized (through sliding contacts) with direct current, and the stator has a polyphase ac winding that produces a rotating magnetic field.* Although the stator usually is wound for three-phase operation, the two-phase representation used here lends simplicity and continuity, and gives substantially the same theoretical insights as does three-phase analysis.

When the stator is energized from an ideal polyphase voltage source, the magnitude and angular velocity of the rotating field in the machine are determined by the source (because voltage and field are related by $v = d\lambda/dt$). The field thus established is the total or resultant air-gap field, and is independent of the conditions of load on the machine.

Figure 4.1.2 illustrates both generator action and motor action for a synchronous machine. Several comments may be made about it.

1. The rotating space phasor $\mathbf{B}_t$ represents the axis and magnitude of the total (cosinusoidally-distributed) air-gap field. Its magnitude and angular frequency are determined by the polyphase voltage applied to the stator.

2. The position chosen for sketching $\mathbf{B}_t$ is arbitrarily (but permanently) selected on the reference axis. This corresponds to its position at the instant when zero instantaneous voltage is being induced into or applied to the reference stator coil.

3. The rotating space phasor $\mu_0\mathbf{H}_r = \mathbf{B}_r$ represents the field from the direct current in the rotor winding and is directed along the axis of the rotor coil, which is turning physically at synchronous speed. It is represented as

---

* The names "field" and "armature" are often given to the dc and ac members, respectively.

(a)

FIGURE 4.1.1. Photographs of 300 megawatt synchronous generator (Courtesy of Allis-Chalmers Manufacturing Company, Milwaukee, Wisconsin). (a) Stator, prior to installation of windings. Large openings at top are for forced cooling. (b) (opposite page) Cylindrical rotor. Workmen are driving slot wedges to hold conductors in place. End turns can be seen on near face of rotor.

$\mu_0\mathbf{H}_r$ rather than $\mathbf{B}_r$ to emphasize that its magnitude is determined by a current rather than by a voltage. Except for i^2R loss, no power enters or leaves the machine at the rotor terminals during normal operation.

4. The phasor $\mathbf{B}_s$ represents the field contribution from the stator windings and is such as to satisfy the phasor summation $\mathbf{B}_t = \mathbf{B}_s + \mu_0\mathbf{H}_r$. Since $\mathbf{B}_t$

(b)

and $\mu_0 \mathbf{H}_r$ are fixed as described above, only $\mathbf{B}_s$ is free to vary, and the balanced polyphase currents in the stator coils automatically take on the value necessary to produce the required $\mathbf{B}_s$.

5. For generator action, external mechanical torque is applied to the shaft so that the rotor field axis is driven ahead of the air-gap field axis, as shown in Figure 4.1.2(a). The electromagnetic torque on the rotor is then positive, in the direction of the torque reference arrow, and the mechanical power $P = T\Omega$ is positive, as is proper for generator action. Electrical energy flows from the electrical terminals of the machine.

6. For motor action, the shaft torque is reversed. The rotor field axis lags the air-gap field axis, as shown in Figure 4.1.2(b). The electromagnetic torque is numerically negative, indicating that mechanical energy is leaving the machine.

7. In steady-state operation, the torque is determined entirely by adjustments of the mechanical load or driving engine attached to the shaft. The torque angle and electrical input vary as necessary to meet the shaft torque requirements.

The torque of the machine, from Equation (3.3.7), is given by

$$T = K_b B_1 B_2 \sin \delta_{12},$$

where B_1 and B_2 represent the axial magnitudes of the two interacting fields, and δ_{12} is the angle between them. The same torque is obtained regardless of

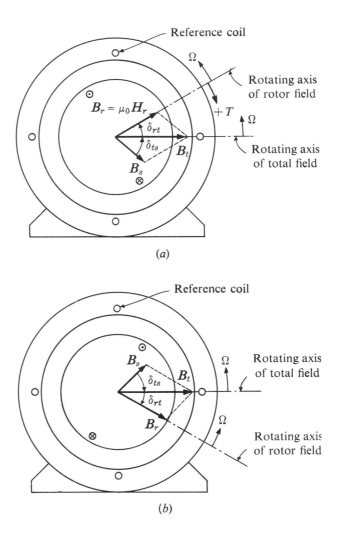

FIGURE 4.1.2. (*a*) Generator action in a synchronous machine. Axis of rotor field $\mathbf{B}_r$ is driven ahead of total air-gap field $\mathbf{B}_t$ by externally-applied torque. Electromagnetic torque is in positive reference direction, and torque angles are numerically positive. Each coil side represents an ideal cosinusoidally-distributed winding. (*b*) Motor action in a synchronous machine. External shaft load causes axis of rotor field $\mathbf{B}_r$ to lag behind total air-gap field $\mathbf{B}_t$. Electromagnetic torque, torque angles, and mechanical shaft power are numerically negative, while electrical input is numerically positive.

whether the two interacting fields are taken to be B_r and B_s, B_t and B_s, or B_r and B_t, provided the correct torque angle is selected in each case. For any of these possibilities, the torque angle becomes zero when the shaft torque is made zero. The angle δ_{12} means $(\delta_1 - \delta_2)$, or the angle of axis 1 with respect to axis 2. The positive senses for the various torque angles are δ_{rs}, δ_{ts}, δ_{rt}, in order to make the electromagnetic torque T numerically positive when the machine is acting as a mechanical load (as a generator).

Since the total field B_t is fixed by the supply voltage, and the rotor field B_r is fixed by the direct current in the rotor winding, it is most convenient to select the angle between these two as the torque angle in synchronous machine calculations. (If the stator were energized from a polyphase current source instead of a polyphase voltage source, the angle between H_s and H_r would be more convenient.)

The torque equation then becomes

$$T = K_b B_r B_t \sin \delta_{rt}, \qquad (4.1.1)$$

where δ_{rt} is the angle of B_r with respect to B_t. This angle is positive for generator action [Figure 4.1.2(a)] and negative for motor action [Figure 4.1.2(b)]. The electromagnetic torque on the rotor is, therefore, positive (clockwise) for generator action and negative for motor action. Equation (4.1.1) is graphed in Figure 4.1.3.

To sum up, B_t is proportional to rms stator voltage, B_r is proportional to the rotor direct current, B_s is proportional to the rms stator current, and all three are related by the phasor equation $\mathbf{B}_t = \mathbf{B}_r + \mathbf{B}_s$ and by the torque equation $T = K_b B_r B_t \sin \delta_{rt}$.

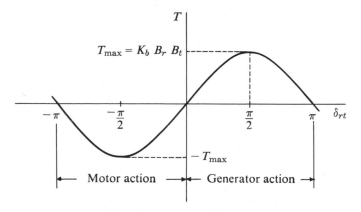

FIGURE 4.1.3. Graph of electromagnetic torque vs. torque angle for a synchronous machine. If shaft torque exceeds T_{max}, the rotor drops out of synchronism, develops a pulsating torque whose average is zero, and stops (if a motor under load) or overspeeds (if being driven as a generator).

PROBLEM 4.1.1. Apply $\mathbf{u} \times \mathbf{B}$ or some similar rule to Figure 4.1.2 and demonstrate that the instantaneous voltage in the reference coil is indeed zero at the instant depicted. Is it zero increasing or zero decreasing? (See Figure 3.8.3 for reference polarities.)

PROBLEM 4.1.2. In the motor of Figure 4.1.2(b), $B_{tm} = 1.2$ webers per square meter, $B_{rm} = 0.7$, and $B_{sm} = 0.8$. Find δ_{rt}, δ_{rs}, and δ_{ts}. A graphical solution is recommended. *Answer:* $\delta_{rt} = -39.6°$; $\delta_{rs} = -73.8°$; $\delta_{ts} = -34.2°$.

PROBLEM 4.1.3. For the results of Problem 4.1.2, show numerically that the same torque results regardless of which δ is chosen as the torque angle.

PROBLEM 4.1.4. The motor of Problem 4.1.2 has its rotor direct current doubled, with the load torque and supply voltage remaining unchanged. Determine the new values of B_r, B_s, B_t, and δ_{rt}. *Answer:* $\delta_{rt} = -18.7°$; $B_s = 0.46$.

PROBLEM 4.1.5. What percentage of its maximum torque is the motor of Problem 4.1.2 developing? Assume fixed rotor direct current and supply voltage. Sketch the $\mathbf{B}$ phasors in the position of maximum torque. *Answer:* 64%.

4.2 Voltage–Current Relationships

The relationships between the rotating field quantities, and the electrical quantities for the reference phase winding, are illustrated in Figure 4.2. The reference phase winding is the coil having its axis along $\theta = 0°$.

Several explanatory comments, based on derivations in Chapter 3, may be made relative to Figure 4.2.

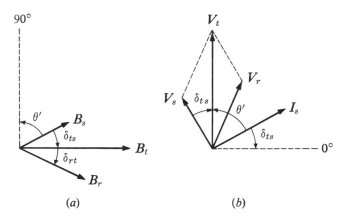

(a)   (b)

FIGURE 4.2. Field and electrical relationships for motor action. (a) Representation of rotating fields (identical with Figure 4.1.2(b). (b) V-I phasor diagram for the stator coil in reference position (with axis at $\theta = 0°$).

1. The phasor V_t represents the voltage induced into (or applied to) the reference stator coil (whose axis is at $\theta = 0°$.) This voltage is at its instantaneous zero when B_t is to the right as shown, so the rotating phasor V_t must be on the vertical axis.

2. The voltage components V_r and V_s represent the voltages induced into the reference coil by B_r and B_s, and sum to V_t, the total or terminal voltage for the reference stator coil.

3. The phasor I_s represents the current flowing in the reference stator coil. This current is at its instantaneous maximum at the instant when B_s is directed along the reference coil axis, and so is shown in the same angular position as B_s.

4. The power factor angle θ' is the negative complement of δ_{ts}, one of the torque angles. If V_t and I_s are taken as phase quantities, the total electrical power is $P_e = nV_tI_s \cos \theta'$, where n is the number of phases. This power is numerically positive when $90° > \theta' > -90°$, and the machine is acting as an electrical load. In Figure 4.2, the machine is the equivalent of an R-L load, since V_t leads I_s.

5. The V-I phasor diagram [Figure 4.2(b)] represents time-varying quantities for only one phase of the polyphase stator winding, whereas the rotating field diagram [Figure 4.2(a)] represents the resultant effect of the mmf's from all phases. However, the phasor diagram is considered to rotate once each cycle in the complex plane, just as does the diagram representing the fields.

The quantitative relationship between the B-field and the applied voltage will now be derived from energy balance considerations. The mechanical power to the machine may be written in terms of field quantities as

$$P_m = T\Omega = \Omega K_b B_{tm} B_{sm} \sin \delta_{ts}. \tag{4.2.1}$$

The particular torque angle δ_{ts} chosen is the most convenient one for the relationships used below. K_b, as given in Equation (3.3.7), is

$$K_b = \pi lrg/\mu_0. \tag{4.2.2}$$

The stator field B_{sm} is related to the stator current by

$$B_{sm} = \mu_0 H_{sm} = \mu_0 N_s I_{sm}/2g. \tag{4.2.3}$$

Since $\theta' + \delta_{st} = 90°$, $\sin \delta_{ts} = -\cos \theta'$. As discussed in Section 3.8, the stator terminal voltage V_{tm} is directly proportional to both the magnitude and the frequency of the total B-field, B_{tm}. If the constant in this proportionality is designated as K_v, the stator voltage magnitude can be expressed as

$$V_{tm} = K_v \Omega B_{tm}. \tag{4.2.4}$$

The various relationships just above may then be substituted into the power equation (4.2.1), giving

$$P_m = \Omega\left(\frac{\pi lrg}{\mu_0}\right)\left(\frac{V_{tm}}{K_v\Omega}\right)\left(\frac{\mu_0 N_s I_{sm}}{2g}\right)(-\cos\theta'). \tag{4.2.5}$$

This equation can be combined with the electrical power input, according to the steady-state relationship,

$$P_e + P_m = 0, \tag{4.2.6}$$

where P_e is seen from Figure 4.2(b) to be (for two phases)

$$P_e = 2V_t I_s \cos\theta' = V_{tm} I_{sm} \cos\theta'. \tag{4.2.7}$$

Upon solving Equation (4.2.6) for K_v, there results

$$K_v = \tfrac{1}{2}\pi lr N_s. \tag{4.2.8}$$

This value, used in Equation (4.2.4), makes it possible to write the instantaneous voltage in the reference winding [see also Equation (3.8.3)] as

$$v_t = -\tfrac{1}{2}\Omega rl\pi N_s B_{tm}\sin\Omega t. \tag{4.2.9}$$

Now for a single· turn, made up of two coil-sides in series, the relationship $v = Blu$ (where $u = \Omega r$) gives

$$V_{tm}' = 2B_{tm}lr\Omega,$$

where V_{tm}' is the voltage in a single turn. This, in combination with Equations (4.2.4) and (4.2.8), gives the ratio $V_{tm}/V_{tm}' = \pi N_s/4$. Thus, a sinusoidally-distributed winding is about 79% as effective in producing voltage as would be the same number of turns wound together in the optimum position. This ratio is called the *distribution factor* for the winding.

PROBLEM 4.2.1. Sketch a *V-I* phasor diagram, similar to Figure 4.2(b), but for, generator action. Is the electrical power positive or negative?

PROBLEM 4.2.2. Sketch the *V-I* phasor diagram for the maximum-torque condition of Problem 4.1.5.

PROBLEM 4.2.3. The machine of Problem 4.1.2 is operated with zero torque. Determine the B's and the δ's if (a) supply voltage and rotor current remain unchanged; (b) supply voltage remains unchanged but rotor current is doubled. In each case, sketch the field diagram and the corresponding *V-I* phasor diagram, and evaluate the power factor angle θ'. *Answer:* (a) $\mathbf{B}_s = 0.5$, $\theta' = 90°$; (b) $\mathbf{B}_s = -0.2$, $\theta' = -90°$.

PROBLEM 4.2.4. For Figure 4.2(b), show that V_s must always lead I_s by 90°, and that the two are always proportional, regardless of operating conditions.

4.3 An Equivalent Circuit

A simple equivalent circuit, commonly used for the steady-state solution of synchronous machine problems, is derived below.

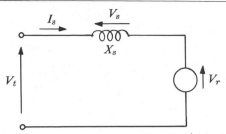

FIGURE 4.3. Equivalent circuit of one phase of a synchronous machine, showing synchronous reactance X_s. V_r is voltage component generated by rotor field, and the power $V_r I_s \cos \theta_{rs}'$ is converted to mechanical form.

The equivalent is based on the fact that $\mathbf{V}_s$ and $\mathbf{I}_s$ are always in quadrature, and are always proportional to each other in magnitude. This suggests that the phasor ratio $\mathbf{V}_s/\mathbf{I}_s$ can be represented as an equivalent reactance, X_s. Reference to Figure 4.2(b) indicates that there can be written

$$\mathbf{V}_s = j\mathbf{I}_s X_s$$
$$\mathbf{V}_t = \mathbf{V}_r + \mathbf{V}_s = \mathbf{V}_r + j\mathbf{I}_s X_s. \tag{4.3.1}$$

Figure 4.3 shows the single-phase equivalent circuit described by Equation (4.3.1), where X_s is properly shown as an inductive reactance. The equivalent voltage source $\mathbf{V}_r$, which represents the mechanical shaft power in electrical terms, is directly proportional to the dc rotor excitation and may be measured experimentally at the terminals when $\mathbf{I}_s = 0$. The reactance X_s, known as the *synchronous reactance*, can be measured by driving the machine as a generator with $\mathbf{V}_t$ reduced to zero. An equivalent series resistance can also be included, but this is small compared with X_s and can be ignored without appreciable error.

PROBLEM 4.3.1. A certain synchronous generator operating at 3600 rpm has a synchronous reactance of 80 ohms and produces 2300 V rms per phase at no load (stator terminals open circuited). It is then connected to a balanced resistive load of 140 ohms per phase, with the dc rotor current unchanged. Determine (a) the terminal voltage V_t; (b) the stator current I_s; (c) the torque angle δ_{rt}; (d) the electromagnetic torque T. *Answer:* (a) 2000 V; (b) 14.3 A; (c) 29.7°; (d) 152 N-m.

4.4 Dynamic Response

When the load on a synchronous machine is abruptly changed, the shaft can be seen (with a stroboscope) to oscillate for a time before assuming the new torque angle. During these oscillations the torque varies according to

$$T(t) = K_b B_r B_t \sin \delta_{rt}, \tag{4.4.1}$$

Raymond P. Jefferis III

where δ_{rt} is a function of time and the other quantities may be considered constant.

If the oscillations are sufficiently small, the approximation $\sin \delta_{rt} = \delta_{rt}$ (in radians) can be made, and the machine appears as a linear torsional spring having an angular displacement proportional to torque. Under these circumstances, the "spring constant" is

$$K_\delta = T/\delta = K_b B_r B_t \quad \text{(for small } \delta) \qquad (4.4.2)$$

The moment of inertia J is determined by all equipment connected to the machine shaft. The damping coefficient D is determined by friction torque and by the electrical damping action of any other electric motor or generator connected to the synchronous machine. Thus, for generator action, oscillations will persist longer when electrical load is removed from the machine than when it is added.

If the oscillations are sufficiently large, the assumption of linearity is no longer valid and the problem of solving a nonlinear differential equation arises. The nonlinearity becomes increasingly significant as δ approaches $90°$, and the machine may pull out of synchronism. The analytical problem is solved readily using step-by-step methods on a digital computer,* or with an analog computer equipped with a function generator that can generate the function $\sin \delta$.

PROBLEM 4.4.1. (*a*) How large can δ be, for the approximation $\sin \delta = \delta$ to hold within 2%? (*b*) Justify the statement in Section 4.4 that B_r and B_t may be considered constant during transient oscillations. Is B_s constant?

4.5   Salient Poles and *d-q* Components

Synchronous machines are often constructed with salient (protruding) poles on the rotor, as shown in Figure 4.5.1. This arrangement provides more physical space for the rotor winding, and also produces a reluctance torque that increases the total torque available at small torque angles. As shown in Section 2.8, reluctance torque varies according to $\sin 2\delta$, and the addition of a reluctance torque component could be expected to modify the torque characteristic in approximately the manner depicted in Figure 4.5.2. This is substantiated by the quantitative theory developed below.†

The effect of the nonuniform air gap produced by saliency is to cause the torque constant $K_b = \pi l r g / \mu_0$, from Equation (3.3.7), to become a function of the torque angle δ. This potentially complicated situation is simplified by referring the machine variables to a new set of coordinate axes, the *direct* and *quadrature* axes of Figure 4.5.1(*a*). These *d-q* axes are attached to the rotor and turn with it. The direct axis is along the rotor axis, in the direction of

---

* For an example, see Reference 4.1, Section 15.7.

† For an alternate analysis in which the air gap is assumed to vary sinusoidally with θ, see Reference 2.2, Chapter 3.

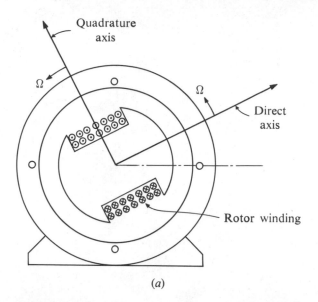

(a)

(b)

FIGURE 4.5.1. (a) Salient-pole synchronous machine, showing nonuniform air gap. Direct axis and quadrature axis rotate with rotor at synchronous speed. (b) (opposite page) Photograph of 1200-rpm salient-pole rotor, showing three of the six poles. Two slip rings can be seen mounted on the shaft at the left of the fan blades.

(c)

FIGURE 4.5.1. (c) Photograph of portion 227-rpm salient-pole rotor showing a few of the twenty-six poles. (Photographs courtesy of Allis-Chalmers Manufacturing Company, Milwaukee, Wisconsin.)

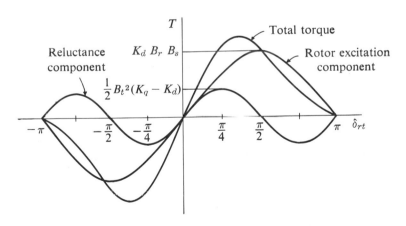

FIGURE 4.5.2. Torque characteristic of salient-pole synchronous machine. Quantitative relationships shown are developed subsequently.

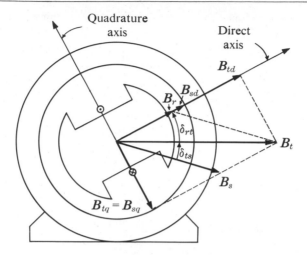

FIGURE 4.5.3. Resolution of $\mathbf{B}_s$ and $\mathbf{B}_t$ into components on direct and quadrature axes. All quantities remain constant in magnitude as rotor turns.

minimum magnetic reluctance. The quadrature axis is advanced 90°, across the rotor axis in the direction of maximum reluctance. Since these axes turn with the rotor, all synchronously revolving quantities appear stationary with respect to them.

If the machine is operating at zero torque, $\delta_{rs} = 0$ and B_s is directed along the direct axis of the rotor. With sufficient mechanical torque, δ_{rs} approaches 90° and B_s is directed along the quadrature axis, where the air gap is considerably larger. Two different torque constants are then required, K_d for the first case and K_q for the second. These constants are evaluated from Equation (3.3.7) as $K = \pi l r g / \mu_0$, where g is the radial length of the air gap, so it results that $K_q > K_d$. Torque is directly proportional to the torque constant, and it may seem surprising that the larger torque constant applies to the quadrature axis, where the air gap is larger. This can be understood in terms of the concept $T = \partial W_f / \partial \theta$; a large air gap means more stored field energy for a given B and therefore more torque. It does not follow that large air gaps are desirable, however, because much more stator current is required to produce a given field along a path of high magnetic reluctance; as was shown in Equation (3.3.5), a small air gap does result in maximum torque per ampere.

In typical operation, B_s is not on either axis, but somewhere in between, as is the case in Figure 4.5.3. Under these conditions, B_s must be resolved into two components, B_{sd} along the direct axis and B_{sq} along the quadrature axis, and the appropriate torque constant applied to each. With reference to Figure 4.5.3, B_{sd} and B_r are both on the same axis and therefore produce no interaction; the developed torque results entirely from the interaction between B_r and B_{sq}, where the torque angle is 90°. Thus, the torque is

$$T = K_q B_r B_{sq}.$$

Unfortunately, this simple form is relatively useless because several inter-related variables are involved in determining B_{sq}. An alternate form involving B_t (the field that is proportional to applied voltage) can be found by resolving both B_t and B_s onto the *d-q* axes, as has also been done in Figure 4.5.3. The torque is then thought of as being composed of two components, one between B_{td} and B_{sq}, and the other between B_{tq} and B_{sd}. In both cases the torque angle is 90°, but careful attention must be given to polarities. It was shown in Section 4.1 that the correct torque angle for interactions between B_s and B_t is δ_{ts} (not δ_{st}), so the torque angle between B_{td} and B_{sq} is $+90°$, and that between B_{tq} and B_{sd} is $-90°$. This leads to the torque expression

$$T = K_q B_{td} B_{sq} - K_d B_{tq} B_{sd}, \tag{4.5.1}$$

where it is noted that each torque constant is associated with the corresponding stator field component. The application of superposition to torques is a permissible procedure whenever the fields are cosinusoidally distributed, for it can then be shown by trigonometric conversions that the torque is always the same, regardless of the components used, as long as the correct torque angles are employed. The validity of the assumption of a cosinusoidal field distribution is discussed further at the end of this section. For a more general field distribution, a rigorous derivation requires that W_f be evaluated and the torque determined by the methods of Section 3.3.

Still another expression for salient-pole torque results when the following trigonometric substitutions, based on the angle δ_{rt}, are made into Equation (4.5.1).

$$B_{td} = B_t \cos \delta_{rt}$$

$$B_{sd} = B_{td} - B_r$$

$$B_{tq} = B_t \sin \delta_{rt} \tag{4.5.2}$$

$$B_{sq} = B_{tq}.$$

With these substitutions, Equation (4.5.1) can be reduced to

$$T = K_d B_r B_t \sin \delta_{rt} + \tfrac{1}{2} B_t^2 (K_q - K_d) \sin 2\delta_{rt}. \tag{4.5.3}$$

Several comments may be made about Equation (4.5.3):

1. The two components predicted, and shown in Figure 4.5.2, are present.
2. K_q does not appear alone, but only in the combination $(K_q - K_d)$. Thus, although $K_q > K_d$, their difference is likely to be small.

3. The second term on the right represents the reluctance torque. It is present even if the rotor current (and $\mathbf{B}_r$) is reduced to zero.

4. For a uniform air gap, $K_q = K_d$, and the expression reduces to that for the cylindrical-rotor machine described in Section 4.1.

PROBLEM 4.5.1. Construct a diagram similar to Figure 4.5.3, but for motor action. In what way is Equation (4.5.1) changed for motor action?

PROBLEM 4.5.2. Carry out the missing steps in the derivation of Equation (4.5.3).

A volt-ampere phasor diagram can be constructed from the field diagram of Figure 4.5.3, using the same methods employed for the cylindrical rotor example of Section 4.2. In Figure 4.5.4, the *d-q* components of $\mathbf{B}_t$, from Figure 4.5.3, define $\mathbf{V}_d$ and $\mathbf{V}_q$, and the *d-q* components of $\mathbf{B}_s$ define $\mathbf{I}_d$ and $\mathbf{I}_q$. Several comments apply to Figure 4.5.4:

1. The power factor angle $\theta' > 90°$ because the figure is drawn for generator action, indicating negative power input at the electrical terminals.

2. Although B_{sd} is shown (in this example) approximately equal to B_{sq}, I_d is smaller than I_q. This is because of the different magnetic reluctances along the two axes, relatively more quadrature axis current than direct axis current being required to set up the specified fields.

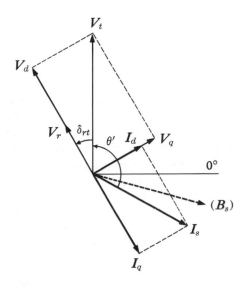

FIGURE 4.5.4. *V-I* phasor diagram for salient-pole synchronous generator. Power factor angle $\theta' > 90°$ because electrical power to generator is negative. $\mathbf{I}_s$ is not "in phase with" $\mathbf{B}_s$, as was the case in the cylindrical-rotor machine of Figure 4.2.

3. V_q leads I_q by 90°, and the two are proportional. Their ratio is called the *quadrature-axis synchronous reactance*, given by $X_q = V_q/I_q$. The *direct-axis synchronous reactance* is defined as $X_d = (V_d - V_r)/I_d$, for I_d is proportional to $V_d - V_r$ rather than to V_d, which is given by $\mathbf{V}_d = \mathbf{V}_r + j\mathbf{I}_d X_d$. Since the direct axis presents the lower-reluctance magnetic path, X_d is greater than X_q.*

4. The electrical power can be read directly from Figure 4.5.4 as

$$P_e = V_q I_d - V_d I_q = V_t I_s \cos \theta'. \qquad (4.5.4)$$

The power factor angle θ' is no longer the negative complement of δ_{ts} because $\mathbf{I}_s$ is not "in phase with" $\mathbf{B}_s$. This is the principal difference in circuit quantities resulting from saliency of the poles.

The treatment of the *d-q* field components as cosinusoidally distributed constitutes the major simplifying assumption of this development. The requirement of cosinusoidal field distribution can be met only approximately even in theory, for a field component centered on one of the two axes can extend only about ±45° from the axis before it encounters a substantially different air gap. However, about 70% of the total flux linkage from such a field occurs within the ±45° range, and a disturbance of the remaining 30% will not usually introduce objectionable error.

The rotor field can be made to approach the desired cosinusoidal distribution by proper shaping of the salient poles. If the stator terminal voltage V_t is sinusoidal, the total air-gap field B_t is constrained to maintain an approximately cosinusoidal distribution regardless of the variation in the air-gap. This distribution is only approximate because *any* arbitrary field distribution will produce a sinusoidal voltage at the terminals of an ideal sinusoidally-distributed winding. On the other hand, a cosinusoidal field distribution is necessary to produce a sinusoidal voltage at the terminals of a winding that is not sinusoidally distributed, and practical windings are usually distributed among uniformly-spaced slots. Thus, it is an acceptable approximation to consider B_t still to be a cosinusoidally-distributed rotating field whose axial magnitude is proportional to the terminal voltage V_t.

If B_t and B_r are both approximately cosinusoidal, then so also must be B_s, for $\mathbf{B}_s + \mathbf{B}_r = \mathbf{B}_t$. The interesting contrast arises between B_s and the stator mmf that produces it, and the reason for resolving B_s along the two axes is to provide an analytical means to allow the direct-axis stator mmf to be more effective than the quadrature-axis stator mmf in producing air-gap field.

---

* Different definitions of V_d and V_q have been used in the literature, with considerable resultant confusion. The original development by Doherty and Nickle, Reference 4.3, introduces the notation used above. Park, Reference 4.4, proposed that the designations for V_d and V_q be interchanged, so that (for example) $X_q = V_d/I_q$. Park's notation relates well to commutator machines, has become more generally accepted, and is used in Chapters 6 and 7.

PROBLEM 4.5.3. Where would the voltage V_s appear on the *V-I* diagram of Figure 4.5.4? Is it in quadrature with I_s or B_s? Why? *Answer:* In quadrature with B_s.

PROBLEM 4.5.4. Construct a *V-I* diagram similar to Figure 4.5.4, but for motor action.

4.6   Fictitious Windings on the *d-q* Axes

A further development of two-axis theory is to imagine that there are no actual stator windings at all, but instead that these are replaced by two fictitious windings, one on the direct axis and one on the quadrature axis, as in Figure 4.6.1. Since the *d-q* axes turn with the rotor, the fictitious coils must also be made to turn with the rotor.

It is desired to have currents flow in these fictitious coils such as to produce a stator field $\mathbf{B}_s$ which is indistinguishable from that produced by the actual stator coils. These currents, designated i_d and i_q, will of necessity be direct currents in the steady state, just as the rotor current is a direct current. Thus, two alternating currents have been replaced by two direct currents, thereby simplifying the mathematical analysis. This is especially useful in transient analysis, where the sinusoidal stator currents are modulated by the transient disturbance. The use of the fictitious currents i_d and i_q has the effect of demodulating, leaving only the transient disturbance to deal with.

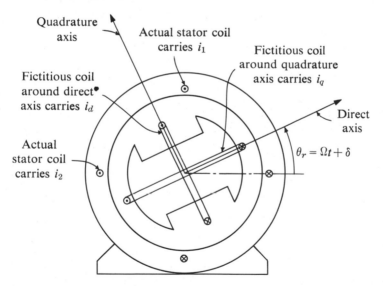

FIGURE 4.6.1. Salient-pole synchronous generator showing fictitious coils about the direct and quadrature axes. Fictitious currents i_d and i_q are to produce the same stator magnetomotive force as the actual currents i_1 and i_2.

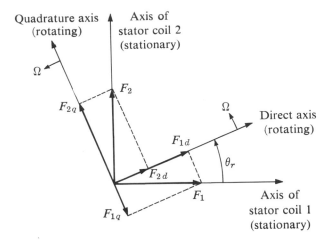

FIGURE 4.6.2. Field components from actual and fictitious currents. In general, the direct and quadrature components change as the rotor turns. For balanced poly-phase excitation of the actual stator coils, *d-q* components remain constant as rotor turns at synchronous speed.

It is to be noted that i_d and i_q are fictitious instantaneous values and may be time-varying, whereas the phasors I_{sd} and I_{sq} of Section 4.5 represent steady-state sinusoidally-varying components of the actual stator current I_s.

The transformation from actual to fictitious coil currents can be developed mathematically in the form of a set of equations that perform a change of variables. For an arbitrary position of the rotor, each actual stator coil contributes both direct-axis and quadrature-axis mmf. Reference to Figures 4.6.1 and 4.6.2 indicates that a positive current in stator coil 1 produces mmf F_1 on the coil axis, but that F_1 can be decomposed into components on the direct and quadrature axes. These mmf components are

$$\text{On direct axis:} \qquad F_{1d} = Ni_1 \cos \theta_r \qquad (4.6.1)$$

$$\text{On quadrature axis:} \qquad F_{1q} = -Ni_1 \sin \theta_r.$$

Similarly, the mmf from stator winding 2 can be decomposed into components:

$$\text{On direct axis:} \qquad F_{2d} = Ni_2 \sin \theta_r \qquad (4.6.2)$$

$$\text{On quadrature axis:} \qquad F_{2q} = Ni_2 \cos \theta_r.$$

The total mmf acting along each of the axes is given by

$$F_d = F_{1d} + F_{2d} \qquad (4.6.3)$$

$$F_q = F_{1q} + F_{2q}.$$

The fictitious coil currents i_d and i_q are, by definition, required to produce identical mmf components to those above. That is, $i_d = F_d/N$ and $i_q = F_q/N$, or

$$i_d = i_1 \cos \theta_r + i_2 \sin \theta_r$$
$$i_q = -i_1 \sin \theta_r + i_2 \cos \theta_r. \qquad (4.6.4)$$

In matrix form, this set of equations is

$$\begin{bmatrix} i_d \\ i_q \end{bmatrix} = \begin{bmatrix} \cos \theta_r & \sin \theta_r \\ -\sin \theta_r & \cos \theta_r \end{bmatrix} \cdot \begin{bmatrix} i_1 \\ i_2 \end{bmatrix}. \qquad (4.6.5)$$

The central 2×2 matrix is commonly called the "rotation matrix" because it changes a set of currents flowing in stationary windings to an equivalent set of currents flowing in rotating windings. As an example of its use, consider that balanced two-phase currents are flowing in the actual stator windings, and that the rotor is turning at synchronous speed. Let

$$i_1 = I_m \cos \omega_s t$$
$$i_2 = I_m \sin \omega_s t \qquad (4.6.6)$$
$$\theta_r = \Omega t + \delta = \omega_s t + \delta.$$

By substituting Equations (4.6.6) into Equations (4.6.5) and simplifying through the use of trigonometric conversions, there results:

$$i_d = I_m \cos \delta$$
$$i_q = -I_m \sin \delta. \qquad (4.6.7)$$

These fictitious currents are steady direct currents as long as δ (which can be a torque angle) is constant. If $\delta = 0$, $i_q = 0$, corresponding to the case where all fields are aligned along the direct rotor axis.

The rotation transformation is also applied to voltages, but the fictitious windings of Figure 4.6.1 do not provide an adequate interpretation of this. For example, the fictitious windings, rotating with the magnetic field in the steady state, would not experience any induced voltage, whereas the transformation yields steady direct voltages for the direct and quadrature axis voltages. In order to visualize this situation adequately, a somewhat more complicated model, employing a commutator, is required. This is discussed in Section 7.8, following the treatment of commutation.

Direct and quadrature analysis has been developed in great detail for the transient analysis of synchronous machines, but will not be carried further here.*

* Reference 4.2.

PROBLEM 4.6.1. What condition on θ_r will make $i_1 = i_d$ and $i_2 = i_q$? Describe the situation physically.

PROBLEM 4.6.2. Solve Equation (4.6.5) for i_1 and i_2 in terms of i_d and i_q. What special relationship exists between the rotation matrix and its inverse?

Advanced Problems

4.1   In Figure P4.1, identify δ_{12}, δ_{1t}, and δ_{t2}. Show by trigonometry that the same torque is given by any of the following: (a) $T = K_b B_1 B_2 \sin \delta_{12}$; (b) $T = K_b B_1 B_t \sin \delta_{1t}$; (c) $T = K_b B_t B_2 \sin \delta_{t2}$.

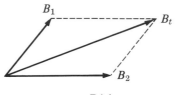

FIGURE P4.1.

4.2   For the motor of Problem 4.1.2, determine the rotor field $\mathbf{B}_r$ required for the machine to operate at unity power factor, with supply voltage and load torque unchanged. Sketch the **B** and *V-I* diagrams, similar to those in Figure 4.2.

4.3   For the motor of Problem 4.1.2, plot curves of B_s vs. B_r with constant stator voltage supply and (a) torque unchanged from Problem 4.1.2; (b) zero torque. A graphical solution is recommended. Note that the results of Problem 4.2 give one point on these curves, which are called "*V*-curves."

4.4   (a) Express the synchronous reactance X_s in terms of machine parameters such as r, N_s, g, etc. (b) Arrange the result of (a) in the form $X_s = \Omega M$, and show that M is dimensionally correct for an inductance.

4.5   When operating as in Problem 4.1.2, a machine is observed to have a terminal voltage $V_t = 120$ V rms and a stator current of 8.0 A rms. The speed is $\Omega = 1000$ rad/s. Evaluate numerically (a) K_v; (b) K_b; (c) X_s; (d) V_r; (e) power converted to mechanical form; (f) electrical power input; (g) developed torque.

4.6   A synchronous motor is delivering 0.5 N-m of torque at 1800 rpm. The load torque is suddenly reduced to zero and the torque angle is observed to oscillate initially over a 12° range with a period of 0.3 s. After 7.5 s, the oscillations have decreased to $(1/e)(12°) = 4.42°$. Calculate K_δ, J, and D for the zero-load condition.

4.7   Show that "any arbitrary field distribution will produce a sinusoidal voltage at the terminals of an ideal sinusoidally-distributed winding" (Section 4.5). If this can be shown for a step distribution (such as that of Figure 3.2.1) the general statement follows by superposition.

4.8   Show that "a cosinusoidal field distribution is required to produce a sinusoidal voltage at the terminals of a winding that is not sinusoidally distributed" (Section 4.5).

4.9   Equation (4.5.1) and Equation (4.5.4) can be related by the power balance of Equation (4.2.6), giving $P_e + T\Omega = 0$. Show that this relationship holds by making appropriate substitutions and simplifying.

4.10   Express the electric power for a salient-pole machine in a form similar to Equation (4.5.3) by writing $P_e = -T\Omega$, where T is given by Equation (4.5.3), and making appropriate substitutions for the field quantities and constants. Sketch a graph of this electric power vs. torque angle.

4.11   During a certain transient the stator currents in a synchronous machine vary according to

$$i_1 = 20 \cos 300t + 10e^{-5t} \cos 300t$$

and

$$i_2 = 20 \sin 300t + 10e^{-5t} \sin 300t$$

(a) Sketch the waveforms of i_1 and i_2. (b) Determine i_d and i_q if the rotor can be assumed to remain at synchronous speed ($\Omega = 300$). (c) Sketch the waveforms of i_d and i_q.

REFERENCES

4.1   W. D. STEVENSON, JR. *Elements of Power System Analysis*. New York: McGraw-Hill, 1962.

4.2   E. W. KIMBARK, *Power System Stability*. Vol. III, *Synchronous Machines*. New York: John Wiley and Sons, Inc., 1956.

4.3   R. E. DOHERTY and C. A. NICKLE, *Synchronous Machines—I and II, Trans. AIEE*, Vol. 45, 1926, pp. 912–947.

4.4   R. H. PARK, *Two-Reaction Theory of Synchronous Machines*, Part I, *Trans. AIEE*, Vol. 48, 1929, pp. 716–727; Part II, *Trans. AIEE*, Vol. 52, 1933, pp. 352–355.

CHAPTER FIVE

Induction Machines

5.1 Rotating Field Relationships

The induction motor is the most durable, inexpensive, and widely used type of motor. Unlike the synchronous motor, it produces torque over a wide range of speeds, and is self-starting. It is mechanically simple because there need be no electrical connections to the rotor.

The induction motor has a polyphase winding on its stator and another polyphase winding on its rotor. Only the stator windings are energized. The rotor windings are (usually) short circuited and receive energy only through electromagnetic induction; hence the name, "induction" motor. A typical induction motor rotor is illustrated in Figure 5.1.1.

The field relationships in the induction motor, sketched in Figure 5.1.2, are more complicated than those in the synchronous machine. The following descriptive comments apply.

1. The phasor $\mathbf{B}_t$ represents the resultant rotating field and is proportional to the applied stator voltage. It rotates at synchronous speed (ω_s), determined by supply frequency.

2. Voltage is induced into the rotor windings only if the $\mathbf{B}_t$ field is moving relative to the rotor, causing a time rate of change of rotor linkages. Obviously, the frequency of this induced voltage is $\omega_r = \omega_s - \Omega$, where Ω is mechanical rotor speed (in the two-pole case).

3. The two short-circuited rotor windings are in space quadrature, so conditions are exactly right for a balanced, polyphase voltage of frequency ω_r to be induced into them. The resulting polyphase rotor currents then produce a rotating field, $\mathbf{B}_r$, rotating at ω_r with respect to the rotor and at $\omega_r + \Omega = \omega_s$ with respect to the stator. Thus, δ_{rt} remains constant even though the rotor is not turning at synchronous speed, and a nonzero average torque can be produced.

FIGURE 5.1.1. Assembling insulated windings onto rotor of 1500-hp wound-rotor inductor motor. The open ends will be properly interconnected to form the desired number of short-circuited phase windings. The stator, not shown, is basically identical with that used for a synchronous machine. (Courtesy of Allis-Chalmers Manufacturing Company, Milwaukee, Wisconsin.)

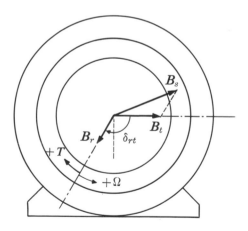

FIGURE 5.1.2. Field relationships in an induction motor. All fields rotate at synchronous speed ω_s, while the rotor turns at the slower shaft speed Ω. No windings are shown because the rotating fields are independent of winding position.

4. The angular position of $\mathbf{B}_r$ will depend on the impedance angle of the rotor windings, and will be between $90°$ and $180°$ behind $\mathbf{B}_t$ for motor action. The exact relationship is developed in detail in Section 5.2.

5. In order that $\mathbf{B}_t = \mathbf{B}_r + \mathbf{B}_s$, the stator field $\mathbf{B}_s$ must lie as shown. It is produced by balanced polyphase stator currents from the line supply.

6. Since δ_{rt} is a negative angle, the torque on the rotor (which is proportional to $\sin \delta_{rt}$) is negative, in the same direction as Ω, and the motor will run continuously. This result can also be seen directly from Figure 5.1.2, where the tendency of $\mathbf{B}_r$ to align with $\mathbf{B}_t$ will urge the rotor in the positive Ω direction.

7. No windings are shown in the drawing since the rotating fields are independent of winding positions so long as the windings are balanced.

PROBLEM 5.1.1. Reproduce Figure 5.1.2 for $B_r = 0$. What rotor speed will produce this condition? *Answer:* Synchronous speed.

5.2 Rotor Field Relationships

It has become evident that the rotor field, $\mathbf{B}_r$, is the variable quantity of most interest in induction motor analysis. To determine the behavior of the rotor field, attention must be directed to the rotor circuit and the polyphase rotor currents that produce $\mathbf{B}_r$.

Figure 5.2.1 shows the rotor windings at a particular instant when they are in line with the stator coil axes. With the total rotating air-gap field $\mathbf{B}_t$

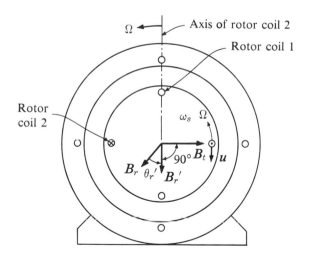

FIGURE 5.2.1. Illustration for showing dependence of δ_{rt} on rotor circuit impedance angle θ_r'. Angles are related by $\delta_{rt} + \theta_r' = -90°$.

momentarily in the 0° position shown, rotor coil 1 can be seen to have zero induced voltage, whereas the voltage induced into rotor coil 2 is at its instantaneous maximum. Since $\omega_s > \Omega$, the $\mathbf{u} \times \mathbf{B}_t$ relationship is, for that instant, as marked next to the right-hand rotor conductor. The velocity $\mathbf{u}$ is that of the wire with respect to the field. The induced rotor voltage is, then, in a direction to cause current to flow out of the right-hand side of the short-circuited rotor coil 2. If the rotor windings were purely resistive, this current in coil 2 would produce a B-field directed for that instant along the coil axis, at $\mathbf{B}_r'$, while coil 1 would have zero current and produce no field. It follows that the rotating field $\mathbf{B}_r'$ would lag behind $\mathbf{B}_t$ by exactly 90°.

There is always a substantial amount of leakage inductance in a short-circuited rotor winding, and neither it nor the winding resistance can be ignored in this case. Thus, the actual rotor currents lag behind the induced voltages by the amount of the rotor-circuit impedance angle. It is readily seen, from the development of Section 3.6, that a phase shift in each of the polyphase currents that are producing a rotating field, will cause a corresponding angular shift in the axis of the rotating field. Thus, the angle between $\mathbf{B}_r$ and $\mathbf{B}_r'$ in Figure 5.2.1 is the (lagging) impedance angle θ_r' of the rotor circuits.

It is to be noted in passing that voltage and current in the rotor of Figure 5.2.1 are taken as positive in the same direction, contrary to the load convention used throughout the text. This violation does not affect the field configuration, and is permitted for the moment to avoid a conceptually confusing array of double negatives. The required reversal is made in Section 5.6, when it first becomes necessary to refer the rotor and stator currents to the same time-reference.

In a given rotor phase winding, the current is given by Ohm's law as

$$\mathbf{I}_r = -\frac{\mathbf{V}_r}{\mathbf{Z}_r} = -\frac{\mathbf{V}_r}{R_r + j\omega_r L_{er}}, \tag{5.2.1}$$

where V_r is the magnitude of the alternating voltage induced into a rotor phase winding by the total rotating field (not the same V_r as in Chapter 4), R_r is the rotor-circuit resistance, and L_{er} is the rotor-circuit leakage inductance, associated with the magnetic flux that links only the rotor circuit and does not cross the air gap. (The air-gap flux itself is constrained by the applied voltage, does not respond to changes in rotor current, and therefore is not related to the leakage inductance).

The induced rotor voltage, $\mathbf{V}_r$, depends both in magnitude and in frequency on the difference between the angular velocities of the rotating air-gap field and of the rotor windings. This velocity difference is used to define a variable called the *slip*, which is a measure of how fast the rotor slips behind the

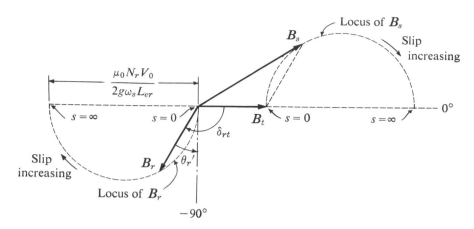

FIGURE 5.2.2. Locus of field variations with slip as a parameter.

synchronously rotating air-gap field. Slip is defined (in the two-pole case) as*

$$s = \frac{\omega_s - \Omega}{\omega_s} = \frac{\omega_r}{\omega_s}. \qquad (5.2.2)$$

When the rotor is stationary, $s = 1.0$; if the rotor is turned at synchronous speed, $s = 0$. If the voltage induced into the rotor winding when the rotor is stationary be designated as $\mathbf{V}_0$, then

$$\mathbf{V}_r = s\mathbf{V}_0. \qquad (5.2.3)$$

It is shown in Figure 4.2 that a voltage phasor "leads" its B-field by 90°; thus $\mathbf{V}_0$, which is produced by $\mathbf{B}_t$, can be expressed as $\mathbf{V}_0 = j V_0$. The rotor field $\mathbf{B}_r$ then becomes

$$\mathbf{B}_r = \frac{\mu_0 N_r \mathbf{I}_r}{2g} = \frac{\mu_0 N_r}{2g} \cdot \frac{-j V_0}{R_r + j s \omega_s L_{er}}, \qquad (5.2.4)$$

which can be shown by analytic geometry to describe the semicircular locus of Figure 5.2.2, where s is a parameter.†

The rotor power-factor angle θ_r' is, from Equations (5.2.1) and (5.2.2),

$$\theta_r' = \tan^{-1} \frac{s \omega_s L_{er}}{R_r}. \qquad (5.2.5)$$

The value of the total field $\mathbf{B}_t$ remains fixed as long as a constant polyphase voltage is applied to the stator. The stator field $\mathbf{B}_s$ takes on whatever value is

* Slip is not to be confused with the variable s of Laplace transforms.
† Reference 5.1, Chapter 15, for example. It is recalled that $\mathbf{B}_r$ is a *phasor*; the complete air-gap field equation would contain additional factors.

required to complete the summation $\mathbf{B}_t = \mathbf{B}_s + \mathbf{B}_r$, and so $\mathbf{B}_s$ also describes a semicircular locus. The operating point on the locus is determined by the torque applied to the rotor shaft, as is described in the next section.

PROBLEM 5.2.1. A two-pole, 60-cps induction motor is operating at 3000 rpm. (a) Calculate the slip. (b) Calculate the rotor-current frequency in cycles per second. *Answer:* (a) 0.167; (b) 10.

PROBLEM 5.2.2. For a certain operating condition, $B_s = 1.0$, $B_r = 0.8$, $\theta_r' = 30°$, and $s = 0.2$. Sketch the field phasors and evaluate (a) δ_{rt}; (b) B_t; (c) diameter of semicircular field locus. *Answer:* (a) $\delta_{rt} = -120°$; (b) $B_t = 0.315$; (c) 1.6.

5.3 Torque Relationships

Torque in the induction motor is given by Equation (3.3.7) as

$$T = K_b B_r B_t \sin \delta_{rt}. \tag{5.3.1}$$

Since B_r is proportional to the polyphase rotor current I_r, and B_t is proportional to the applied polyphase stator voltage V_t, Equation (5.3.1) may also be written as

$$T = -K_2 I_r V_t \cos \theta_r'. \tag{5.3.2}$$

The negative sign in Equation (5.3.2) is necessary to describe motor action, whereas it is unnecessary in Equation (5.3.1) because δ_{rt} is negative for motor action. Analytically, the negative sign comes from the relationship $\delta_{rt} + \theta_r' = -90°$, where δ_{rt} is numerically negative as in Figure 5.2.2. It follows that $\cos \theta_r' = -\sin \delta_{rt}$.

Several substitutions will now be made into Equation (5.3.2). First it is noted that V_0, the induced rotor voltage when $\Omega = 0$, is proportional to V_t. This follows because both voltages are related to the same rotating air-gap field $\mathbf{B}_t$. Then from Equation (5.2.1), there follows

$$I_r = \frac{sV_0}{\sqrt{R_r^2 + (s\omega_s L_{er})^2}}$$

and

$$\cos \theta_r' = \frac{R_r}{Z_r} = \frac{R_r}{\sqrt{R_r^2 + (s\omega_s L_{er})^2}}.$$

These three substitutions are then made into Equation (5.3.2), and with several constants combined into one, there results

$$T = -k \frac{sV_t^2 R_r}{R_r^2 + (s\omega_s L_{er})^2}. \tag{5.3.3}$$

This general equation for induction motor torque leads to several important operating characteristics.

1. Other things being constant, torque is proportional to the square of the applied voltage.

2. If the slip is so small that $(s\omega_s L_{er})^2 \ll R_r{}^2$, the torque expression becomes

$$T = -k \frac{V_t^2}{R_r} s = -k's, \qquad (5.3.4)$$

which is a straight-line characteristic.

3. If the slip is sufficiently large that $(s\omega_s L_{er})^2 \gg R_r{}^2$, the torque expression becomes

$$T = -k \frac{V_t^2 R_r}{s\omega_s{}^2 L_{er}{}^2} = -k'' \frac{1}{s}, \qquad (5.3.5)$$

which is a hyperbolic function of slip.

4. A typical operating characteristic can be deduced by combining Equations (5.3.4) and (5.3.5) for a case where slip is the only variable, as in Figure 5.3.

5. For $s < 0$, the rotor must be externally driven forward at greater than synchronous speed. The machine then becomes an induction generator, a

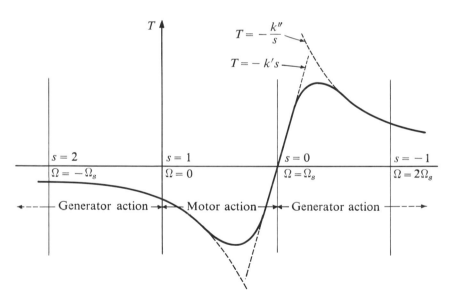

FIGURE 5.3. Torque–speed curve for induction motor. Abscissa shows values both of speed (Ω) and slip (s). Dashed lines show approximations used in constructing curves. Curves as supplied by manufacturer would normally be plotted in first quadrant for motor action.

mode of operation that can be successfully maintained only while the stator remains connected to a polyphase voltage supply.

6. For $s > 1$, the rotor must be externally driven backward against the direction of the rotating field. Operation in this region (see Figure 5.3) can be achieved momentarily by reversing the phase sequence of the applied voltage while the motor is running, producing a slip just under 2. This procedure, which brings the rotor to a rapid halt, is known as regenerative braking or "plugging."

7. Differentiation of Equation (5.3.3) reveals that the maximum torque occurs when $R_r = s\omega_s L_{er} = X_r$, or when $\theta_r{}' = 45°$.

PROBLEM 5.3.1. Derive the condition for maximum torque [Section 5.3(7)], and develop an equation for maximum torque in a form that shows it to be independent of rotor-circuit resistance.

PROBLEM 5.3.2. A certain four-pole, 50-cps induction motor develops rated output power at 1200 rpm, operating in the linear (low-slip) portion of its characteristic. What per cent of rated output power will it develop at 1300 rpm? *Answer: 72.2%.*

5.4   Power Loss Associated with Slip

Further insight into induction motor operation can be gained by examining the torque reactions with the rotating magnetic field, $\mathbf{B}_t$, that couples rotor and stator. In the steady state, equilibrium requires that the coupling field react back on the stator with a torque equal to that with which it drives the rotor forward. The stator is not "aware" of the presence of the rotor except through the coupling $\mathbf{B}_t$ field, which rotates at ω_s, not Ω, with respect to the stator. Thus, the power delivered to the field by the stator is

$$P_s = T\omega_s,$$

while the power delivered by the rotor to the shaft is

$$P_r = T\Omega = T(1 - s)\omega_s = T\omega_s - Ts\omega_s,$$

or

$$P_r = P_s - sP_s.$$

The term sP_s represents a power loss due to slip, much like the friction loss in a fluid coupling or clutch. It does not contain any actual friction loss (which may be accounted for as part of the mechanical output), but occurs as $I^2 R$ loss in the rotor windings.

This power loss due to slip renders the induction motor relatively inefficient at any but very low slips, and large induction motors are designed so that the slip rarely exceeds 0.05 at rated load. In small motors such as servomotors, where the total power involved is unimportant, resistance may purposely be added to the rotor circuit to give certain desired operating characteristics.

5.5   The Effect of Changing the Rotor-Circuit Resistance

The maximum torque occurs, according to Section 5.3(7), at a slip $s_m = R_r/\omega_s L_{er}$, which is proportional to rotor resistance. Figure 5.5 shows torque–speed curves for several values of rotor resistance. Curve (*a*) is for normal low-slip operation, but exhibits relatively low starting torque (at $\Omega = 0$).

In curve (*b*), the rotor circuit resistance has been increased until the maximum torque occurs at $\Omega = 0$. This produces good starting, but is inefficient at normal running speeds. If the rotor windings, instead of being short-circuited, are connected to sliding contacts (slip rings), a variable resistance can be inserted externally for starting, and then reduced to zero for running. This arrangement also makes it possible to adjust the speed of the motor while it is operating under load.

In curve (*c*), the rotor resistance is so great that the operating curve is practically linear, a characteristic that is desired in control systems for analytical reasons.

PROBLEM 5.5.1. A certain four-pole, 50-cps induction motor develops rated output power at 1200 rpm, operating in the linear (low-slip) portion of its characteristic. At what speed will the motor develop rated torque if its rotor circuit resistance is doubled? Discuss the effect of this change on the efficiency of the motor. *Answer:* 900 rpm.

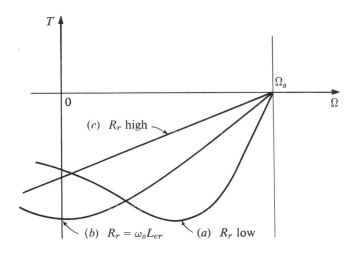

FIGURE 5.5. Effect of rotor resistance on torque–speed characteristic.

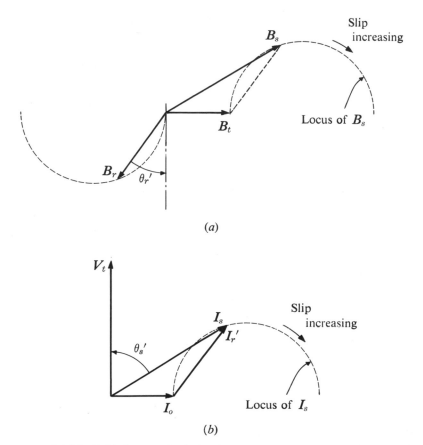

FIGURE 5.6.1.(*a*) Field diagram for induction motor, reproduced from Figure 5.2.2. (*b*) *V-I* phasor diagram for induction motor, showing stator current locus as slip varies. In comparison with (*a*), $\mathbf{I}_0$ and $\mathbf{I}_s$ are in phase with $\mathbf{B}_t$ and $\mathbf{B}_s$, while $\mathbf{I}_r'$ is reversed with respect to $\mathbf{B}_r$. The reversal of $\mathbf{I}_r'$ occurs because the current reference direction assigned to $\mathbf{I}_r$ in Figure 5.2.1 is opposite that assigned for the stator currents.

5.6   An Equivalent Circuit

The voltage–current relationships for the induction motor can be deduced in a manner similar to that used for the synchronous machine. The *V-I* phasor diagram (for the stator coil having its axis along $\theta = 0°$) is developed in Figure 5.6.1(*b*) from the field locus diagram [Figure 5.2.2, and reproduced in Figure 5.6.1(*a*)] as follows:

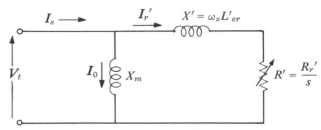

FIGURE 5.6.2. Parallel-branch equivalent circuit of induction motor, for one phase.

1. Since $\mathbf{B}_t$ is shown in the position where it induces zero instantaneous voltage into the reference coil, the reference coil voltage $\mathbf{V}_t$ is shown [in Figure 5.6.1(b)] as a time phasor in the 90° position.

2. The stator reference coil current, $\mathbf{I}_s$, is shown "in phase with" $\mathbf{B}_s$ (see Section 4.2). This establishes $\theta_s{}'$, the power-factor angle of the stator.

3. The stator current $\mathbf{I}_s$ can be resolved into two components, $\mathbf{I}_0$ and $\mathbf{I}_r{}'$. $\mathbf{I}_0$ is the limiting value of $\mathbf{I}_s$ as rotor current approaches zero, and is constant as long as $\mathbf{V}_t$ is constant. When acting alone, $\mathbf{I}_0$ produces the rotating field $\mathbf{B}_t$.

4. $\mathbf{I}_r{}'$ is the rotor current expressed in equivalent stator terms. That is, $\mathbf{I}_r{}'$ flowing in the stator coils would produce the same field, $\mathbf{B}_r$, as does $\mathbf{I}_r$ flowing in the rotor coils. $\mathbf{I}_r{}'$ is shown "reversed" from $\mathbf{B}_r$ because of a difference in choice of positive reference directions for stator and rotor currents.

5. The resolution of $\mathbf{I}_s$ into two components, $\mathbf{I}_0$ and $\mathbf{I}_r{}'$, suggests a parallel equivalent circuit, as shown in Figure 5.6.2. The magnetizing reactance X_m is determined by the quotient V_t/I_0, which two quantities are always proportional and always in quadrature. It is somewhat similar to the synchronous reactance in the synchronous machine, but appears as a parallel equivalent instead of as a series equivalent.

6. The R'-L' series branch in Figure 5.6.2 is the proper circuit to produce a current (or admittance) locus of semicircular shape, like that of $\mathbf{I}_r{}'$, when R' is a variable quantity.* Since this R' is the only element in the equivalent circuit capable of absorbing power, it must represent the shaft power output plus the slip power loss.

The variable resistor R' in Figure 5.6.2 can be evaluated by rearranging the $\mathbf{I}_r$ expression, Equation (5.2.1), as follows, noting that $V_0/V_t = N_r/N_s$ (because both voltages are produced by the same $\mathbf{B}_t$), and $N_r I_r = -N_s I_r{}'$ (from definition of $I_r{}'$).

$$\mathbf{I}_r{}' = -\frac{N_r \mathbf{I}_r}{N_s} = \frac{N_r}{N_s}\frac{s\mathbf{V}_0}{R_r + j s \omega_s L_{er}} = \left(\frac{N_r}{N_s}\right)^2 \frac{\mathbf{V}_t}{\dfrac{R_r}{s} + j\omega_s L_{er}} = \frac{\mathbf{V}_t}{\dfrac{R_r{}'}{s} + j\omega_s L_{er}{}'}. \quad (5.6.1)$$

* Reference 5.1, Chapter 15.

The primed quantities R_r' and L_{er}' are seen to be the actual rotor quantities transformed by the square of the stator-to-rotor turns ratio, just as impedances are transformed by a stationary transformer.*

From the expression for I_r', Equation (5.6.1), the series branch of Figure 5.6.2 can be seen to consist of $X' = \omega_s L_{er}'$ and $R' = R_r'/s$. These quantities can be evaluated numerically by calculation from the locus diagram (often called the "circle diagram"), which can be determined experimentally from actual load tests on the machine.

The mechanical power output of the machine, P_r, was shown in Section 5.4 to be

$$P_r = P_s - sP_s = P_s(1 - s), \qquad (5.6.2)$$

where P_s is the power delivered to the air gap. The air-gap power must be equal to the resistance loss in the equivalent circuit, or

$$P_s = n(I_r')^2\left(\frac{R_r'}{s}\right), \qquad (5.6.3)$$

where n is the number of phases. The slip power loss, sP_s, is found from Equation (5.6.3) to be

$$sP_s = n(I_r')^2(R_r'), \qquad (5.6.4)$$

and the remaining power (the mechanical power) becomes

$$P_r = P_s - sP_s = n(I_r')^2 R_r'\left(\frac{1 - s}{s}\right). \qquad (5.6.5)$$

Thus the equivalent circuit can be rearranged, as illustrated in Figure 5.6.3, to show two components of resistance in the I_r', branch, one (R_r') representing the slip power loss, an actual I^2R loss, and the other representing the power converted from electrical to mechanical form.

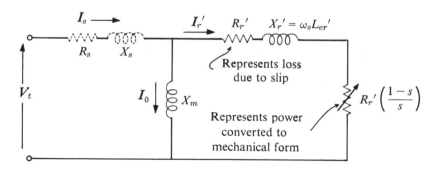

FIGURE 5.6.3. Modified equivalent circuit showing separation of slip loss and mechanical power. R_s and X_s, shown dotted, represent stator impedance actually present but not included in the theoretical development.

* Appendix, Section A.3.

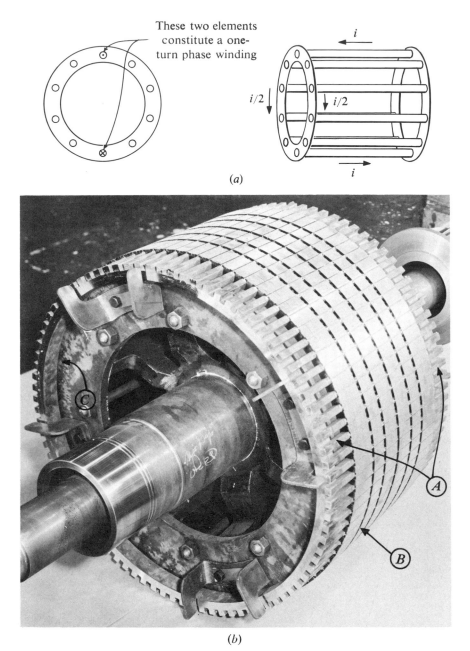

These two elements constitute a one-turn phase winding

i

$i/2$ $i/2$

i

(a)

(b)

FIGURE 5.7.1. *N*-phase rotor construction. (*a*) Diagrammatic sketch. (*b*) Squirrel-cage induction motor rotor. Rectangular conductors (*A*) can be seen emerging from iron (*B*) and joining the end ring (*C*). (Courtesy of Allis-Chalmers Manufacturing Company, Milwaukee, Wisconsin.)

The equivalent circuit of Figure 5.6.3 is similar in appearance to the usual equivalent circuit representation of the iron-core transformer, and its constants are determined experimentally by running-light and blocked-rotor tests, very similar in theory to the open-circuit and short-circuit tests performed on transformers.

PROBLEM 5.6.1. Evaluate the variable resistance in the equivalent circuit of Figure 5.6.3 for the condition of (*a*) zero speed; (*b*) synchronous speed; (*c*) maximum torque; (*d*) operation as an induction generator. *Answer:* (*a*) short circuit; (*b*) open circuit; (*c*) $\omega_s L_{er}' - R_r'$; (*d*) negative resistance.

5.7   The *N*-Phase Rotor

The short-circuited rotor windings of an induction motor may have any number of balanced phase windings without affecting the resultant field. A common and very rugged arrangement uses a large number of phases with common end connections, as shown in Figure 5.7.1. Each pair of diametrically opposite conductors constitutes one two-pole phase winding, with the current finding its way properly between coil sides around the common connecting rings at the ends. The entire structure is imbedded in the laminated iron rotor assembly, often being injected by die-casting methods. The relatively small voltages induced in the one-turn windings makes insulation unnecessary, adding to the ruggedness of the assembly. This type of rotor was dubbed "squirrel cage" after the cylindrical wire cages sometimes employed for exercising small animals, and this descriptive name is commonly used.

The torque–speed characteristic of a squirrel-cage motor is indistinguishable from that of the wound-rotor type. However, it is a simple matter to modify the squirrel-cage rotor to form the double-cage rotor of Figure 5.7.2. The outer winding has high resistance and low inductance, and is designed

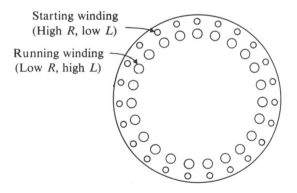

Starting winding
(High *R*, low *L*)

Running winding
(Low *R*, high *L*)

FIGURE 5.7.2.   Double-cage rotor construction.

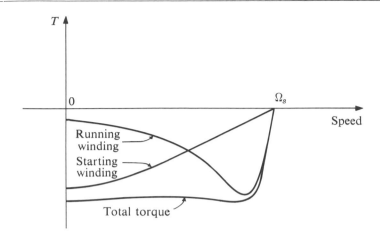

FIGURE 5.7.3. Improved torque characteristic of double-cage induction motor.

to produce maximum torque at starting. The inner winding has high inductance (since it is buried in the low-reluctance rotor iron) and low resistance (since the conductors have large cross-sectional area). It is designed to produce maximum torque at rated operating speed. The total torque produced can be made by the designer to vary in almost any desired way with speed; a typical "flat" curve is shown in Figure 5.7.3. A particularly desirable feature of the double-cage motor is that the current in the starting winding drops to a low value at running speeds.

5.8 Unbalanced Operation and Counter-Rotating Fields

Although any polyphase machine may sometimes be subject to operation from an unbalanced power supply, unbalanced operation is deliberately used in two important forms of induction motor, the servomotor and the single-phase motor. There are several approaches to the analysis of unbalanced operation, including a variation of the direct- and quadrature-axis method of Section 4.5. In the present discussion, the effect of unbalanced operation is represented by the superposition of two rotating fields that move in opposite directions around the air gap. The analysis for balanced operation may then be applied to each field separately, and the results superimposed.

Attention is first directed to the single-phase machine of Figure 5.8.1(*a*), which carries but a single sinusoidally-distributed winding. The air-gap field produced by current in this winding is cosinusoidally distributed about the winding axis, and varies in magnitude proportionally with the current. It can be represented by a reciprocating phasor (Section 3.6) that varies in

magnitude but always lies along the coil axis and does not rotate. That is,

$$\mathscr{B}(\theta, t) = \mathbf{a}_r \text{ Re } [\mathbf{B}_m e^{-j\theta}]$$

where the phasor $\mathbf{B}_m$ is

$$\mathbf{B}_m(t) = B_m e^{j0°} = \frac{\mu_0 Ni}{2g} e^{j0°}.$$

It will be recalled that B_m represents the maximum value of the B-field on the field axis, and the term $e^{j0°}$ indicates that the field axis is fixed along the reference axis, and does not rotate.

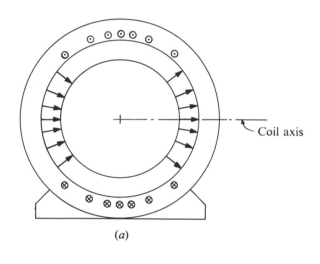

(a)

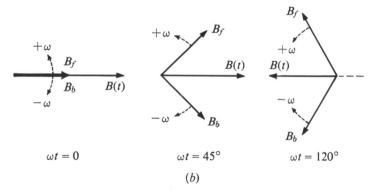

$\omega t = 0$ $\omega t = 45°$ $\omega t = 120°$

(b)

FIGURE 5.8.1.(a) Air-gap field for single-phase machine. Field reciprocates on its axis but does not rotate. (b) Forward and backward components of a single-phase field sketched for several successive instants of time.

If now, the current is made to vary cosinusoidally with time, according to $i = I_m \cos \omega t$, the space phasor representation becomes

$$\mathbf{B}_m = \frac{\mu_0 N I_m \cos \omega t}{2g} e^{j0°} = [B_m \cos \omega t] e^{j0°} = B_m \frac{[e^{j\omega t} + e^{-j\omega t}]}{2}.$$

The exponential terms represent two counter-rotating components of equal magnitude, which always sum to the actual nonrotating field located on the coil axis. The forward component $\mathbf{B}_f = \frac{1}{2} B_m e^{j\omega t}$, and the backward component $\mathbf{B}_b = \frac{1}{2} B_m e^{-j\omega t}$, are depicted in several successive positions in Figure 5.8.1(*b*).

This analysis can be extended to the unbalanced two-phase case by adding a quadrature winding that carries current of the same frequency, shifted by 90°, but of a different magnitude. If the two currents are designated as $i_1 = I_{1m} \cos \omega t$ and $i_2 = I_{2m} \cos \left(\omega t - \frac{\pi}{2} \right)$, the total field can be expressed as

$$\mathbf{B}_T = \mathbf{B}_1 + \mathbf{B}_2$$

$$= B_{1m} \cos \omega t \, e^{j0°} + B_{2m} \cos \left(\omega t - \frac{\pi}{2} \right) e^{j90°}$$

$$= B_{1m} \frac{e^{j\omega t} + e^{-j\omega t}}{2} + B_{2m} \frac{e^{j\omega t} - e^{-j\omega t}}{2}$$

$$= \frac{B_{1m} + B_{2m}}{2} e^{j\omega t} + \frac{B_{1m} - B_{2m}}{2} e^{-j\omega t}$$

$$= \mathbf{B}_{fm} e^{j\omega t} + \mathbf{B}_{bm} e^{-j\omega t}$$

$$= \mathbf{B}_f + \mathbf{B}_b.$$

The total field is seen to be the sum of two counter-rotating components, $\mathbf{B}_f$ and $\mathbf{B}_b$, having different amplitudes. The amplitudes, $\mathbf{B}_{fm}$ and $\mathbf{B}_{bm}$, may be complex amplitudes, although they are not complex in this example. The total field $\mathbf{B}_T$ is not constant, nor does it rotate uniformly. The phasor representation is sketched in Figure 5.8.2 for the instant that $\omega t = 30°$.

PROBLEM 5.8.1. Determine and sketch the forward and backward rotating field components, $\mathbf{B}_f$ and $\mathbf{B}_b$, for a two-phase induction motor if the currents are (*a*) $i_1 = 15 \cos \omega t$ and $i_2 = 10 \sin \omega t$; (*b*) $i_1 = 10 \sin \omega t$ and $i_2 = 10 \cos \omega t$; (*c*) $i_1 = 10 \cos \omega t$ and $i_2 = 15 \cos (\omega t + 60°)$; (*d*) $i_1 = 10 \sin \omega t$; $i_2 = 0$. *Answer*: (*a*) $\mathbf{B}_f = 12.5 \, k \, e^{j\omega t}$, $\mathbf{B}_b = 2.5 \, k \, e^{-j\omega t}$, where $k = \mu_0 N/2g$; (*b*) $\mathbf{B}_f = 0$, $\mathbf{B}_b = 10 \, k \, e^{-j(\omega t - 90°)}$; (*c*) $\mathbf{B}_f = 4.1 \, k \, e^{j(\omega t + 112°)}$, $\mathbf{B}_b = 12.1 \, k \, e^{-j(\omega t - 18°)}$; (*d*) $\mathbf{B}_f = -j5 \, k \, e^{j\omega t}$, $\mathbf{B}_b = j5 \, k \, e^{-j\omega t}$.

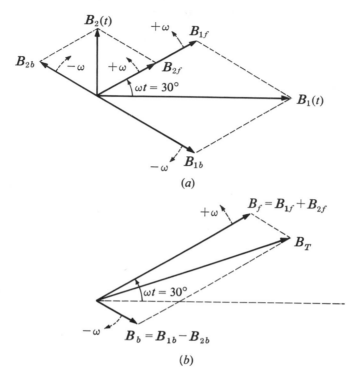

FIGURE 5.8.2. Forward and backward field components for unbalanced operation. (*a*) Resolution of separate fields into forward and backward components. (*b*) Summation of components into one forward field and one backward field. Total field, $\mathbf{B}_T = \mathbf{B}_f + \mathbf{B}_b$, is not of constant magnitude, nor does it rotate uniformly.

5.9   Torque from Counter-Rotating Field Components

As was shown in the previous section, the pulsating, nonuniform field resulting from unbalanced excitation can be resolved into two counter-rotating components. Each of these components has associated with it a stator field $\mathbf{B}_s$, a rotor field $\mathbf{B}_r$, and a torque angle, and will by itself produce a torque in the same manner as was described for balanced polyphase operation. Each torque is in the angular direction of its field component, so the two subtract to produce the actual torque developed at the shaft. (See Figure 5.9.1.) For a particular rotor speed, if the slip with respect to the forward field component is s, the slip with respect to the backward field component is $2 - s$. At synchronous speed, the backward torque has a finite value; unlike the balanced case, an unbalanced motor does *not* approach

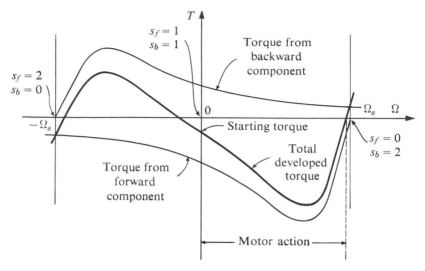

FIGURE 5.9.1. Torque in unbalanced operation of polyphase induction motor. The symbols s_f and s_b represent slip with respect to forward and backward rotating field components.

synchronous speed as a limit as its torque requirement goes to zero. These conclusions are illustrated in Figure 5.9.1, where the forward and backward torques are combined graphically.

The torques shown in Figure 5.9.1 are average torques. The forward component was determined by considering the reaction between two forward-rotating fields: one stator field and the corresponding rotor field. The backward component was determined by considering the reaction between two backward-rotating fields: one stator field and the corresponding rotor field. In addition, there is interaction between the forward stator field and the backward rotor field, and also between the backward stator field and the forward rotor field. These latter are oscillating torques because of their rapidly changing torque angles, and produce zero average torque. However, they may produce objectionable mechanical vibrations in some systems.

5.10 Voltages in Unbalanced Operation

It was shown in Section 5.8 that unbalanced polyphase currents flowing in the stator windings produce an air-gap field that can be represented as the sum of two counter-rotating fields of differing magnitudes. This analysis can be extended to voltages by considering the voltages induced into each of the stator windings by the counter-rotating fields.

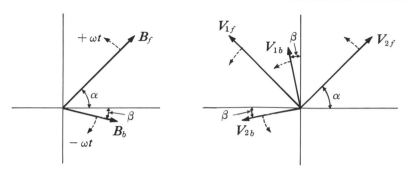

FIGURE 5.10.1. Counter-rotating air-gap fields and corresponding rotating voltage phasors for stator windings. V_{1b} and V_{2b}, the voltages induced by the backward-rotating field B_b, have the opposite phase sequence from V_{1f} and V_{2f}.

The forward-rotating component of field, B_f, will induce into the two-phase stator windings a balanced two-phase set of voltages, with V_{1f} leading V_{2f}. The backward-rotating component, B_b, will induce a balanced two-phase set of voltages of a different magnitude, and also of opposite phase sequence, with V_{2b} leading V_{1b}. The fields and corresponding voltage phasors are represented in Figure 5.10.1. It is to be noted that while the fields rotate in opposite directions, the voltage phasors (by generally-accepted convention) all rotate the same way, differing instead in phase sequence. A reversal of the direction of the rotating field is accompanied by a reversal in the phase sequence of the terminal voltage.

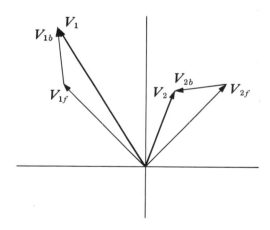

FIGURE 5.10.2. Summation of symmetrical (balanced) components of Figure 5.10.1 to form unbalanced polyphase voltages V_1 and V_2.

The total voltages appearing at the terminals are found by summing components, giving

$$\mathbf{V}_1 = \mathbf{V}_{1f} + \mathbf{V}_{1b}$$
$$\mathbf{V}_2 = \mathbf{V}_{2f} + \mathbf{V}_{2b}. \qquad (5.10.1)$$

This process is shown graphically in Figure 5.10.2, where it is seen that $\mathbf{V}_1$ and $\mathbf{V}_2$ constitute an unbalanced two-phase set of voltages. Since the relationship between voltage and field is reversible, it follows that such an unbalanced set of voltages applied to the stator terminals will produce an air-gap field which can be represented by the counter-rotating fields $\mathbf{B}_f$ and $\mathbf{B}_b$ of Figure 5.10.1.

PROBLEM 5.10.1. Show that each of the voltage components in Figure 5.10.1 is properly related to its corresponding rotating field component.

5.11 Symmetrical Components

In Figure 5.10.2, two symmetrical (balanced) sets of voltages having opposite phase sequences were added to form a single set of unbalanced voltages, $\mathbf{V}_1$ and $\mathbf{V}_2$. The inverse process can also be performed, by solving Equations (5.10.1) for $\mathbf{V}_{1f}$ and $\mathbf{V}_{1b}$, giving

$$\mathbf{V}_{1f} = \tfrac{1}{2}(\mathbf{V}_1 + j\mathbf{V}_2)$$
$$\mathbf{V}_{1b} = \tfrac{1}{2}(\mathbf{V}_1 - j\mathbf{V}_2). \qquad (5.11.1)$$

The voltages $\mathbf{V}_{1f}$ and $\mathbf{V}_{1b}$ are called the *symmetrical components* of $\mathbf{V}_1$ and $\mathbf{V}_2$, and form the basis of an important method of analysis used in the solution of machinery and polyphase power system problems. They are usually referred to as *positive-sequence* and *negative-sequence* symmetrical components.*

PROBLEM 5.11.1. Calculate the symmetrical components, and then check by recombining the results graphically, as in Figure 5.10.2, if (a) $\mathbf{V}_1 = 100e^{j30°}$ and $\mathbf{V}_2 = 50e^{j90°}$; (b) $\mathbf{V}_1 = 100e^{j30°}$ and $\mathbf{V}_2 = 100e^{j30°}$; (c) $\mathbf{V}_1 = 100e^{j30°}$ and $\mathbf{V}_2 = 0$; (d) $v_1 = 50 \sin \omega t$ and $v_2 = 100 \cos \omega t$. (e) In each case, sketch the counter-rotating **B** fields at the instant when $\omega t = 30°$. *Answer:* (a) $\mathbf{V}_{1f} = 31.0e^{j53°}$, $\mathbf{V}_{1b} = 73e^{j20°}$; (b) $\mathbf{V}_{1f} = 70.7e^{j75°}$, $\mathbf{V}_{1b} = 70.7e^{-j15°}$; (c) $\mathbf{V}_{1f} = \mathbf{V}_{1b} = 50e^{j30°}$; (d) $\mathbf{V}_{1f} = 25e^{j90°}$, $\mathbf{V}_{1b} = 75e^{-j90°}$.

5.12 The Servomotor

The two-phase induction motor is widely used as a control motor or servomotor, in ratings of a few watts. A fixed alternating voltage is applied

---

* Reference 4.1, Chapter 13, for example.

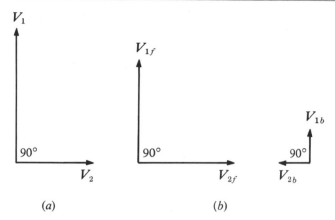

FIGURE 5.12.1.(*a*) Unbalanced voltages constrained to 90° phase relationship. (*b*) Symmetrical components of voltages related to counter-rotating field components have opposite phase sequence and are referred to as "positive-sequence" and "negative-sequence" symmetrical components.

to one winding (for example, winding 1), and a control voltage of variable magnitude, but lagging by 90°, is applied to the other winding. It is desired that the torque of the motor be proportional to the magnitude of the control voltage.

As a result of the constraint that the two phase-voltages be kept in quadrature, the form of the symmetrical components is considerably simplified. Let the ratio of the magnitude of control voltage V_2 to fixed voltage V_1 be designated by a constant c. Then, with V_1 leading V_2 by 90° as in Figure 5.12.1,

$$V_2 = -jcV_1, \tag{5.12.1}$$

and from Equation (5.11.1),

$$V_{1f} = \tfrac{1}{2}V_1(1 + c)$$
$$V_{1b} = \tfrac{1}{2}V_1(1 - c). \tag{5.12.2}$$

These symmetrical components are also shown in Figure 5.12.1.

The rotor resistance of the servomotor is made sufficiently high that its torque characteristic approximates the straight-line curve of Figure 5.5(*c*). Then the torque for each voltage component is given by Equation (5.3.4), repeated here:

$$T = -k\frac{V_t^2}{R_r}s. \tag{5.3.4}$$

Under unbalanced operation, the total torque can be found by summing the forward and backward torques produced by the two symmetrical components of voltage. When the slip for the forward component is s, the slip for the backward component, at the same shaft speed, is $(2 - s)$. Thus the total torque is

$$T = T_f - T_b = -k \frac{V_1^2}{4R_r} [(1 + c)^2 s - (1 - c)^2 (2 - s)]. \quad (5.12.3)$$

The two components and their sum are shown for a typical case in Figure 5.12.2.

Control motors operate most of the time near zero speed, turning slowly a few turns one way and then the other. Thus, their characteristics near zero speed are of special interest. When $s = 1$, Equation (5.12.3) becomes

$$T\big|_{s=1} = -k \frac{V_1^2}{R_r} c = -k \frac{V_1 V_2}{R_r}, \quad (5.12.4)$$

showing that the torque at zero speed is proportional to the control voltage V_2. Since the torque curve is a straight line, it can be constructed easily by determining one other point, such as that for synchronous speed, where $s = 0$ and $T_f = 0$, and

$$T\big|_{s=0} = +k \frac{V_1^2}{2R} (1 - c)^2. \quad (5.12.5)$$

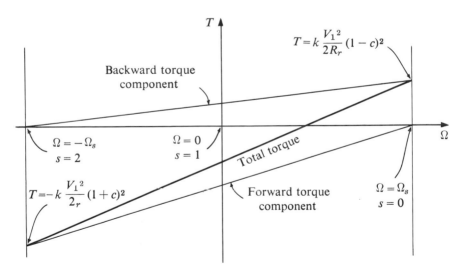

FIGURE 5.12.2. Summation of forward and backward torque components in unbalanced operation of induction motor. Curves are assumed linear because of high rotor resistance. Total torque curve shows motor would (in this case) run about half synchronous speed with no shaft load.

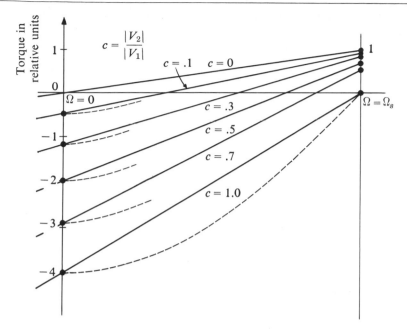

FIGURE 5.12.3. Family of servomotor torque–speed curves for various values of $c = V_2/V_1$, with V_1 constant. Curves are straight lines because of assumption of high rotor resistance. Practical machine curves, shown as dashed lines, all have approximately the same slope near zero speed.

A family of such curves is shown in Figure 5.12.3. Of special interest is the curve for $c = 0$, where the control winding is short circuited. This curve represents the characteristic for ideal viscous damping, where torque is proportional to speed, or

$$T = D_\theta \Omega. \tag{5.12.6}$$

The damping constant D_θ is equal to the slope of the $c = 0$ curve, and can be evaluated as

$$D_\theta = \frac{T|_{s=0}}{\Omega_s} = \frac{kV_1^2}{2\omega_s R_r}, \tag{5.12.7}$$

where ω_s is the supply-voltage frequency and equals the synchronous speed Ω_s.

In practical designs, the rotor resistance is decreased until the torque–speed curves depart from linearity and appear approximately as the dashed curves in Figure 5.12.3. This has the effect of making the slope of all of the curves approximately the same as that for the $c = 0$ curve, in the region up to about

25% of synchronous speed. Within this region, the torque-speed relationship can be shown to have the linear form

$$T = -\frac{kV_1^2}{R_r}\left[c - \frac{\Omega}{2\omega_s}\right].$$

(5.12.8)

This approximation permits the servomotor to be represented by a combination of an ideal torque source and an ideal frictional damping element, greatly simplifying the analysis of systems using this motor as a component.

PROBLEM 5.12.1. Derive in detail (*a*) Equation (5.12.3); (*b*) Equation (5.12.8).

PROBLEM 5.12.2. A certain servomotor develops 0.02 N-m of torque at zero speed when connected to a *balanced two-phase supply*, of frequency 100 rad/s. It is to be operated with its fixed winding connected to the same supply. (*a*) Determine the numerical expression for Equation (5.12.8). (*b*) Represent the motor as a combination of an ideal torque source and a damping element. (*c*) Draw an analogous electric circuit for (*b*). *Answer:* $T = -0.02\,(c - \Omega/200)$.

5.13 Single-Phase Motors

A single-phase induction motor has only one stator winding, and it might be expected that this would lead to a simplification of the analysis over that of the two-winding polyphase servomotor. Such is not the case, however, for the absence of the second winding removes a constraint on the relationship between the counter-rotating field components. This is best illustrated by examining the related symmetrical components of voltage.

In Figure 5.13.1 are shown a single-phase applied voltage $\mathbf{V}_1$, and its appropriate set of symmetrical components, calculated by Equations (5.11.1),

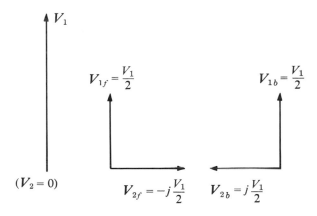

FIGURE 5.13.1. Symmetrical components of single-phase voltage $\mathbf{V}_1$ when $\mathbf{V}_2 = 0$.

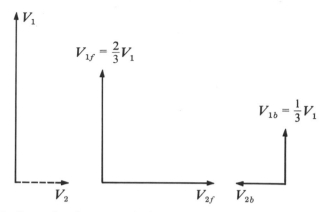

FIGURE 5.13.2. Example of symmetrical components produced by single-phase voltage V_1 when V_2 is not constrained. An infinite number of combinations is possible.

for $\mathbf{V}_2 = 0$. It is seen that the voltage components are equal in magnitude, corresponding to two equal, counter-rotating field components. In the single-phase motor there is actually no such constraint as $\mathbf{V}_2 = 0$, however, for there is no actual second winding present that could be short circuited to constrain $\mathbf{V}_2$ to zero. Therefore, *any* set of symmetrical components that fulfil the requirement $\mathbf{V}_{1f} + \mathbf{V}_{1b} = \mathbf{V}_1$ can possibly exist. The constraint on $\mathbf{V}_{2f} + \mathbf{V}_{2b}$ has been removed. One example of this is shown in Figure 5.13.2, where it is arbitrarily set that $\mathbf{V}_{1f} = \tfrac{2}{3}\mathbf{V}_1$. The other relationships shown follow from Equation (5.11.1), and result in a hypothetical $\mathbf{V}_2 = -j\tfrac{1}{3}\mathbf{V}_1$. Thus the rotating fields correspond to those in a polyphase machine with $c = \tfrac{1}{3}$, and the torque will be considerably higher than would be expected from the invalid assumption that $c = 0$. The hypothetical voltage $\mathbf{V}_2$ would actually appear at the terminals of a second phase winding if one were present.

For the single-phase induction motor, the values of $\mathbf{V}_{1f}$ and $\mathbf{V}_{1b}$ can be determined most readily by use of the induction motor equivalent circuit, originally developed in Figure 5.6.2 for balanced operation. Since the slips seen by the forward and backward field components are different, two diagrams are needed. Figure 5.13.3 shows the two diagrams connected in such a way that the requirement $\mathbf{V}_{1f} + \mathbf{V}_{1b} = \mathbf{V}_1$ is met. A similar development for symmetrical components of current (see Problem 5.13.1) shows that since $\mathbf{I}_2$ *is* constrained to zero, $\mathbf{I}_{1f} = \mathbf{I}_{1b}$, a condition that is also fulfilled by the series connection.

The two equivalents present different impedances (except at $s = 1$), and after evaluation of these impedances the values of $\mathbf{V}_{1f}$ and $\mathbf{V}_{1b}$ can be found

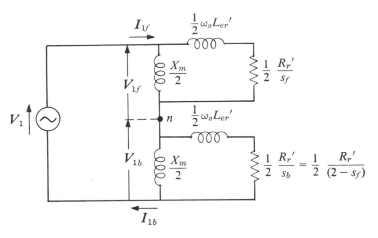

FIGURE 5.13.3. Equivalent circuit for single-phase motor operation. Node n is hypothetical and inaccessible, and at a floating potential, so that $\mathbf{V}_{1f}$ and $\mathbf{V}_{1b}$ can take on any values whose phasor sum is $\mathbf{V}_1$. Factors of $\frac{1}{2}$ appear because parameters are normally measured at standstill, when $\mathbf{V}_{1f} = \mathbf{V}_{1b} = \frac{1}{2}\mathbf{V}_1$, and are defined in terms of $\mathbf{V}_1/\mathbf{I}$.

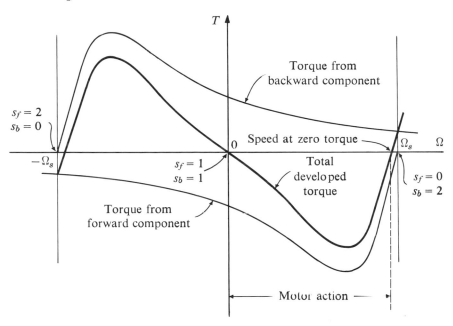

FIGURE 5.13.4. Torques in single-phase motor. The symbols s_f and s_b represent slip seen by forward and backward rotating field components.

from the voltage divider relationship. It is to be noted that the special 90°
relationships of Figure 5.12.1 are no longer required, and the more general
conditions of Figures 5.10.1 and 5.10.2 apply.

The upper and lower parts of the equivalent circuit of Figure 5.13.3 are
called, respectively, the *positive-sequence network* and the *negative-sequence
network*. Similarly, the impedances of these two parts are called the *positive-
sequence impedance* and the *negative-sequence impedance*.

The forward and backward components of torque calculated using $\mathbf{V}_{1f}$ and
$\mathbf{V}_{1b}$ can be superimposed, giving a result like that of Figure 5.13.4. It is noted
that since $\mathbf{V}_{1f} = \mathbf{V}_{1b}$ at standstill ($s = 1$), the single-phase motor produces
zero torque at standstill and will not start unless some auxiliary means is
provided. Early single-phase motors were started by pulling on a rope wound
around the shaft. A more convenient method uses a second winding, in space
quadrature with the main winding, as illustrated in Figure 5.13.5. The current
in this second winding is shifted in phase with respect to that in the main

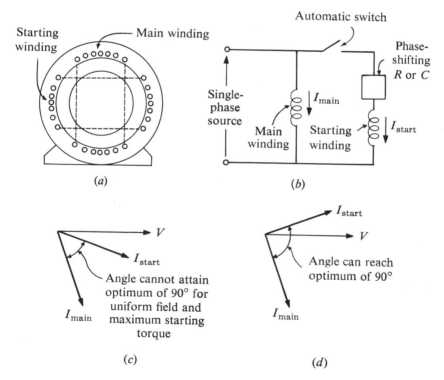

(a)

(b)

(c)

(d)

FIGURE 5.13.5. Starting of single-phase motors. (*a*) Windings. (*b*) Circuit diagram.
(*c*) Phasor diagram for resistive starting. (*d*) Phasor diagram for capacitive start.

winding by the use of a series resistor or capacitor, so that the motor becomes a two-phase motor during starting.

During operation, normal changes in loading would require continual adjustments of the phase-shifting element to maintain effective two-phase operation, so it is usually more practical to disconnect the second winding entirely, by means of a centrifugal switch, as the motor comes up to speed, and let the motor run as a single-phase motor.

PROBLEM 5.13.1. Symmetrical components of current take on the same form as those for voltage, as given in Equation (5.11.1). Show that if $I_2 = 0$, $\mathbf{I}_{1f} = \mathbf{I}_{2f}$.

PROBLEM 5.13.2. A single-phase motor with no starting winding is connected to a voltage supply and then has its shaft driven externally in the $-\Omega$ direction. Is it operating as a motor or as a generator? What will happen if the external driver is removed?

5.14   Example. The Induction Tachometer

An interesting application of the symmetrical-component concept is the analysis of the induction tachometer, illustrated in Figure 5.14.1. This is basically a small single-phase motor to which a second winding has been added. With inproper limitations, the alternating voltage $\mathbf{V}_2$ appearing at the terminals of this second winding will be proportional in magnitude to the shaft speed of the tachometer.

For the purpose of providing a numerically simple example, the parameter values in Figure 5.14.1(b) were chosen so that both X_m and X' can be ignored

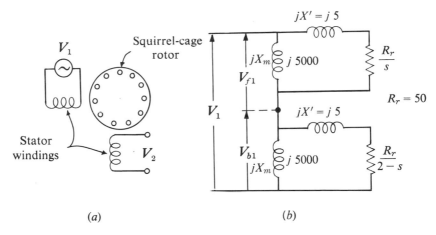

(a)   (b)

FIGURE 5.14.1. Induction tachometer. (a) Connection diagram; (b) equivalent circuit.

with little error. The equivalent circuit then becomes a simple circuit consisting of resistances R_r/s and $R_r/(2 - s)$ connected in series. After application of the voltage-divider rule and substitution into Equation (5.10.1), there results

$$V_2 = -jV_1 \frac{\Omega}{\Omega_s},\qquad (5.14.1)$$

which is the desired proportionality. If a larger number of turns is placed on the second winding, high sensitivity can be achieved.

PROBLEM 5.14.1. Derive Equation (5.14.1). For what range of speeds are the assumptions likely to be invalid?

Advanced Problems

5.1 Prove analytically that Equation (5.2.4) gives a semicircular locus in the complex plane.

5.2 In Figure 5.2.2, let $B_t = 1.0$, $B_r = 0.8$, $\theta_r' = 30°$, and $s = 0.15$ for a particular operating condition. Sketch to scale the locus variations, similar to Figure 5.2.2, marking to scale the points on the locus where slip has the values of 0.05, 0.15, 0.30, 0.50, and 1.0.

5.3 Extend the plot of Problem 5.2 to include slips of 2.0 and −0.15. Explain what is happening under these two conditions.

5.4 Calculate and plot a curve of T vs. Ω from the data of Problem 5.2, using the relationship $T = K_b B_r B_t \sin \delta_{rt}$, with $K_b = 10.0$. Cover the range from $s = 2$ to $s = -1$.

5.5 Sketch a family of curves like those of Figure 5.5, except that L_r instead of R_r is varied.

5.6 Evaluate, in terms of machine parameters such as g, r, N_s, etc., the constant in (a) Equation (5.3.2); (b) Equation (5.3.3).

5.7 A two-pole, two-phase induction motor is operated at 120 V rms (per phase), with no shaft load, and the stator current measured at 0.5 A. The speed is practically synchronous speed. Then, with the rotor blocked so that it cannot turn, a voltage of 30 V is found to produce 4.0 A, with a power input of 20 W/phase. Calculate X_m, X_r', and R_r'.

5.8 A high-slip induction motor has a linear torque-speed characteristic like that of Figure 5.5(c). Calculate (a) the speed for maximum mechanical power output, in terms of synchronous speed; (b) the efficiency P_r/P_s for this speed.

5.9 Represent the linear torque characteristic of Figure 5.5(c) as a combination of an ideal torque source and a linear damping element D_θ, and draw an analogous electric circuit.

5.10   Make sketches similar to the *V-I* phasor diagram of Figure 5.6.1, showing the effect on the locus of I_s if the rotor resistance R_r' is (*a*) increased; (*b*) decreased. (*c*) Use these diagrams to plot the approximate variation of I_s with rotor speed. (*d*) Comment on the effect of rotor resistance on the starting-current ($\Omega = 0$) requirement.

5.11   The squirrel-cage rotor of Figure 5.7.1(*a*) is placed in a cosinusoidally-distributed rotating air-gap field. (*a*) Show by means of a phasor diagram the relationship between the voltages induced into each of the uniformly-spaced one-turn phase windings. (*b*) Make a graph of instantaneous current vs. rotor coil position for one instant of time. (*c*) From the graph of (*b*) make a graph of *rotor field* vs. rotor coil position, similar to those of Problem 3.1. This should show that the uniformly-distributed winding can in this case produce a cosinusoidally-distributed air-gap field.

5.12   In Figure P5.12(*a*) is shown a single-phase representation of a large induction motor being started from an ac supply line of voltage *V* (the other phases are identical). The torque at starting ($\Omega = 0$) is T_a; the corresponding starting current, I_a, proves to be too high, so a transformer (also polyphase) is connected as in Figure P5.12(*b*) to remedy this. (*a*) Find the turns ratio N/N_s so that the new starting current, I_b, is reduced to 50% of I_a. (*b*) With the transformer as in (*a*), determine the starting-torque ratio T_b/T_a.

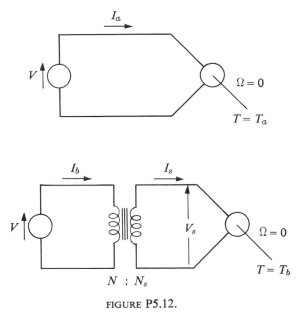

FIGURE P5.12.

5.13   A double-cage rotor (Figure 5.7.2) has the same torque constant for both rotor windings, and has the following parameter values, expressed in terms of equivalent stator quantities:

	Starting winding	Run winding
Inductance	0.3 H	0.5 H
Resistance	30 ohms	2.5 ohms

The supply frequency is 100 rad/s. Sketch a torque-speed curve similar to Figure 5.7.3, showing (*a*) numerical values for the speed at which each component maximum occurs; (*b*) the relative magnitudes of these maxima; (*c*) the relative magnitudes of the components of starting torques.

5.14 Use the equivalent circuit of Figure 5.6.3 to determine the mechanical power and torque output from a polyphase induction motor that is supplied from a balanced polyphase *current* source. Deduce and sketch the approximate torque-speed curve.

5.15 Determine and sketch the symmetrical components of each of the current sets given in Problem 5.8.1.

5.16 Two cosinusoidally-distributed windings, each represented by only a single coil in Figure P5.16, are wound with their axes as shown. The currents are $i_1 = I_m \cos \omega t$ and $i_2 = I_m \sin \omega t$. Evaluate $\mathbf{B}_f$ and $\mathbf{B}_b$ as space phasors, and sketch them approximately to scale for the instant when $\omega t = 30°$.

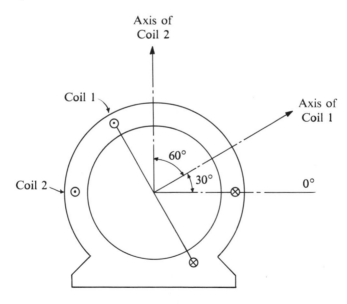

FIGURE P5.16.

5.17 A two-phase *synchronous* motor is running in the steady state at synchronous speed, when one phase of the stator supply is disconnected. (*a*) Explain, in terms of counter-rotating field theory, how the motor can continue to run at synchronous speed. (*b*) What frequency of voltage will be induced into the rotor during single-phase operation? (*c*) Obtain an expression for the torque produced by each component of the air-gap field, assuming that the rotor current remains a steady direct current.

5.18 Figure 5.13.4 shows that a single-phase induction motor produces backward torque at synchronous speed. Explain this phenomenon in terms of the equivalent circuit of Figure 5.13.3.

5.19 Modify the equivalent circuit of Figure 5.13.3 to apply to a polyphase motor with unbalanced voltages applied. Is node *n* still at a floating potential?

REFERENCE

5.1   E. BRENNER and M. JAVID. *Analysis of Electric Circuits.* New York: McGraw-Hill, 1959.

CHAPTER SIX

Commutator Machines

6.1 The Purpose of Commutation

Rotating machines depend for their operation on there being some way to maintain a constant torque-angle between the stator field and the rotor field, as the rotor turns. The rotating field produced by polyphase windings is an important answer to this problem, but is lacking in flexibility because of the requirement that the field be in synchronism with the terminal frequency. The synchronous machine must always turn at synchronous speed; the induction machine overcomes this problem but is grossly inefficient at low speeds because of high slip loss. The commutator machine provides complete freedom from synchronous requirements; in fact, it can operate efficiently at zero frequency.

Commutation is a switching process, accomplished either through solid-state devices or mechanically. The conventional commutator is a mechanical switch attached to the rotor shaft and rotating with it. When the electrical connections to the rotor are made through a commutator, there result two important modifications which are listed below, and are to be developed in detail in later sections.

1. The axis of the rotor field is not affected by mechanical rotation of the rotor. Rotation of the rotor does not produce a corresponding rotation of the rotor field.

2. The frequency of voltages generated by a rotor (turning in a magnetic field, or stationary in a rotating field) is not affected by mechanical rotation of the rotor. The magnitude of these voltages, however, *is* affected.

This remarkable ability to separate some of the rotational effects from others makes the commutator machine a versatile device with many desirable operating characteristics, but limited in use by the relatively high cost of the commutator.

6.2 Physical Commutator Construction

Before proceeding further, it is desirable to investigate the construction of a commutator, and see how it may be connected to a winding. The early "Gramme Ring" winding (Figure 6.2.1), although inefficient and impractical, provides easy visualization of commutator action.

The following comments may be made about Figure 6.2.1(*a*).

1. The toroidal rotor carries a single uniform winding of many turns which closes upon itself (is "re-entrant").

2. Two sliding contacts, or "brushes," bear on opposite sides of the winding. These are wide enough so that they always contact at least one turn of the winding, to avoid abrupt breaking of the electrical circuit as the rotor turns. In practice, the brushes are sufficiently wide always to contact at least two turns of the winding.

3. Any current entering the winding (say, from the top brush) will divide equally, half flowing downward around the turns on each side, and leave at the bottom brush. This equal division will occur whether the rotor is stationary or turning, provided the electrical time constants are short compared with the turning speed.

4. The mmf from the two sides will be equal and in the same direction (down, in this case). These two mmf's are magnetically in parallel, so that

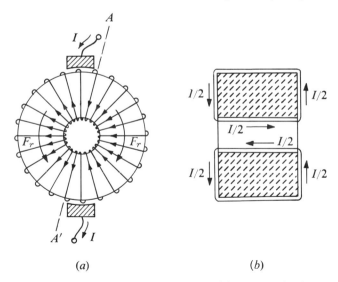

(*a*) (*b*)

FIGURE 6.2.1. Gramme ring commutated rotor. (*a*) Rotor winding and brushes. Arrows on windings indicate current directions through winding. (*b*) Sectional view from side at *AA'*.

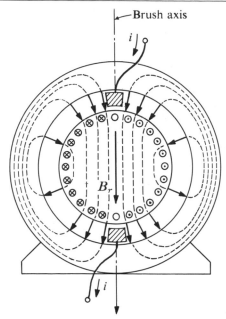

FIGURE 6.2.2. Commutated rotor modified to cylindrical form. Details of winding interconnections are not shown, but are considered such that current flow into brush determines direction of field along brush axis.

their resultant is the same as either one. Also, the net mmf *around* the toroid is zero.

Inspection of the cross-sectional sketch of Figure 6.2.1(*b*) reveals that each current through the small center hole is in close proximity to another equal current in the opposite direction, so that the net magnetic effect is zero. Thus, the center hole may be eliminated if some way can be found to reconnect the wires.

Numerous ingenious wiring arrangements exist and are discussed at length in standard textbooks on dc machinery.* After elimination of the center hole the rotor becomes a single cylinder and appears as in Figure 6.2.2, with the current directions in the remaining circumferential conductors corresponding to those of Figure 6.2.1.

It is seen that the coil-sides are uniformly spaced around the rotor, rather than being sinusoidally distributed. This uniform spacing is necessary if the rotor field is to be unaffected by the angular position of the rotor, and will produce a triangular field distribution rather than a cosinusoidal field distribution. Since the use of phasor methods for adding air-gap fields

---

* For example, see Reference 6.1.

FIGURE 6.2.3. Details of practical commutator. Brush springs (*A*) press graphite brushes (*B*) against commutator surface (*C*). Many brushes are used (instead of one) for mechanical reasons. Each wedge-shaped copper commutator bar is insulated separately, and connected by riser (*D*) to appropriate rotor winding (*E*). (Courtesy of Allis-Chalmers Manufacturing Company, Milwaukee, Wisconsin.)

depends on there being a cosinusoidal field distribution, an approximation is made that disregards all but the fundamental component of the triangular space distribution of the field.

The line drawn through the brushes, along which the field is directed, is known as the "brush axis." The positive direction of the brush axis is defined by the reference direction assigned to the brush current; in Figure 6.2.2, for example, the current enters at the upper brush and leaves at the lower brush, establishing the brush axis direction as downward. The rotor is assumed to be wound such that positive current produces a rotor field in the positive axial direction.

If both brushes are moved through the same angle, the brush axis shifts and the rotor field turns a corresponding amount. If the assembly holding the brushes is so mounted that it can rotate continuously about the rotor shaft axis, a steady direct current into the brushes will result in a rotating magnetic field. Such a rotating brush assembly is featured on the educational Generalized Machine by Westinghouse, but is too complex to be of value in industrial applications. However, some practical machines do use brush assemblies that can be rotated through a small angle.

In a practical machine, the brushes do not rub directly on the wires, but rather on a thickened, cylindrical extension (Figure 6.2.3) which provides a surface adequate for wear. It is this extension that is ordinarily called the commutator.

PROBLEM 6.2.1. The rotor of Figure 6.2.1 has 24 turns and the brush current is 6.0 A. Calculate the mmf F_r. *Answer:* 33 amp-turns.

PROBLEM 6.2.2. A steady direct current of 4.0 A flows in the brushes of Figure 6.2.2, while the rotor is driven at 300 rpm in the counterclockwise direction. Determine the rpm and direction of rotation of the rotor field. *Answer:* Stationary.

6.3   Polyphase Commutation

Figure 6.3.1 illustrates a two-phase commutated rotor, with the brushes connected to a two-phase supply. Several comments apply.

1. Phase 1 produces a vertical field and phase 2 produces a horizontal field, each along its own brush axis.

2. The phase currents superimpose as they flow between opposite brushes in the single re-entrant winding. If electrical isolation between phases were

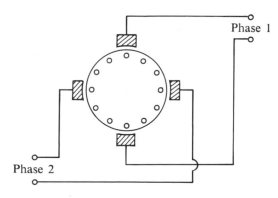

FIGURE 6.3.1. Polyphase commutated rotor.

necessary, two separate windings, each with its own commutator, would be required.

3. The polyphase currents produce a rotating field in the usual manner, rotating at supply frequency but with respect to the *brushes*, not with respect to the rotor. The commutator insures that changes in the rotor position do not affect the field.

4. If the assembly holding the brushes is so mounted that it can be rotated continuously about the rotor shaft axis, this rotation *will* affect the speed of the rotating field.

Torque is produced as the rotor field tries to line up with whatever field is produced by the stator. This alignment may be thought of as proceeding in a series of small oscillations. The rotor advances, carrying its field with it through a small angle. Then the brushes slip off of a rotor coil and on to the next one, returning the field to its original position. It is the "carrot and donkey" trick applied to a machine.

Example 6.3. Figure 6.3.2 shows a two-phase commutated rotor inside a two-phase stator. The connection diagram shows that each stator phase is connected in series with one rotor phase, and the machine is energized from a two-phase source.

(a) At what speed must the rotor turn for torque to be produced?

(b) How is the torque angle to be varied?

Solution. (a) The stator will produce a revolving field that rotates at ω_s, the supply frequency. The rotor will also produce a field rotating at ω_s, and as a result of the commutation this rotation will be unaffected by rotor speed. Therefore, torque may be produced at any rotor speed.

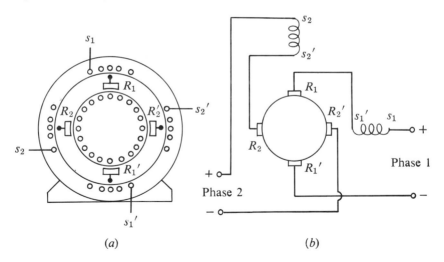

(a)   (b)

FIGURE 6.3.2. Machine for Illustrative Example 6.3. (*a*) Machine. (*b*) Connection diagram with symbolic representation of stator windings.

(b) For the arrangement shown, the rotating fields produced by stator and rotor are always at right angles with respect to each other, giving optimum torque angle for all operating conditions (the reader should inspect the connections carefully to verify this). The relative position of the rotor field can be varied by shifting all of the brushes through the same angle. By this means the torque angle can be changed to any value, either positive or negative.

PROBLEM 6.3.1. The polyphase commutated rotor of Figure 6.3.1 has a two-phase voltage of frequency $\omega_r = 40$ applied at the brushes, while the rotor is turned physically at $\Omega = 30$. Determine the speed of the rotating field if (a) field and rotor turn in the same direction; (b) field and rotor turn in opposite directions. *Answer:* (a) 40; (b) 40.

PROBLEM 6.3.2. The machine of Figure 6.3.2 has its stator windings interchanged in such a way that the stator field rotates in the opposite direction. How does this affect the situation? Explain. *Answer:* Torque oscillates about an average of zero.

PROBLEM 6.3.3. In a machine similar to that of Figure 6.3.2(a), the stator winding S_1 is energized with direct current, the stator winding S_2 is open circuited, and the brushes are energized from a two-phase supply of frequency ω_s. What must be done in order for a nonzero average torque to be developed? *Answer:* Rotate brushes at $-\omega_s$.

PROBLEM 6.3.4. The machine of Problem 6.3.3 is reconnected so that the two-phase supply energizes the stator and the direct current flows in the rotor brushes $R_2 - R_2'$. What must be done so a nonzero average torque can be developed?

6.4 The Effect of Commutation on Rotor Voltages

The effect of commutation on rotor terminal voltages can be seen with reference to Figure 6.4.1, where a Gramme ring rotor is shown in a machine having a rotating air-gap field produced by stator windings and given by

$$\mathscr{B} = \mathbf{a}_r B_m \cos{(\omega t - \theta)}. \tag{6.4.1}$$

Now let the rotor be held *stationary*, so that $\Omega = 0$. The field then sweeps past the stationary rotor winding, generating on the outside of each coil a voltage given by

$$v = (\mathbf{u} \times \mathscr{B}) \cdot \mathbf{l} = [\mathbf{a}_z \omega r B_m \cos{(\omega t - \theta_0)}] \cdot \mathbf{l}$$
$$= \omega r l B_m \cos{(\omega t - \theta_0)}, \tag{6.4.2}$$

where r is the rotor radius, $\mathbf{l}$ is the directed axial length of the coil side, ω is the angular velocity of the air-gap field, θ_0 is the angular position of the coilside, measured from the $0°$ axis, $\mathbf{u}$ is the velocity of the coilside relative to the field $(u = \omega r)$, and $\mathbf{a}_z$ indicates that the electric field is directed parallel to the rotor shaft axis.

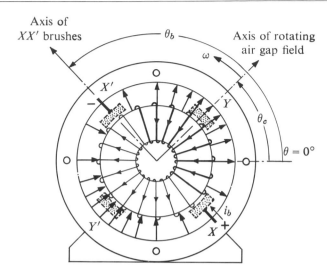

FIGURE 6.4.1. Illustration for discussion of commutated voltages. Air-gap field is produced by polyphase stator windings. Reference directions and brush positions are located as the discussion in Section 6.4 proceeds. The angle θ_c is measured to the central coil of the winding between brush positions X and X', and only coincidentally to the axis of the rotating air-gap field.

At the instant that the rotating field has the position shown in Figure 6.4.1, the resulting positive direction of the instantaneous induced voltage around each turn is as shown by the arrows on the wires. These voltages add up around the turns in the direction of the arrows, so that the net voltage around the re-entrant winding is zero. The voltage between the diametrically opposite points X and X', however, is seen to equal the sum of the voltages induced into the turns connected in series between X and X'. The total winding is seen to be divided into two equal parts, connected electrically in parallel between X and X'. If the winding is tapped with brushes at points X and X', the maximum instantaneous voltage will be obtained, with brush X positive. Brushes at Y and Y' tap zero instantaneous voltage at the same instant, and brushes at other points would provide a value between zero and the maximum.

According to an argument illustrated in Figure 3.8.5, and proved in Section 4.2, the alternating voltages induced into the individual coils add to give a total voltage between tap points that is $\pi N/4$ times the voltage of the central coil, and in phase with the voltage of the central coil. This phase relationship can be verified by inspection of Figure 6.4.1; for example, the coil just under brush X is in position to have induced into it zero instantaneous voltage, and this same coil is the central turn for the winding between brushes Y and Y', where the instantaneous voltage is also zero.

For the brush pair X and X', the brush at X was shown to be positive at the instant sketched in Figure 6.4.1. Assignment of the brush current i_b as being directed into the positive brush, according to the load convention, establishes the brush axis direction as shown. Then, if θ_b is the angle of the XX' brush axis, and θ_c is the angular position of the corresponding central coil, $\theta_c = \theta_b - 90°$. With these modifications, setting $\theta_0 = \theta_c$ in Equation (6.4.2) gives the brush voltage for *any* brush axis as

$$v_{bb'} = \tfrac{1}{4}\omega rl\pi N B_m \cos\left(\omega t - \theta_b + 90°\right),$$

or

$$v_{bb'} = -V_{bm} \sin\left(\omega t - \theta_b\right). \tag{6.4.3}$$

The symbol N represents the number of turns when each turn is taken as having two active coil sides. Half of the active coil sides are effectively in parallel with the other half between the brushes, and so produce only half the voltage that would be produced in an ac phase winding, where all the coil sides are in series between winding terminals.

As the rotating air-gap field turns past the stationary rotor, the voltages at the brushes vary sinusoidally with time, $v_{XX'}$ being 90° ahead of $v_{YY'}$. If the rotor be moved to a new angular position, there is no change in the configuration seen by the brushes and therefore, no change in the brush voltages.

Now let the rotor be *driven mechanically* at angular speed Ω. The effect of this on the magnitude and on the frequency of the brush voltage will be considered separately.

1. The *magnitude* of the alternating brush voltage is seen from Equation (6.4.2) to depend on **u**, the relative velocity between the coil sides and the field. The rotating rotor is now trying to "catch up" with the air-gap field, so the new relative velocity equals the difference between the two speeds. Thus, the magnitude of the brush voltage becomes

$$V_{bb'm} = (\omega - \Omega)rl\pi N B_m/4.$$

2. The *frequency* of the brush voltage is determined by noting that the changing configuration of coil voltages goes through one complete cycle each time the rotating field makes one revolution *relative to the brushes*. Starting at the position shown in Figure 6.4.1, the air-gap field sweeps around the air gap until it has returned to its starting position, at which time the coil voltage configuration is exactly the same as it was originally. Turning the rotor has no effect on this voltage configuration. Thus, the frequency at the brushes is the same as the angular velocity of the air-gap field, ω. If the brush assembly were so mounted that it could rotate continuously about the rotor shaft axis at a mechanical speed Ω_b, this *would* alter the cycle time at

the moving brush position, so that in general, the brush-voltage frequency becomes $\omega_b = (\omega - \Omega_b)$. This same result is obtained from substitution of $\theta_b = \Omega_b t$ in Equation (6.4.3), which with these modifications takes the general form,

$$v_{bb'} = -\tfrac{1}{4}(\omega - \Omega)rl\pi NB_m \sin(\omega - \Omega_b)t, \qquad (6.4.4)$$

where $v_{bb'}$ is the motionally-generated voltage at the brushes (with $i_b = 0$), ω is the angular velocity of the air-gap field, B_m is the magnitude of the air-gap field on its own (rotating) axis, Ω is the mechanical angular velocity of the rotor, Ω_b is the mechanical angular velocity of the assembly holding the brushes, measured to the brush axis; for stationary brushes the substitution $\theta_b = \Omega_b t$ is made.

It is to be noted that mechanical shaft speed affects only the magnitude of the voltage and not the frequency, whereas rotation of the brushes affects the frequency and not the magnitude. The student should review the rotating field relationships involved until these results seem entirely sensible.

PROBLEM 6.4.1. Show, by the application of appropriate rules, that the directions of induced voltage in Figure 6.4.1 are indeed correct.

PROBLEM 6.4.2. Refer to Figure 6.4.1, and explain how each of the following depends on the mechanical rotor speed Ω: (*a*) frequency of the voltage induced into a single coil of the rotor; (*b*) frequency of the voltage appearing at the brushes; (*c*) magnitude of the voltage induced into a single coil of the rotor; (*d*) magnitude of the voltage appearing at the brushes.

PROBLEM 6.4.3. The reference stator coil of a commutator machine carries a steady direct current of I. The rotor turns at a speed Ω. Use Equation (6.4.4) to calculate the voltage at each set of brushes, if the brushes are fixed on the stator coil axes. *Answer:* 0, $\Omega rl\pi u_0 N_r N_s I/8g$ (a constant value).

6.5   Example. A Frequency Converter

Variable-frequency alternating voltage can be generated by driving a *synchronous generator* at varying speeds, producing [from Equation (4.2.9)] the voltage

$$v = -\tfrac{1}{2}\Omega rl\pi NB_m \sin \Omega t, \qquad (4.2.9)$$

where Ω is the shaft speed.

It is noted that the magnitude of this voltage is proportional to the frequency, so that to produce a useful voltage at very low frequency requires unreasonably large values of B_m. The device of Figure 6.5.1 is one solution to this problem. A polyphase voltage source is connected to the rotor through slip rings, and the variable frequency is taken off at brushes. There are no windings at all on the stator.

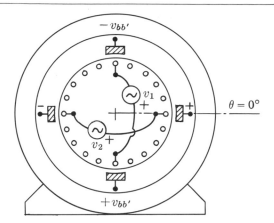

FIGURE 6.5.1. Frequency converter for example problem. Machine has brushes and slip rings on rotor, and no stator winding. Generators v_1 and v_2 represent external two-phase source connected to rotor slip rings.

For rotor excitation (through the slip rings) with the voltages as given in Equations (3.8.4), which are

$$v_1 = -V_m \sin \omega_r t$$

$$v_2 = V_m \cos \omega_r t,$$

it was shown in Section 3.8 that the associated air-gap field is described (relative to the rotor) as the rotating field

$$\mathscr{B} = \mathbf{a}_r B_m \cos (\omega_r t - \theta),$$

where $B_m = 4V_m/lr\pi N\omega_r$ for the re-entrant winding [see Equation (6.4.3)]. If, now, the rotor is *turned mechanically* so that $\theta_r = \Omega t$, the air-gap field advances at the combined angular velocity of $\omega = (\omega_r + \Omega)$, but does not change in magnitude, giving

$$\mathscr{B} = \mathbf{a}_r B_m \cos [(\omega_r + \Omega)t - \theta].$$

The resulting commutated voltage $v_{bb'}$ at the brushes is found by taking $\theta_b = 90°$ in Equation (6.4.4) and noting that the air-gap field angular velocity is $\omega = \omega_r + \Omega$, with the result that

$$v_{bb'} = V_m \cos (\omega_r + \Omega)t.$$

Thus, the voltage magnitude is unchanged by rotation of the shaft but the frequency *is* changed. If the shaft is turned backward (Ω numerically negative), very low frequencies are produced at a constant voltage level.

In this example, the shaft torque is theoretically zero, since there is no stator field to interact with the rotor field. Thus, a very small adjustable-speed motor could drive a large-capacity frequency converter and convert large amounts of power between any two frequencies, including direct current. There are many specialty uses for frequency converters, although the conversion is often effected more economically with solid-state devices.

PROBLEM 6.5.1. In the frequency converter of Figure 6.5.1, (*a*) derive an expression for the voltage at the unmarked brushes (on the $\theta = 0°$ axis); (*b*) determine the voltage that would be induced into a stator winding on the reference axis if one were present. Express the magnitude of these voltages in terms of V_m, the magnitude of the voltage applied to the slip rings. *Answer:* (*a*) $V_m \sin(\omega_r + \Omega)t$; (*b*) $v_s = [-2(\omega_r + \Omega)V_m N_s/N_r\omega_r] \sin(\omega_r + \Omega)t$.

6.6 Torque in the Commutated Machine

The axis of the field produced by a commutated rotor has been shown to be independent of rotor rotation, being affected only by the position of the brushes and by the polyphase frequency applied to the brushes. Thus, the production of a *uniform* torque requires that the same frequency be applied

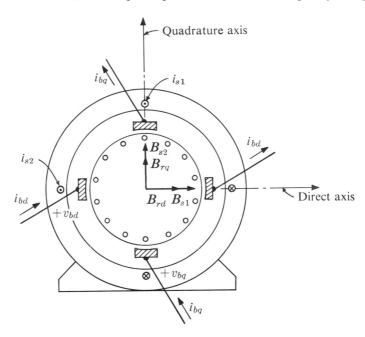

FIGURE 6.6.1. Reference directions on two-axis commutator machine. Rotor brushes are identified with reference to direct and quadrature axes, which are fixed to stator and do not rotate. In machines having salient stator poles, direct axis is assigned to salient pole axis.

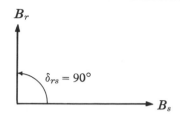

FIGURE 6.6.2. Representation of rotating fields with constant 90° torque angle.

both to the stator windings and to the brushes, so that both fields may rotate with a constant torque angle between them. No restriction is placed on the speed of the rotor itself, which if not checked by other system constraints may race to destructively high values.

Figure 6.6.1 shows a two-axis commutator machine with positive reference directions for the torque, speed, voltages, currents, and fields. It is assumed that the rotor is wound as shown in detail in Figure 6.2.1, such that the current direction into and out of a pair of brushes determines the direction of the resulting rotor field. That is, the brush axis and the positive field axis are in the same direction.

It is desired to have the optimum torque angle of 90° between the rotor field and the stator field. One possible choice having this desired alignment is given by

$$\mathscr{B}_s = \mathbf{a}_r B_{sm} \cos(\omega t - \theta)$$
$$\mathscr{B}_r = -\mathbf{a}_r B_{rm} \sin(\omega t - \theta),$$

$$(6.6.1)$$

which are sketched as phasors in their positions for $t = 0$ in Figure 6.6.2. The torque for this configuration is given by

$$T = K_b B_{sm} B_{rm} \sin \delta_{rs} = K_b B_{sm} B_{rm}. \qquad (6.6.2)$$

The torque angle δ_{rs} is positive, indicating that if Ω is also positive, the machine is a mechanical load (a generator).

From the original development of the rotating field concept in Section 3.6, it is seen that the rotating field $\mathscr{B}_s$ of Equation (6.6.1) could be produced by currents

$$i_{s1} = I_{sm} \cos \omega t$$
$$i_{s2} = I_{sm} \sin \omega t,$$

$$(6.6.3)$$

where

$$I_{sm} = 2g B_{sm}/\mu_0 N_s.$$

Similarly, the rotating field $\mathscr{B}_r$ could be produced by currents leading those above by 90°, or

$$i_{bd} = -I_{bm} \sin \omega t$$
$$i_{bq} = I_{bm} \cos \omega t,$$

$$(6.6.4)$$

where the subscripts bd and bq designate quantities for the brushes on the direct and quadrature axes, as defined in Figure 6.6.1. Thus, $i_{s1} = i_{bq}$ and $i_{s2} = -i_{bd}$ will fulfill the requirements for a constant 90° torque angle. It will now be recalled that the example problem of Figure 6.3.2 was an attempt to do just the sort of thing suggested here. The student should re-examine Figure 6.3.2, note that the current equalities above are not satisfied, and determine what torque angle will result from the connection of Figure 6.3.2.

The torque can be expressed in terms of the four separate instantaneous currents, i_{s1}, i_{s2}, i_{bd}, and i_{bq}. Each of these produces an (approximately) cosinusoidal field along its appropriate axis, shown for positive currents in Figure 6.6.1. For each current, the magnitude of the corresponding field component is given by $B = \mu_0 Ni/2g$, is time-varying with i, and does not rotate. The total torque is the sum of a positive component produced by B_{rq} and B_{s1}, plus a negative component from B_{rd} and B_{s2}, or

$$T = K_b(B_{s1}B_{rq} - B_{s2}B_{rd}). \qquad (6.6.5)$$

Equation (6.6.5) can also be derived from Equation (6.6.2) by resolving B_r and B_s into their components on the direct and quadrature axes, and performing appropriate trigonometric manipulations. This process is similar to the one used in the analysis of the salient-pole synchronous machine (Section 4.6), and would be identical if the complications of saliency were removed.

PROBLEM 6.6.1. Express the torque of Equation (6.6.5) in terms of the currents of Equations (6.6.3) and (6.6.4). (*a*) Is a nonzero average torque produced? (*b*) Is an oscillating component of torque produced? (*c*) Determine the torque if all four brushes are advanced 90° without changing the electrical connections. *Answer:* (*a*) $T = K_b N_s N_r \mu_0^2 I_{sm} I_{rm}/4g^2$; (*b*) none; (*c*) $T = 0$.

6.7 Solid-State Commutation

Commutator machines have many desirable operating characteristics, but suffer from the disadvantage of commutator wear and sparking. Electronic and solid-state switching devices have been used in experimental machines to replace the mechanical commutator, and rapid advances in solid-state technology suggest that practical machines of this type will be available for special applications.

Solid-state commutation is more readily applied to the stator, rather than to the rotor, making it unnecessary for the switching devices to rotate physically. As an introduction to this idea, Figure 6.7.1 shows a mechanically commutated stator, with brushes rotating at Ω_b to produce a rotating magnetic field from a direct current source. Figure 6.7.2 shows how the same

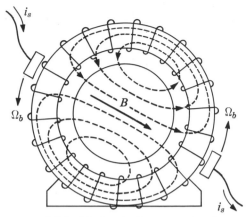

FIGURE 6.7.1. Mechanically commutated stator.

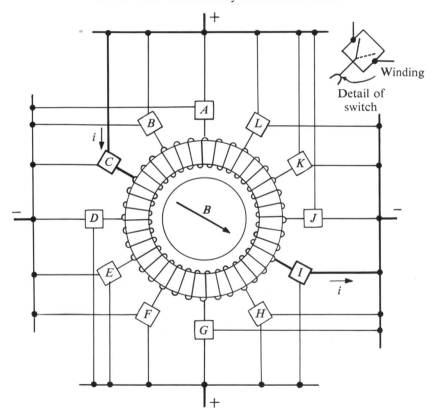

FIGURE 6.7.2. Solid-state stator commutation. Terminals marked + and − are connected to direct current supply.

result is obtained using many solid-state switches (mechanical switches could also be used but would provide no advantage over the conventional mechanical commutator). The switches are shown as double-pole single-throw, but in practice each such switch would be replaced by two on–off solid-state switches connected together at one end. The heavy lines in Figure 6.7.2 indicate the current path that produces the *B*-field shown. A moment later, the *C* and *I* switches will be opened, switch *D* will close to the positive side, and switch *J* will close to the negative side, causing the *B*-field axis to shift in a counterclockwise direction. This process is repeated for all of the switches consecutively, causing the *B*-field to rotate.

A great many possibilities exist for the switching circuitry, which will be influenced by the desired application. Two principal alternatives are:

1. *Switching speed controlled externally.* This leads to such applications as synchronous or induction motors with widely adjustable synchronous speeds, including very slow speeds for the synchronous machine.

2. *Switching speed the same as the rotor shaft speed*, but with stator and rotor fields permanently in quadrature. This insures maximum torque at all speeds, but requires some sort of device for sensing the rotor position (possibly a magnetic pickup).

The details of the switching circuitry are complicated, because transistors and silicon-controlled rectifiers (SCR's) have appreciable leakage coupling to their control circuits, so that some form of isolation is necessary. In addition, steps must be taken to hold the proper cut-off voltage on all of the switches that are not conducting. These and other difficulties suggest the refinements necessary for solid-state commutation to compete economically with conventional mechanical commutators, except in special applications

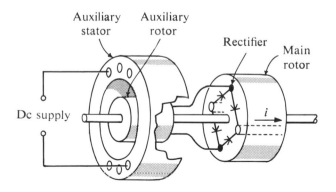

FIGURE 6.7.3. Method of eliminating sliding contacts for excitation of synchronous machine rotor. Auxiliary rotor generates alternating votage that is connected directly to rectifier shown symbolically on main rotor. Main stator is not shown.

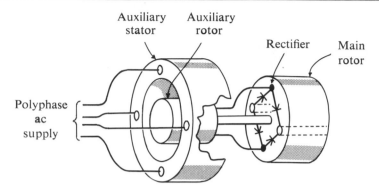

Auxiliary   Auxiliary
stator   rotor

Rectifier   Main
rotor

Polyphase
ac
supply

FIGURE 6.7.4. Contact-free excitation of synchronous machine rotor. Auxiliary stator field rotates in direction opposite to shaft rotation, producing double-frequency alternating voltage that is connected directly to rectifier on main rotor.

such as explosive atmospheres, high altitudes where commutator wear is excessive, and isolated locations where servicing is impractical.*

Another somewhat simpler application of solid-state devices to rotating machinery is in the elimination of slip rings for dc rotor excitation of *synchronous* machines. This application uses an auxiliary machine on the same shaft as the rotor of the synchronous machine, and a rectifier that rotates with the shaft. In Figure 6.7.3, the dc supply produces a stationary stator field that induces an alternating voltage into the auxiliary rotor, which is on the same shaft as the main rotor. This voltage is then rectified and applied to the main rotor of the synchronous machine.†

In Figure 6.7.4 the dc supply is eliminated. The polyphase voltage supply is applied to the auxiliary stator so as to produce a field rotating in the direction *opposite* to the shaft rotation. The auxiliary rotor then generates an alternating voltage of double the supply frequency, which is rectified and applied to the main rotor. In both of these arrangements the main rotor field current is adjusted by changing the auxiliary stator current, so no sliding connections are required.

6.8   Direct   Current   Machines

The most important commutator machine is the single-axis direct current machine, in which the stator and the rotor fields both are stationary in space.‡

* Reference 6.2.
† Reference 6.3.
‡ Stator and rotor for dc machines are commonly called "field" and "armature," respectively. In most synchronous machines, however, the stator is called the "armature" and the rotor is called the "field." An exploded view of a typical dc machine is shown in Figure 6.8.1.

FIGURE 6.8.1. Dc Machine. Exploded view shows (*A*) armature (rotor) with cooling fan and commutator; (*B*) stator field assembly; (*C*) brush mounting; (*D*) interpole. Four brush positions are used because this is a four-pole machine. (Courtesy of General Electric Company.)

Alternating voltages and currents are to be found in the rotor when it turns, but all fields are stationary with respect to the brushes, and only direct voltages and currents appear at the brushes.

Figure 6.8.2(*a*) depicts a two-pole dc machine with all reference polarities shown. There is only one stator winding (instead of two) and only one pair of brushes, because the fields are not required to rotate. In the simplified diagram of Figure 6.8.2(*b*), the symbolic stator coil is oriented to produce a field along the same axis as does the actual stator winding. The stator and rotor are both assumed to be wound so that the current reference arrows also indicate the directions of the field axes.

The torque angle between $\mathbf{B}_r$ and $\mathbf{B}_s$ is permanently fixed, at the optimum of 90°, so long as the brush axis is not changed. The magnitude of the torque can be controlled by adjusting either the stator current or the rotor current. The commutator renders the torque and torque angle independent of rotor position.

The stator winding is in an unusual situation. Since the air-gap field does not rotate, there is no $\mathbf{u} \times \mathbf{B}$ voltage induced into the stator winding. Also, because of the 90° relationship between the stator and rotor field axes, there is no mutual coupling between them. These conditions result in the stator circuit being unaffected by rotor fields or speeds, and governed only by the simple relationship

$$v_s = (R_s + pL_s)i_s. \tag{6.8.1}$$

The magnitude of the voltage generated at the brushes depends on the rotor speed and on the magnitude of the (stationary) air-gap field, B_s. This is shown analytically from Equation (6.4.4) by substituting $\omega = 0$ and $\theta_b = +90°$, giving

$$v_b = -\Omega r l \pi N_r B_m / 4, \tag{6.8.2}$$

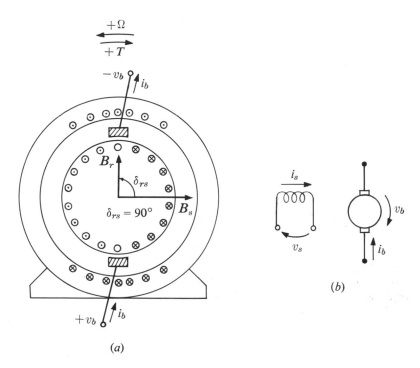

FIGURE 6.8.2. (*a*) Reference polarities for a single-axis machine. (*b*) Simplified diagram.

where in this case $B_m = B_s$. It is again to be noted that the brush axis and the stator coil axis are at right angles, the required configuration both for optimum torque and for optimum motionally-generated voltage at the brushes. Were the brushes and the stator coil to be placed on the same axis, there would be zero motionally-generated voltage as well as zero torque.

The voltage v_b in Equation (6.8.2) is numerically negative if both Ω and B_s are positive, which means that the upper brush is numerically positive in Figure 6.8.2. This is the correct orientation for generator action, for the current emerges from the positive terminal of an electrical source. Also, the torque angle δ_{rs} is positive, as it should be for a mechanical load.

In Figure 6.8.3, the dc machine is shown in operation as a motor, with its stator winding and brushes connected to separate, adjustable dc sources. The rotor field is shown reversed, to give the negative torque angle required for motor action; to accommodate this, the reference polarities for brush voltage and current have also been reversed. This change also reverses the sign of the torque expression, Equation (6.6.2). Introducing at the same time

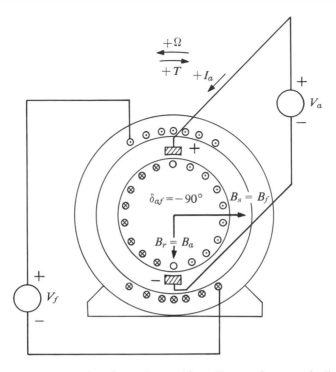

FIGURE 6.8.3. Motor action in a dc machine. Torque is numerically negative. Brush voltage and current reference polarities have been reversed from Figure 6.8.2 for convenience. New subscripts a and f stand for conventionally-used terms "armature" and "field."

the conventional designations *armature* (for rotor) and *field* (for stator), the variables of Figure 6.8.2 and Figure 6.8.3 are related according to

$$v_a = -v_b \qquad v_f = v_s$$
$$i_a = -i_b \qquad i_f = i_s. \tag{6.8.3}$$

Then Equations (6.8.1), (6.8.2), and (6.6.2) become

$$v_f = (R_f + pL_f)i_f, \tag{6.8.4}$$

$$v_a = +\Omega r l N_a B_f/4, \tag{6.8.5}$$

$$T = -K_b B_a B_f. \tag{6.8.6}$$

These polarity changes are not essential for the solution of problems, but are a conceptual aid because without them, so many of the variables of interest may be numerically negative that the situation becomes difficult to interpret. The reference polarities of Figure 6.8.3 are, therefore, used throughout the rest of this chapter.

As an example of motor operation, the stator field B_f is first established in the machine of Figure 6.8.3, and the armature (rotor) is then energized from the direct voltage source V_a.* Equation (6.8.5) requires that the armature speed increase to, and remain steady at, the value needed to generate a voltage equal to V_a. During the speed transient, the armature current will take on whatever value is required to provide the necessary torque; series starting resistors are often needed to limit the armature current to an acceptable level. When the motor is operating in the steady state, a change in V_a causes the speed to change in proportion.

Variation of V_f also affects the speed, but in an inverse manner. If V_f is increased, with V_a constant, B_f will increase. Then the armature (rotor) must slow down so that its generated voltage will still equal V_a. If the source at V_f becomes disconnected, so that I_f falls to zero, it might be supposed that the torque would go to zero and the motor coast to a stop. This is not the case, however, for the residual magnetism in the machine is sufficient to maintain B_f at about 10% of its normal value, and the motor will race toward approximately ten times its normal speed. A dc motor that loses its field excitation is extremely hazardous, as it can "run away"·and fly apart physically within just two or three seconds.

PROBLEM 6.8.1. As discussed in connection with Figure 6.8.2, it is not possible for all terminal quantities to be numerically positive at the same time in the steady state. In Table P6.8.1, the + and − signs indicate that the various quantities are numerically positive or negative with respect to the reference directions marked on Figure 6.8.2. If any two terminal polarities are assigned, all others are uniquely determined. (*a*) With the stator field current in the positive direction shown in

TABLE P6.8.1

Polarity Combinations that Permit Steady-State Operation

v_b	i_b	P_e	δ_{rs}	T	Ω	P_m	Mode
+	+	+	+	+	−	−	Motor
+	−						?
					+		Generator
	−				+		?

* The capitalized symbols V and I are used when it is desired to emphasize steady-state dc behavior, in contrast to transient behavior.

Figure 6.8.2, complete Table P6.8.1. The first row has been completed as an illustrative example. (*b*) Repeat (*a*), except with the stator field current reversed.

PROBLEM 6.8.2. Repeat Problem 6.8.1(*a*) for the revised polarity conventions of Figure 6.8.3.

6.9 Compensating Winding

The armature current produces the field $\mathbf{B}_a$ which interacts with $\mathbf{B}_f$ to provide torque. The resultant of $\mathbf{B}_a$ and $\mathbf{B}_f$, shown as $\mathbf{B}_t$ in Figure 6.9.1, is the net field, and its axis is not on the brush axis. This has three undesirable results.

1. There is a voltage induced into the single turn of the armature winding that is momentarily short-circuited by the brushes, causing a large short-circuit current in that turn and perhaps causing arcing at the brushes. (If only $\mathbf{B}_f$ is present, zero voltage is induced into the shorted turn.)

2. Since $\mathbf{B}_t$ is larger than $\mathbf{B}_f$, excessive voltages will be induced into certain turns of the armature, and arcing between the corresponding commutator segments may occur.

3. The increased $\mathbf{B}_t$ produces magnetic saturation effects that lead to partial demagnetization, reducing the stator field component $\mathbf{B}_f$.

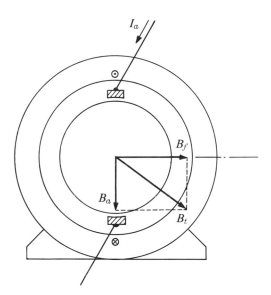

FIGURE 6.9.1. Effect of armature field on total air-gap field in dc machine. Shift of field axis and increase in air-gap magnitude produce undesirable effects. Stator field winding is represented by single turn.

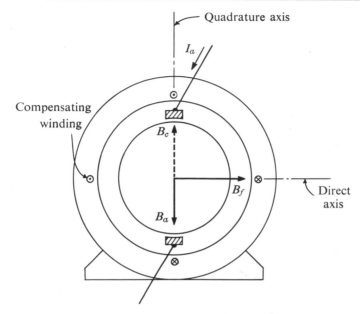

FIGURE 6.9.2. Compensating winding and compensating field. Compensating winding is in series with brushes and carries armature current.

To eliminate these undesirable effects of armature current, often called "armature reaction," a quadrature stator winding may be employed, as shown in Figure 6.9.2. This quadrature-axis winding is connected in series with the brushes, in such a way as to produce a compensating field, $\mathbf{B}_c$, that exactly cancels the armature field, $\mathbf{B}_a$. Since both $\mathbf{B}_a$ and $\mathbf{B}_c$ are produced by the armature current, they will be equal and opposite for any value of armature current.

It might at first be thought that since $\mathbf{B}_c$ cancels $\mathbf{B}_a$, there will be no torque produced. However, the torque angle between $\mathbf{B}_c$ and $\mathbf{B}_a$ is always 180°, so $\mathbf{B}_c$ produces no armature torque (sin 180° = 0). It does produce torque with $\mathbf{B}_f$, but this results only in mechanical stresses within the stator. Treated thus by superposition, the torque between $\mathbf{B}_a$ and $\mathbf{B}_f$ can be seen to remain unaffected.

A compensating winding of this type, or a somewhat different kind of series winding called a "commutating" or "interpole" winding,* is used on practically all modern dc machines. It is usually not shown in the subsequent discussion, but its presence is implied.

Practical dc machines are usually constructed with salient (protruding) stator field poles. These and other features are illustrated in the photographs

* Reference 6.1, Chapter 6.

of Figures 6.9.3 and 6.9.4. Problem 6.4 at the end of this chapter deals with a salient-pole dc machine.

PROBLEM 6.9.1. The dc machine of Figure 6.9.2 has Z active coil sides on its armature. Calculate the number of turns required for a compensating winding. *Answer:* $Z/2$ turns.

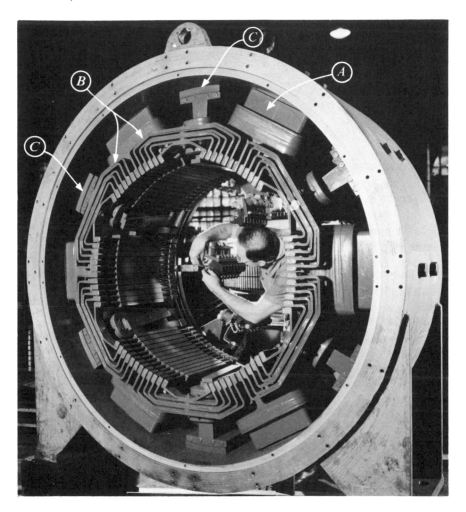

FIGURE 6.9.3. Stator field assembly for six-pole, 1000 kw dc generator, showing (*A*) salient field pole; (*B*) compensating winding in pole faces; (*C*) commutating poles ("interpoles") which aid in supression of sparking at the brushes. Workman is assembling brush mount. (Courtesy of Allis-Chalmers Manufacturing Company, Milwaukee, Wisconsin.)

FIGURE 6.9.4. Dc machine during assembly. Circumferential banding of armature and commutator is provided to increase physical strength. (Courtesy of General Electric Co.)

6.10   Equations of dc Machine Performance

Three relationships can now be written to summarize the performance of dc machines.

1. *Voltage generation.* The dc voltage generated at the brushes is [according to Equation (6.8.5)] proportional to B_f and Ω. Thus,

$$E_a = k_e I_f \Omega, \tag{6.10.1}$$

where the circuit quantity I_f has been substituted for the proportional field quantity B_f. The symbol E_a represents the motionally-generated voltage and often must be distinguished from V_a, the voltage actually appearing at the brushes.

2. *Kirchhoff's voltage law.* The difference between E_a and V_a is due to internal $I_a R_a$ drop in the armature circuit. That is,

$$V_a = E_a + I_a R_a. \tag{6.10.2}$$

The armature current I_a is numerically positive for motor action and numerically negative for generator action, in accord with the load convention. The inductance of the armature circuit is normally quite small, and of course has no effect in the steady state.

Equation (6.10.2) suggests the simple equivalent circuit shown in Figure 6.10.1. The equation may be multiplied by I_a to give a power balance:

$$V_a I_a = E_a I_a + I_a^2 R_a.$$

The first term ($V_a I_a$) is the total power input to the brushes, the last term ($I_a^2 R_a$) is resistive dissipation, and the remaining term, $E_a I_a$, represents the power converted between electrical and mechanical form.

3. *Torque production.* The familiar torque equation, $T = K_b B_r B_s \sin \delta_{rs}$, reduces to

$$T = -k_t I_a I_f, \tag{6.10.3}$$

where the circuit quantities I_f and I_a are substituted for the proportional field quantities B_s and B_r, and where δ_{rs} is fixed at $-90°$ by the brush location. The negative sign indicates correctly that the machine is a motor for positive I_a, I_f, and Ω.

The constants k_e and k_t, appearing in Equations (6.10.1) and (6.10.3), are identical. This follows from the power balance,

$$P_e + P_m = P_f,$$

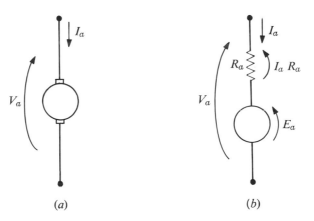

(a)   (b)

FIGURE 6.10.1. Equivalent circuit for commutated rotor (armature). (*a*) Armature; (*b*) equivalent circuit.

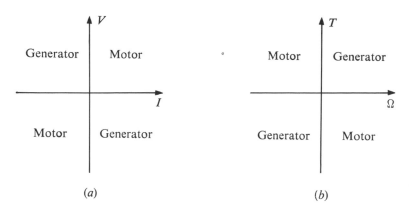

(a)   (b)

FIGURE 6.10.2. Coordinates used to display dc machine characteristic curves, showing quadrants for motor and generator action. All variables are referenced according to the load convention. (a) Constant shaft speed. (b) Constant terminal voltage.

where $P_f = 0$ in the steady state. By substituting $P_m = T\Omega$ and $P_e = E_a I_a$, and using Equations (6.10.1) and (6.10.3), there results

$$k_e I_f \Omega I_a - k_t I_f I_a \Omega = 0,$$

from which $k_e = k_t = k$. Since k depends only on machine constants, which do not change during operation, the equality holds for dynamic as well as steady-state operating conditions.

The three basic dc machine equations developed in this section are used subsequently to determine a number of typical steady-state performance characteristics. Those characteristics most commonly presented are the voltage–current curve for constant-speed generator action, and the torque–speed curve for constant-voltage motor action. Figure 6.10.2 shows the coordinates for these curves, with motor and generator regions indicated. These regions are not affected by the reversal of electrical polarities made in Section 6.10.

6.11   Operating Characteristics of dc Generators

Direct-current generators are commonly driven at as nearly a constant speed as can be achieved practically. The motionally-generated voltage, Equation (6.10.1), then becomes

$$E_a = k' I_f. \qquad (6.11.1)$$

The electrical terminals are usually connected to a resistive load, rather than to an ideal source, with the result that the terminal voltage is not constrained to be constant.

Series Generator. If the field winding is connected in series with the armature in such a way that $I_a = -I_f = I$, there results

$$E_a = -k''I. \tag{6.11.2}$$

This idealized characteristic curve is plotted in Figure 6.11.1(a), along with the *external characteristic* curve of V_t versus I, which includes the effect of

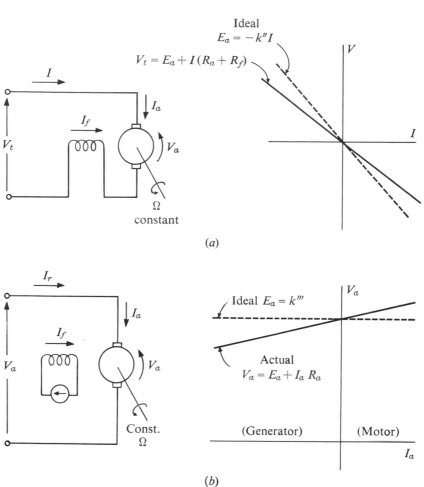

(a)

(b)

FIGURE 6.11.1. (*a*) Series generator. Characteristic approximates that of negative resistance. If voltage source (such as battery) is connected at V_t, current I is proportional to V_t but is negatively directed, such as to charge the battery. If resistor is connected at V_t, current and voltage will approach theoretical infinity until limited by saturation effects in generator. (*b*) Separately-excited generator. Actual and ideal curves differ by internal $I_a R_a$ drop in rotor. Manufacturer's curves for generators are normally plotted in first quadrant for generator action.

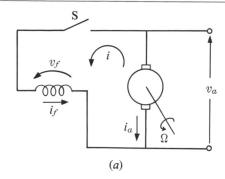

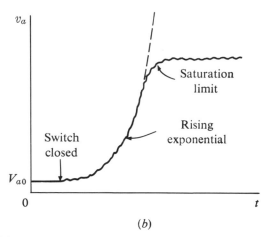

FIGURE 6.11.2. (*a*) Self-excited dc generator. Switch is closed after armature is brought up to speed. (*b*) Voltage build-up of self-excited shunt generator.

internal resistance drop. The series generator has the properties of a "negative resistance."

Separately-Excited Generator. If the stator field winding is energized from a separate constant-current source, the generated voltage becomes

$$E_a = k''', \qquad (6.11.3)$$

a constant generated voltage in the ideal case, as shown in Figure 6.11.1(*b*).

Self-Excited Generator. An obvious economy is to energize the stator field winding from the armature brushes. This arrangement, usually termed the *shunt* connection because the field is "shunted" across the armature terminals, depends on the presence of residual magnetism to start voltage build-up and on magnetic saturation to keep the voltage from rising toward a theoretical infinity.

The build-up process is illustrated in Figure 6.11.2(*a*), where the switch *S* is closed after the generator has been brought up to speed. Initially, a small

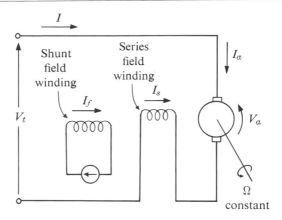

FIGURE 6.11.3. Compound dc generator for Example 6.11. Shunt field is ordinarily self-excited, rather than separately excited as shown here.

residual magnetic field produces a small initial armature voltage $v_a = V_{a0}$. The interconnection makes $v_a = v_f$ and $-i_a = i_f = i$. Thus,

$$v_f = v_a$$

$$(R_f + L_f p)i = k\Omega i.$$

Upon transforming and solving for the natural frequency, s,

$$s = \frac{k\Omega - R_f}{L_f}$$

and

$$v_a = V_{a0}e^{st}.$$

This shows that if $R_f < k\Omega$, there is a pole in the right half s-plane. Voltage and current will rise exponentially until limited by magnetic saturation, which in effect reduces k. Figure 6.11.2(b) reproduces a recording of such a voltage build-up.

The steady-state characteristic of the self-excited dc generator is similar to that for the separately-excited generator.*

Compound Generator. This arrangement, which is used in most dc generators that do not employ automatic voltage regulators, combines a self-excited, relatively constant-current stator field winding with a second stator field winding on the same magnetic axis (not the quadrature axis), but connected in series with the armature (Figure 6.11.3). Depending on the relative strengths of these two fields, the compound generator may produce anything

* For a detailed analysis, see Reference 6.1, Chapter 7.

from a rising characteristic similar to the series generator to the drooping characteristic of the self-excited generator. In the case where the series-connected field boosts the generated voltage by exactly enough to compensate for the $I_a R_a$ voltage drop, the terminal voltage is unaffected by loading and the machine is said to be "flat compounded."

Example 6.11. A modified compound generator having a separately-excited shunt field winding, and also a series field winding, is shown in Figure 6.11.3. The series field connections are such that when the machine is operating as a generator (with the current I numerically negative), the series and shunt field mmf's add.
Data:
    The number of turns on each stator field winding is

$$\text{Series winding: } N_s = 40 \text{ turns}$$
$$\text{Shunt winding: } N_f = 2000 \text{ turns.}$$

The resistances are:

$$R_s = 0.1 \text{ ohm}$$
$$R_a = 0.4 \text{ ohm}$$
$$R_f = 250 \text{ ohms.}$$

When $I = 0$ and $I_f = 0.5$, $V_a = E_a = 120$ V.

Find the terminal voltage V_t when $I = -30$ A.

Solution. From the data on the number of turns, the series winding is $(40/2000) = 1/50$ as effective as the shunt winding in producing mmf per ampere. Thus, the generated voltage expression becomes:

$$E_a = k\Omega(I_f + 0.02I_s)$$
$$= k\Omega(I_f - 0.02I).$$

The same constant k applies to both windings because both are wound on the same machine axis. To evaluate $k\Omega$, with shaft speed held constant, the $I = 0$ data gives

$$E_a = k\Omega I_f,$$
from which
$$k\Omega = 120/0.5 = 240 \text{ V/A.}$$
Then for $I = -30$,
$$E_a = 240[0.5 + 0.02(30)] = 264 \text{ V.}$$
Finally,
$$V_t = E_a + I_a(R_a + R_s)$$
or
$$V_t = 264 - (30)(0.5) = 249 \text{ V.}$$

The large rise in terminal voltage with loading indicates that this machine has a much higher degree of compounding than is normally encountered.

PROBLEM 6.11.1. A dc shunt generator is driven at $\Omega = 500$ rad/s, with zero armature current and a constant stator field current, and a voltage of 100 V appears at the brushes. The resistance of the armature circuit (R_a) is 2.0 ohms. Determine (*a*) the terminal voltage V_a when a current of 10.0 A flows from the armature to a resistive load; (*b*) the armature current and terminal voltage if a resistor of 6.0 ohms is connected across the V_a terminals; (*c*) the electromagnetic torque required for the condition of part (*a*). *Answer:* (*a*) 80 V; (*b*) 75 V; (*c*) 2.0 N-m.

PROBLEM 6.11.2. Show the effect on the generator characteristic curves of Figures 6.11.1(*a*) and (*b*) when the speed is reduced to one-half its original value.

PROBLEM 6.11.3. A series generator has $k = 0.2$, $\Omega = 100$, and $R = 4$. Calculate the numerical value of the negative resistance which can represent the generator. *Answer:* $R_{eq} = -16$ ohms.

PROBLEM 6.11.4. The series generator characteristic of Figure 6.11.1(*a*) extends into the second and fourth quadrants, while that of the separately-excited generator of Figure 6.11.1(*b*) extends into the first and second quadrants. Comment on this in a manner that best illustrates your understanding of the situation.

6.12 Characteristics of dc Motors

The characteristics of dc motors are usually presented as torque–speed curves for constant-voltage operation. These curves are readily derived from the three basic equations of Section 6.10.
Series Motor. If the stator and rotor are connected in series, as in Figure 6.12.1, the three basic dc machine equations become

$$E_a = kI\Omega,$$

$$V = E_a + IR,$$

$$T = -kI^2,$$

where $R = R_s + R_a$ and $I_s = I_a = I$. These may be manipulated algebraically to give

$$T = -\frac{kV^2}{R^2 + 2kR\Omega + k^2\Omega^2}.$$ (6.12.1)

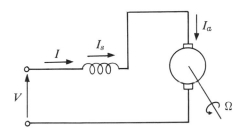

FIGURE 6.12.1. Connection diagram for series motor.

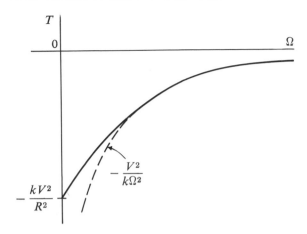

FIGURE 6.12.2. Torque–speed curve for series motor, showing actual curve and hyperbolic approximation. Manufacturer's performance curves for motors are normally plotted in first quadrant for motor action.

In machines of this type, R is made very small, so the torque is approximately

$$T \cong -\frac{V^2}{k\Omega^2}. \tag{6.12.2}$$

This indicates that the torque–speed curve is approximately hyperbolic, as shown in Figure 6.12.2. The starting torque, found by substituting $\Omega = 0$, is

$$T\big|_{\Omega=0} = -\frac{kV^2}{R^2} = -kI^2. \tag{6.12.3}$$

As a result of its dependence on the square of the current, the starting torque of a series motor is outstandingly high, leading to its use in traction and lifting applications. However, the undefined no-load speed requires special precautions against dangerous overspeeding.

The *shunt* motor, in which the stator field is "shunted" across the brushes, has quite different characteristics. This connection, shown in Figure 6.12.3, is not interchangeable with the series connection, for the stator is wound with many turns of relatively small wire, making R_f large. In the steady state, $I_f = V/R_f$. This leads to the torque–speed relationship

$$\begin{aligned}
T &= -\frac{kV^2}{R_f R_a} + \frac{k^2 V^2}{R_f{}^2 R_a}\Omega \\
&= \frac{k^2 V^2}{R_f{}^2 R_a}\left[\Omega - \frac{R_f}{k}\right],
\end{aligned} \tag{6.12.4}$$

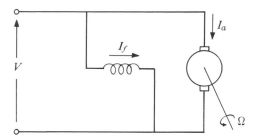

FIGURE 6.12.3. Connection diagram for shunt motor.

which gives the linear curve of Figure 6.12.4. The starting torque on the shunt-connected motor is not as high as on the series motor, but it has a definite no-load speed which, quite conveniently, is proportional to R_f. From the expression for the slope, it is seen that if the product $R_f^2 R_a$ is small, the slope will be large, giving a fairly constant speed over a reasonable range of torque. This is accomplished by keeping R_a very small. A well-designed shunt motor will hold its speed within a few percent over its rated operating range, and this nearly constant speed is readily adjustable by changing R_f. Here is an important advantage over ac motors, whose speed is closely tied to synchronous speed.

The *compound* motor, shown in Figure 6.12.5, has both series and shunt windings. It can be analyzed if the relative turns ratio of the two windings is known so that the magnetic effects of the two currents can be compared. The torque–speed curve for a compound motor is shown in Figure 6.12.6, along with curves for the series and the shunt motor. For purposes of

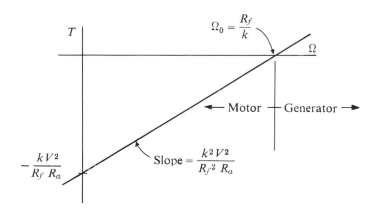

FIGURE 6.12.4. Torque–speed curve for shunt motor.

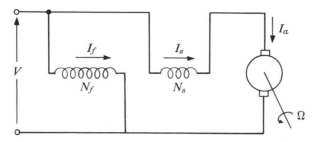

FIGURE 6.12.5. Connection diagram for compound motor. Both windings are on same stator axis, but $N_f \gg N_s$. Series field connection is reversed from that of compound generator, Figure 6.11.3.

comparison all three machines have been assigned the same rated torque and speed. If the rated torque is exceeded, excessive currents flow and the machine soon overheats, causing damage to the electrical insulation.

Example 6.12. A certain dc shunt motor has $R_a = 0.5$ ohm, $R_f = 80$ ohms, and $k = 0.02$. Under steady-state operation from a 120 V dc supply, the armature current is observed to be $I_a = 20$ A.
   (a) Determine the speed and torque.

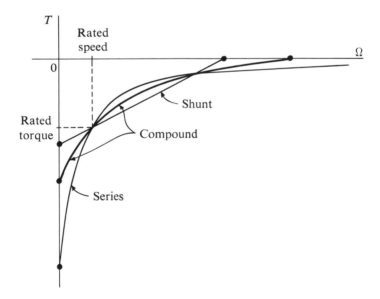

FIGURE 6.12.6. Comparison of dc motor characteristics. Only series motor lacks definite no-load speed. If rated torque is exceeded for extended period, motors overheat.

From the voltage law, Equation (6.10.2),

$$E_a = V_a - I_a R_a = 120 - (20)(0.05) = 110 \text{ V}.$$

Then, from the generated voltage expression, Equation (6.10.1), and using $I_f = 120/80 = 1.5$ A,

$$E_a = k\Omega I_f, \quad \text{or} \quad \Omega = 110/(0.02)(1.5) = 3670 \text{ rad/s}.$$

The torque expression, Equation (6.10.3), gives

$$T = -kI_a I_f = -(0.02)(20)(1.5) = -0.6 \text{ N-m}.$$

As a check, the energy conversion balance is

$$T\Omega + E_a I_a = 0$$

$$-(0.6)(3670) + (110)(20) = -2200 + 2200 = 0.$$

(b) The field resistance is increased so that $I_f = 1.0$ A, with the terminal voltage and shaft torque remaining constant. Evaluate the armature current and electromagnetic torque (1) immediately after the field current changes and (2) in the new steady state.

Substitution of the generated voltage from Equation (6.10.1) into Equation (6.10.2) gives a useful relationship for the armature current:

$$I_a = \frac{V_a - k\Omega I_f}{R_a} \tag{6.12.5}$$

Immediately after the field current has decreased to 1.0 A (from 1.5 A), the armature current rises to

$$I_a = \frac{120 - (0.02)(3670)(1.0)}{0.5} = 93.2 \text{ A}.$$

The electromagnetic torque increases to:

$$T = -kI_f I_a = -(0.02)(1.0)(93.2) = -1.86 \text{ N-m}.$$

Since this is larger than the (constant) shaft torque, angular acceleration begins. The speed rises and simultaneously I_a decreases, until the electromagnetic torque is again equal to the shaft torque in magnitude. The new steady-state armature current is

$$I_a = \frac{-T}{kI_f} = \frac{0.6}{(0.02)(1)} = 30 \text{ A}.$$

The corresponding generated voltage is

$$E_a = V_a - I_a R_a = 120 - (30)(0.5) = 105 \text{ V},$$

and the new steady-state speed is

$$\Omega = \frac{E_a}{kI_f} = \frac{105}{(0.02)(1)} = 5250 \text{ rad/s}.$$

If, now, the field current is abruptly increased to its original value, Equation (6.12.5) gives

$$I_a = \frac{120 - (0.02)(5250)(1.5)}{0.5}$$

$$= \frac{120 - 157.5}{0.5} = -75 \text{ A}.$$

The reversal of current indicates that the machine has temporarily become a generator, converting the mechanical rotational energy from its decelerating armature into electrical form and delivering it back to the electrical source.

In this example, only the initial and steady-state values of the variables were determined. The complete transient solution is found in the next section.

PROBLEM 6.12.1. Derive the torque–speed relationship for a series motor, as given by Equation (6.12.1).

PROBLEM 6.12.2. Derive the torque–speed relationship for a shunt motor, as given by Equation (6.12.4). Start from the three basic dc machine equations.

PROBLEM 6.12.3. A series motor drives a constant-torque load requiring 10.0 N-m, and draws 20.0 A from a 120 V dc supply. The armature-circuit resistance is 1.0 ohm. (*a*) Find the speed. (*b*) An additional series resistance of 4.0 ohms is inserted into the circuit. Find the new current and speed. *Answer:* (*a*) 200 rad/s. (*b*) $I = 20.0$, $\Omega = 40$.

PROBLEM 6.12.4. A dc shunt motor is driving a mechanical load requiring 5.0 N-m of torque, at a speed $\Omega = 200$ rad/s, from a voltage source of 120 V. The armature resistance is 2.0 ohms. (*a*) Find the armature current. There will be two values; which is more practical? (*b*) If torque is doubled, find the new steady-state speed. (*c*) For the condition of (*a*), let the field current be doubled, and find the new steady-state speed. *Answer:* (*a*) $I_a = 10$ A. (*b*) $\Omega = 160$. (*c*) $\Omega = 110$.

PROBLEM 6.12.5. For the series motor of Problem 6.12.3, operating as given in the problem, assume that the shaft load is frictional with a constant D_θ. Find the new steady-state speed and armature current if the stator field current is doubled. *Answer:* $I_a = 5.7$ A; $\Omega = 114$.

6.13   Dynamic Performance

In addition to the three equations deduced in Section 6.10, it is necessary to have a fourth relationship to completely describe a rotating electro-mechanical system. This is the torque characteristic for whatever is connected to the rotating shaft. In the case of motor action, the external load will normally have friction and inertia, and may also have stiffness if the armature is connected to a coiled spring, as is the case with most indicating instruments. In such a case, the instantaneous torque can be represented as

$$T_m(t) = J\frac{d^2\theta}{dt^2} + D\frac{d\theta}{dt} + K\theta, \tag{6.13.1}$$

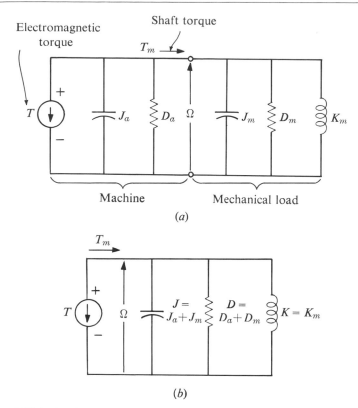

FIGURE 6.13.1. Analogous representation of loaded motor. Electromagnetic torque T is represented as current source, marked according to load convention. (*a*) Complete diagram showing torque at mechanical terminals. (*b*) Simplified diagram lumping machine intertia and damping as part of mechanical load.

where T_m is the mechanical load torque in N-m, J is the moment of inertia in N-m-s²/rad, D is the damping coefficient in N-m-s/rad, K is the stiffness in N-m/rad, and θ is angular shaft position, in radians. This equation can also be written in terms of angular velocity where $\Omega = d\theta/dt$ in radians per second.

The relationship between the mechanical load torque, T_m, and the electromagnetic torque T is given ideally by

$$T + T_m = 0. \qquad (6.13.2)$$

However, the machine is not an ideal source. Its armature has a substantial moment of inertia, and frictional effects, although less significant, are present. The analogous circuit describing this situation is shown in Figure 6.13.1(*a*), where the electromagnetic torque T is represented as a current source. Unless it is important to know the actual shaft torque, it is convenient to lump the inertia and friction terms from the motor with those of the load, as in Figure 6.13.1(*b*), and then Equation (6.13.2) applies.

The four dynamic dc machine equations, grouped together for convenience, are

$$e_a = ki_f\Omega. \tag{6.13.3}$$

$$v_a = e_a + i_a R_a. \tag{6.13.4}$$

$$T = -ki_f i_a. \tag{6.13.5}$$

$$T_m = (Jp + D + K/p)\Omega. \tag{6.13.6}$$

Equation (6.13.4) contains only electrical quantities, and Equation (6.13.6) contains only mechanical quantities. These two equations are linear if ideal components are assumed. The remaining equations relate electrical and mechanical quantities, and contain product terms ($i_f\Omega$ and $i_f i_a$), thus exhibiting the potential nonlinearity of electromechanical energy conversion.

Nonlinear differential equations are solved by computer methods, by classical procedures in certain special cases, and by linearization. Although it is not the intent of this text to explore these solutions in detail, the two examples that follow illustrate two common methods of linearization. Once linearized, the equations are subject to all of the concepts developed in linear analysis (Laplace transforms, transfer functions, natural frequencies, superposition, etc.).

Example 6.13.1. A dc shunt-connected motor (Figure 6.13.2) is supplied from a constant-voltage source and is driving a linear load (constant D and J) at a uniform speed Ω_0, when the stator-circuit resistance is suddenly doubled. Determine and sketch the equation of the speed. Armature-circuit inductance is negligible.

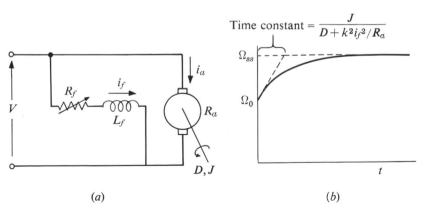

$$\text{Time constant} = \frac{J}{D + k^2 i_f^2 / R_a}$$

(*a*)   (*b*)

FIGURE 6.13.2. Illustration for Example 6.13.1. (*a*) Circuit; (*b*) response.

Solution. Substitution of Equation (6.13.3) into Equation (6.13.4) gives

$$i_a = \frac{v_a - ki_f\Omega}{R_a}.$$ (6.13.7)

Also, from Equations (6.13.5) and (6.13.6),

$$(Jp + D)\Omega = ki_f i_a.$$ (6.13.8)

These two equations may be solved simultaneously to eliminate the current i_a, giving

$$\left(Jp + D + \frac{k^2 i_f^2}{R_a}\right)\Omega = \frac{ki_f V}{R_a}.$$ (6.13.9)

This equation is nonlinear in i_f and Ω. However, there is no mutual coupling from the armature circuit into the field circuit as long as the field axes are in quadrature, so that i_f is independent of i_a and Ω, and is given simply by

$$i_f = \frac{V}{R_f + L_f p}.$$ (6.13.10)

Thus, i_f is an exponential with a time constant of L_f/R_f, and Equation (6.13.9) becomes a linear differential equation with time-varying coefficients, a type that can be solved by the use of an integrating factor. In many practical cases, however, the electrical time constant is so much shorter than the mechanical time constant that the electrical response is substantially over before the mechanical response has begun. That is, i_f can be assumed to step immediately to its new value and remain constant thereafter. This makes the time-varying coefficients into constants, and Equation (6.13.9) becomes an ordinary linear differential equation.

The left side of Equation (6.13.9) shows that an increase in the level of stator direct current, or a decrease in R_a, has the same effect on transient behavior as an increase in viscous damping. Also, there will be only one exponential in the response, with a time constant $J/(D + k^2 i_f^2/R_a)$, if i_f is assumed constant. In the steady state, $Jp\Omega$ goes to zero and the new steady-state speed is

$$\Omega_{ss} = \frac{ki_f V}{DR_a + k^2 i_f^2}.$$ (6.13.11)

In the special case of no shaft load, $D = 0$ and

$$\Omega_{ss} = \frac{V}{ki_f}.$$ (6.13.12)

Thus, in the problem as stated above, the speed will approximately double as field-circuit resistance is doubled (i_f is halved). Even though D is made zero, there is electrical damping which enters into the establishment of the mechanical time constant. A formal solution including D can be made by Laplace transforms or an equivalent procedure. A typical response is sketched in Figure 6.13.2(*b*).

Example 6.13.2. A series-connected dc motor (as in Figure 6.12.1) is driven from a constant-voltage source and drives a reciprocating load such that

$$T_m = T_0 + T_1 \cos \Omega t, \text{ where } T_1 \ll T_0. \tag{6.13.13}$$

The symbol Ω represents the shaft speed. Linearize the problem and find the transfer function relating torque to speed.

Solution. Upon letting $i = i_a = i_s$, $L = L_a + L_s$, and $R = R_a + R_s$, Equations (6.13.3) through (6.13.6) become

$$e_a = ki\Omega. \tag{6.13.14}$$

$$e_a = V - (R + Lp)i. \tag{6.13.15}$$

$$T = -ki^2. \tag{6.13.16}$$

$$T_m = T_0 + T_1 \cos \Omega t. \tag{6.13.17}$$

The linearization assumption used here is that when each variable varies about some quiescent value by small increments, these small incremental variations are approximately linear. That is, they are proportional to each other in amplitude, and are all of the same frequency. This same small-signal linearization was used in Section 2.4, but in the present example the increments are sinusoidal, so time-phasor methods are employed. For the torque variation, which is the given quantity in this example, the quiescent value is T_0 and the incremental variation is cosinusoidal with amplitude T_1.

Each of the other variables is assumed to have the same form. That is,

$$\begin{aligned} i(t) &= I_0 + I_1 \cos(\omega t + \phi_i), \\ \Omega(t) &= \Omega_0 + \Omega_1 \cos(\omega t + \phi_\omega), \\ e_a(t) &= E_0 + E_1 \cos(\omega t + \phi_a). \end{aligned} \tag{6.13.18}$$

For clarification, Figure 6.13.3 shows the relationship between ω, Ω, Ω_0, and Ω_1. Now let $i(t)$, above, be substituted into Equation (6.13.16), giving

$$T_0 + T_1 \cos \Omega t = -k[I_0 + I_1 \cos(\omega t + \phi_i)]^2,$$

or

$$T_0 + T_1 \cos \Omega t = -kI_0^2 - 2kI_0I_1 \cos(\omega t + \phi_i) - kI_1^2 \cos^2(\omega t + \phi_i).$$

If $I_1 \ll I_0$, the third term on the right will be very small and can be neglected. The remaining equality demands that $T_0 = -kI_0^2$ (the quiescent solution), that $\omega = \Omega$, and that $\phi_i = 0$. The sinusoidal portion of the equality, written in phasor form, is

$$\mathbf{T_1} = -2kI_0\mathbf{I_1}, \tag{6.13.19}$$

where

$$\mathbf{T_1} = \text{Re}\ \{[T_1 e^{j0}]e^{j\Omega t}\} \text{ and } \mathbf{I_1} = \text{Re}\ \{[I_1 e^{j\phi_i}]e^{j\Omega t}\}.$$

Application of the same reasoning to Equations (6.13.14) and (6.13.15) gives

$$\mathbf{E_1} = kI_0\mathbf{\Omega_1} + k\mathbf{I_1}\Omega_0. \tag{6.13.20}$$

$$\mathbf{E_1} = -\mathbf{I_1}(R + j\Omega L). \tag{6.13.21}$$

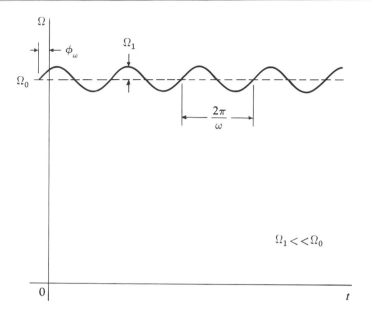

FIGURE 6.13.3. Graph of $\Omega(t) = \Omega_0 + \Omega_1 \cos(\omega t + \phi_\omega)$.

The solution of Equations (6.13.19), (6.13.20), and (6.13.21) for the desired transfer function results in

$$\frac{\Omega_1}{T_1} = \frac{(R + k\Omega_0) + j\Omega L}{2k^2 I_0{}^2}.$$

The complex numerator of the transfer function shows that the sinusoidal speed variations lead the torque variations by a phase angle that approaches zero as the circuit inductance is made negligible. The quantity Ω_0 is the average shaft speed, and Ω_1 is the amplitude of the sinusoidal variation in the shaft speed Ω. It is seen that the above transfer function will be constant only if Ω_0 and I_0 remain unchanged, which is indeed one of the conditions underlying the linearization process used in this example.

PROBLEM 6.13.1. For Example 6.13.1, determine and sketch the time variation of armature current i_a. Do not neglect D. *Answer:*

$$i_a = \{V - k i_s[\Omega_{ss} + (\Omega_0 - \Omega_{ss})]e^{-t/t_c}\}/R_a,$$

where Ω_{ss} is given in Equation (6.13.11) and $t_c = J/(D + k^2 i_f{}^2/R_a)$.

PROBLEM 6.13.2. Derive Equations (6.13.20) and (6.13.21).

PROBLEM 6.13.3. In Example 6.13.2, why does not the inertia J appear in the equations?

Advanced Problems

6.1   The machine of Figure 6.3.2 has a single-phase voltage applied to the "phase 1" terminals, with the other phase terminals not energized. (*a*) Make sketches of the counter-rotating fields and determine whether a nonzero average torque will be produced. (*b*) Determine whether an oscillating torque will be produced.

6.2   In Figure 6.4.1, the brushes are caused to turn with the air-gap field at ω rad/s. Modify Equation (6.4.4) to determine the magnitude and frequency of $v_{XX'}$ and $v_{YY'}$. Explain the result briefly.

6.3   In Section 4.2 there is developed a voltage constant $K_v = rl\pi N/2$. Find the analogous constant in Equation (6.4.4) and explain why they differ by a factor of two.

6.4   A commutator machine with salient stator poles is shown in Figure P6.4. It may be assumed that the air-gap field is uniform and constant under the pole faces ($\pm\theta_p$) at a value B, and is negligible elsewhere. There are a total of Z uniformly spaced coil sides on the rotor, which turns at Ω radians per second. Determine the magnitude and polarity of the voltage at each pair of brushes.

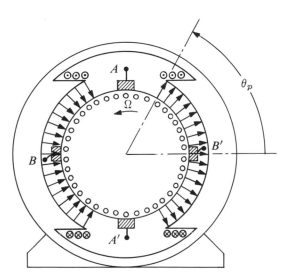

FIGURE P6.4.

6.5   In the device known as a *synchronous converter*, a single stator-winding carries a steady direct current, rotor slip rings are energized from a polyphase alternating voltage supply, and the output is taken from rotor brushes. (*a*) At what speed must the rotor turn, if it is to drive itself as a motor? (*b*) Determine the magnitude and frequency of the voltage at the brushes, as a function of the magnitude and frequency of the voltage applied to the slip rings.

6.6   Derive Equation (6.6.5) from Equation (6.6.2) by resolving B_r and B_s into their time-varying components on the direct and quadrature axes, and performing appropriate trigonometric manipulations.

6.7   A separately-excited dc generator, driven at constant speed, is observed to produce $V_a = 150$ V when $I_a = 0$, and $V_a = 110$ V when $I_a = -20$ A. (*a*) Calculate R_a. (*b*) What external load resistance will give $V_a = 120$ V?

6.8   For the compound dc generator of Example 6.11, find (*a*) the value of V_t when $I = -30$ but no series winding is present; (*b*) the number of series turns needed to produce flat compounding.

6.9   Evaluate the constant k of Section 6.10 in terms of machine parameters such as g, r, N_s, etc.

6.10   Two motors, one series-connected and one shunt-connected, are designed to have the same rated operating characteristics (same rated voltage, same rated armature current, same rated torque, and same rated speed). For these two motors, derive the defining equations and sketch together their curves of (*a*) torque vs. armature current; (*b*) speed vs. armature current.

6.11   The shunt motor of Problem 6.12.4 is to be started from a 120-V supply, but the starting current ($\Omega = 0$) is not to exceed 15 A. (*a*) Determine the additional series resistance required in the armature circuit. (*b*) Find the steady-state speed with the additional resistance included, if the load torque is 5.0 N-m. (*c*) With the steady-state speed as in (*b*), what increment of armature-circuit resistance may be removed without exceeding the 15-A limitation on armature current?

6.12   The voltage supply for the motor of Problem 6.12.4 drops to 100 V. This supply energizes both the field and the armature circuits. Determine the new steady-state armature current and speed, if the load torque remains constant at 5 N-m.

6.13   From consideration of the characteristics of Figure 6.12.6 and Problem 6.10, which type of dc motor would you recommend to drive (*a*) a hoist; (*b*) a machine lathe; (*c*) a punch press; (*d*) a fan.

6.14   A separately-excited dc motor is to start a high-inertia load, having high J and negligible D, from a constant-voltage source V. Determine and sketch the equations for speed (Ω) and armature current (i_a). What limits the speed if friction is negligible?

6.15   In a procedure known as dynamic braking, the supply voltage is disconnected and a short circuit placed across the armature terminals. Determine and sketch the equations for Ω and i_a if dynamic braking is applied, assuming a high J, negligible D load, and an initial steady-state speed of Ω_0. The machine is a shunt motor and the field circuit remains energized throughout.

6.16   The series motor of Example 6.13.2, is operating in the steady state when it is subjected to a small step change in torque, $T_1 U(t)$. Calculate and sketch the time response of the speed.

6.17   The series motor of Example 6.13.2, is driving a load consisting of inertia J and damping D. The applied voltage is caused to vary by a small amount. Calculate the linearized functions (*a*) Ω/V; (*b*) I/V.

6.18   A series motor is driving a friction (D) and inertia (J) load in the steady state, but a bad bearing causes the friction coefficient to vary according to $D_\theta = D_0 + D \cos \theta_r$, where $D \ll D_0$. Analyze the situation by small-signal linearization and calculate the time variation of (*a*) i; (*b*) Ω.

REFERENCES

6.1   R. C. KLOEFFLER, R. M. KERCHNER, and J. L. BRENNEMAN. *Direct-Current Machinery*. New York: The Macmillan Company, 1949.
6.2   T. G. WILSON and P. H. TRICKEY. D-c Machine with Solid-State Commutation, *Electrical Engineering*, Nov., 1962, 879–884.
6.3   G. M. ROSENBERRY, JR. "Brushless D-c Excited Rotating Field Synchronous Motor," *AIEE Transactions*, Part II, *Applications and Industry*, 49, July 1960, 136–139. K. M. SPARROW. "A New Frequency Converter Excitation System for A-c Generators," *AIEE Transactions*, Part III, *Power Apparatus and Systems*, 55, Aug. 1961, 369–373.

CHAPTER SEVEN

The Rotating Machine as a Circuit Element

7.1 The Circuits Approach

The analysis of electromechanical energy conversion began in Chapter 2 with the idea that there must be variation in some circuit parameter (capacitance or inductance) in order to permit physical motion. This changing parameter introduces opportunities for the nonlinearities whose presence is characteristic of energy conversion systems. In most of the rotating machines considered in this text, the mutual inductance is the parameter that changes with angular position and thus makes possible the production of torque. The self-inductances are constant because the air gap is uniform, and so do not contribute to the torque. Many practical machines have protruding (salient) poles, and may produce reluctance torque.

Throughout the treatment in Chapters 3, 4, 5, and 6, the rotating field served as a conceptual and analytical link between the electrical and mechanical circuits. In this chapter, the rotating field is replaced by the varying circuit-parameters of inductance and flux linkage. This procedure reduces the rotating machine to a device whose terminal characteristics are known, but whose principles of operation are concealed, as it were, within a "black box." The resulting equations of operation are the same, but it is more difficult to interpret them in a conceptually meaningful manner. On the other hand, the circuits approach is superior when the machine is a part of a larger system, for it fits well into orderly procedures for solving large system problems.

7.2 A Generalized Machine

Historically, the various types of rotating machines have developed almost independently of each other. Since all electromechanical devices operate on the same basic principles, an attractive possibility is an all-purpose or "generalized" machine that can operate as any type when connected in different ways. Theoretical models of such a generalized machine were treated mathematically about 1935 by Gabriel Kron, W. J. Gibbs, and others. More recently, the Massachusetts Institute of Technology designed and tested an experimental educational generalized machine* which was later revised and manufactured by the Westinghouse Electric Corporation, and furnished to most engineering schools. This device can be made to assume almost any practical operating mode, plus some that are interesting but impractical laboratory curiosities. The present discussion is based primarily on a generalized machine of this type, and so applies equally well to a variety of conventional machines.

The basic generalized machine [Figure 7.2(a)] has a uniform air gap, and thus produces no reluctance torque. It carries a two-phase, two-pole stator winding, designed to give a stator field distribution that is approximately sinusoidal. The rotor winding is connected to slip rings at v_{r_1} and v_{r_2}, but it is a uniform and re-entrant winding in order that it may also be connected to a commutator for those operating modes requiring commutation. This arrangement is not identical with the phase windings encountered in a normal polyphase rotor winding, but will produce substantially the same results, as explained below.

In Figure 7.2(a) the generalized machine is depicted, for simplicity, as having a Gramme ring rotor. Figure 7.2(b) illustrates a sinusoidally-distributed rotor winding for comparison (only the r_1 phase winding is shown; the r_2 phase winding would be shown advanced by 90° and there would be some degree of overlapping if each were complete).

It can be seen that the terminals for observing v_{r_1} are in the same angular position on the two rotors. In either case, the mutual coupling between stator winding s_1 and rotor winding r_1, and that between s_2 and r_2, are at a positive maximum when $\theta_r = 0$. The active coils comprising the r_1 phase winding are in the same location in each case, but are connected together in different manners.

The *direct axis* is selected arbitrarily as the axis of stator coil s_1. (In other types of machines having salient stator poles, the direct axis is chosen as the salient pole axis.) The *quadrature axis* is advanced 90° from the direct axis.

The commutated rotor winding is uniform and not sinusoidally distributed, so the mutual coupling does not actually vary cosinusoidally with θ_r. However, it can be shown that very little error results if only the fundamental component of the variation is considered. As a result of symmetry, the variable mutual inductances all have the same maximum value, designated as M. The mutual inductance between, say, s_2 and r_1 is designated as $M_{s_2 r_1}$.

* Described in detail in Reference 2.2.

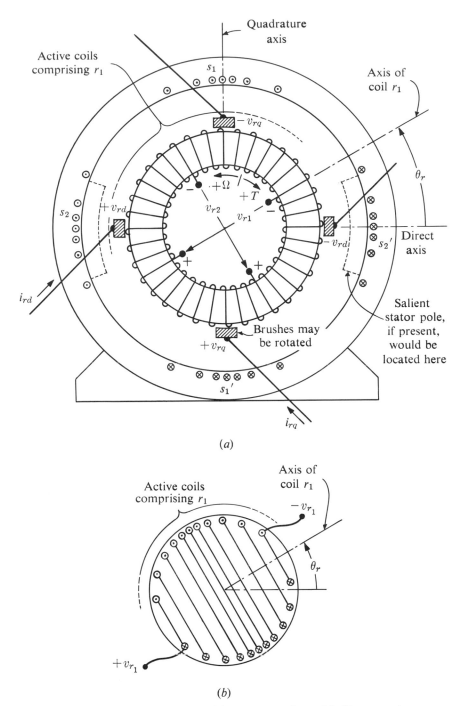

FIGURE 7.2. A generalized machine. (*a*) Representation with Gramme ring rotor. (*b*) Sinusoidally distributed rotor winding for comparison. Winding r_2 is not shown.

The four mutual inductances that vary with θ_r are, from inspection,

$$M_{s_1 r_1} = M \cos \theta_r,$$
$$M_{s_2 r_2} = M \cos \theta_r,$$
$$M_{s_1 r_2} = -M \sin \theta_r,$$
$$M_{s_2 r_1} = M \sin \theta_r. \tag{7.2.1}$$

The mutual inductances between the two stator windings, and those between the two rotor winding terminal sets, are always zero because they are always in quadrature. This is a simplification that does not hold in the case of three-phase windings.

The self-inductances are constant, and are designated as L_s for either stator winding and L_r for either rotor winding. The self-inductances enter into voltage calculations but not into the torque relationships.

The winding resistances are considered negligible except in those cases where it is essential to include them.

The flux linkage with the various windings can be expressed in terms of self and mutual inductances (see Section 2.7) as follows:

$$\lambda_{s_1} = L_s i_{s_1} + M_{s_1 r_1} i_{r_1} + M_{s_1 r_2} i_{r_2},$$
$$\lambda_{s_2} = L_s i_{s_2} + M_{s_2 r_1} i_{r_1} + M_{s_2 r_2} i_{r_2},$$
$$\lambda_{r_1} = L_r i_{r_1} + M_{s_1 r_1} i_{s_1} + M_{s_2 r_1} i_{s_2},$$
$$\lambda_{r_2} = L_r i_{r_2} + M_{s_1 r_2} i_{s_1} + M_{s_2 r_2} i_{s_2}. \tag{7.2.2}$$

From these equations, the voltage at any winding terminals can be determined by $v = d\lambda/dt$, plus an iR drop that can be neglected in many cases.

The electromagnetic torque is determined from the rate of change of field energy by $T = -(\partial W_f / \partial \theta_r)$, with currents the independent variables. The stored field energy in a multiwinding system was shown in Section 2.7 (and Problem 2.7.4) to consist of two types of terms, those of the form $\frac{1}{2} L_1 i_1{}^2$ and those of the form $M_{12} i_1 i_2$. In the case of the generalized machine with uniform air gap, the self-inductances do not vary with θ_r, so only the mutual terms will remain after the partial differentiation. After a rather lengthy calculation, there results

$$T = -\frac{\partial W_f}{\partial \theta_r} = M(i_{s_1} i_{r_2} - i_{s_2} i_{r_1}) \cos \theta_r + M(i_{s_1} i_{r_1} + i_{s_2} i_{r_2}) \sin \theta_r \tag{7.2.3}$$

PROBLEM 7.2.1. Explain why a negative sign appears in one of Equations (7.2.1), but not in the others.

PROBLEM 7.2.2. Arrange Equations (7.2.2) in matrix form.

PROBLEM 7.2.3. Write the expression for W_f and use it to derive Equation (7.2.3).

7.3 Synchronous Machine Equations

The circuit equations will be used to develop some of the synchronous machine equations of Chapter 4. As a simplification, it is assumed that both stator and rotor are energized from *current* sources; this restriction will be removed later. The terminal conditions for a synchronous machine are

$$i_{r_1} = I_r; \qquad i_{r_2} = 0 \quad \text{(not used)};$$

$$i_{s_1} = I_s \cos \omega_s t;$$

$$i_{s_2} = I_s \cos (\omega_s t - 90°) = I_s \sin \omega_s t.$$

The torque is found by substituting these terminal conditions into Equation (7.2.3), giving

$$T = MI_r I_s \sin (\theta_r - \omega_s t). \tag{7.3.1}$$

This is an oscillating torque whose peak value is constant at $MI_r I_s$ and occurs at different times depending on θ_r. The average torque over one complete cycle is zero, so the machine will not start unless the frequency is very low.

Now let the rotor turn at a uniform speed Ω, such that $\theta_r = (\Omega t + \alpha)$. That is, $\theta_r = \alpha$ at $t = 0$. After an analysis similar to that of Section 2.8, it is seen that a nonzero average torque is produced only when $\Omega = \omega_s$, in which case

$$T = +MI_r I_s \sin \alpha. \tag{7.3.2}$$

The positive sign implies that when α is positive, the torque is positive and the machine is acting as a generator. The similarity of Equation (7.3.2) to the familiar torque equation of rotating-field theory is obvious; this will be pursued further, following the development of the voltage equations.

The voltages at the terminals of the two stator windings are, from Equations (7.2.2),

$$v_{s_1} = -\omega_s L_s I_s \sin \omega_s t - \omega_s I_r M \sin (\omega_s t + \alpha),$$

$$v_{s_2} = \omega_s L_s I_s \cos \omega_s t + \omega_s I_r M \cos (\omega_s t + \alpha). \tag{7.3.3}$$

These constitute a set of balanced two-phase voltages, since all terms are of the same magnitude and frequency, and v_{s_1} is 90° ahead of v_{s_2}. It follows, therefore, that the application of a balanced voltage source will lead to the same steady-state performance as does the assumed current source.

Equations (7.3.3) may be written as phasors:

$$\mathbf{V}_{s_1} = \omega_s L_s I_s e^{j90°} + \omega_s MI_r e^{j(\alpha+90°)},$$

$$\mathbf{V}_{s_2} = \omega_s L_s I_s e^{j0°} + \omega_s MI_r e^{j\alpha}. \tag{7.3.4}$$

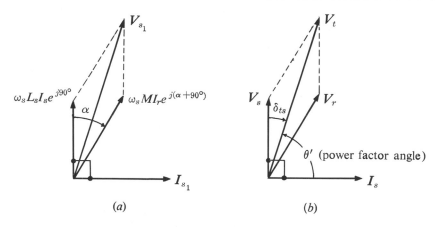

FIGURE 7.3. Phasor representation of synchronous motor terminal quantities for one phase. (a) Phasor representation of Equation (7.3.4a). (b) Figure 4.2(b) with $\mathbf{I}_s$ made the reference phasor.

The graphical representation for $\mathbf{V}_{s_1}$, but with α numerically negative to indicate motor action, is shown in Figure 7.3(a). Comparison with Figure 4.2(b), which is repeated here as Figure 7.3(b) (but with the current as the reference phasor), shows the correspondence between the results by the two methods.

PROBLEM 7.3.1. Carry out the derivation of Equation (7.3.1).

PROBLEM 7.3.2. Show that Equation (7.3.2) follows from Equation (7.3.1).

PROBLEM 7.3.3. Derive Equation (7.3.3) from Equation (7.2.2).

PROBLEM 7.3.4. Sketch the equivalent circuit of Figure 4.3, labeling it with the notation developed in Section 7.3.

PROBLEM 7.3.5. Show analytically that $v_{r_1} = 0$ in the synchronous machine of Section 7.3, so long as the torque angle is constant. Explain the result in terms of rotating field theory.

7.4   Induction Motor Equations

For balanced operation in the steady state, the induction motor terminal conditions are:

$$v_{s_1} = V_s \cos \omega_s t,$$
$$v_{s_2} = V_s \sin \omega_s t, \tag{7.4.1}$$
$$v_{r_1} = v_{r_2} = 0 \text{ (short circuited).}$$

For a specific constant shaft speed, Ω is a constant and $\theta_r = \Omega t + \alpha$.

Before beginning the analysis, it is worthwhile to note that all currents and voltages can be expected to be sinusoidal in the steady state, since there are no reluctance terms to introduce harmonics. Also, the stator and rotor currents can be expected, from symmetry considerations, to be balanced two-phase sets. Thus only one stator current and one rotor current need be determined.

It is convenient to set down the solutions in advance, in a general form:

$$i_{s_1} = I_s \cos (\omega_s t + \beta) \qquad i_{r_1} = I_r \cos (\omega_r t + \gamma).$$

$$i_{s_2} = I_s \sin (\omega_s t + \beta) \qquad i_{r_2} = I_r \sin (\omega_r t + \gamma).$$

The only known quantity in these equations is ω_s, the frequency of the stator current. This will of necessity be the same as the frequency of the supply voltage if energy is to be delivered to the motor in the steady state.

The procedure for determining the terminal equations is straightforward, if sometimes tedious. The various quantities are substituted into the equations of flux linkages (7.2.2) which are then differentiated and set equal to the stated terminal voltages. For example, for stator winding s_1,

$$\lambda_{s_1} = L_s I_s \cos (\omega_s t + \beta) + M I_r \cos (\omega_r t + \gamma) \cos (\Omega t + \alpha)$$
$$- M I_r \sin (\omega_r t + \gamma) \sin (\Omega t + \alpha),$$

which by trigonometric conversion becomes

$$\lambda_{s_1} = L_s I_s \cos (\omega_s t + \beta) + M I_r \cos [(\omega_r + \Omega)t + \gamma + \alpha].$$

Then, taking $v_{s_1} = d\lambda_{s_1}/dt$,

$$V_s \cos \omega_s t = -\omega_s L_s I_s \sin (\omega_s t + \beta)$$
$$- M I_r(\omega_r + \Omega) \sin [(\omega_r + \Omega)t + \gamma + \alpha]. \quad (7.4.3)$$

This trigonometric equation can be valid only if $(\omega_r + \Omega) = \omega_s$, which is exactly the condition for torque production developed from rotating field theory. With this substitution, the equation may be rewritten in phasor form:

$$\mathbf{V}_{s_1} = \omega_s L_s I_s e^{j(90°+\beta)} + \omega_s M I_r e^{j(90°+\gamma+\alpha)}. \quad (7.4.4)$$

The approximation of ignoring winding resistance cannot be made in writing the rotor equation, for (it will be recalled) rotor resistance is an important parameter in induction motor theory. Were it to be neglected in the calculations, a zero torque angle would always result. With the rotor resistance R_r included, the voltage equation for the short-circuited winding r_1 is derived from the appropriate linkage equation as:

$$0 = R_r I_r \cos (\omega_r t + \gamma) - \omega_r L_r I_r \sin (\omega_r t + \gamma)$$
$$- (\omega_s - \Omega) M I_s \sin [(\omega_s - \Omega)t + \beta - \alpha].$$

Again, the equation requires that $(\omega_s - \Omega) = \omega_r$, which is the same condition as before. With this substitution the rotor equation may be written in phasor form as

$$0 = (R_r + j\omega_r L_r)I_r e^{j\gamma} + j\omega_r M I_s e^{j(\beta - \alpha)}. \qquad (7.4.5)$$

Since $\mathbf{I}_{s_1} = I_s e^{j\beta}$, it is desirable to modify the two phasor equations so that this form appears, before solving for $\mathbf{I}_{s_1}$. This is done by letting Equation (7.4.4) be multiplied by $j = e^{j90°}$, and Equation (7.4.5) be multiplied by $e^{j\alpha}$. Then they become

$$j\mathbf{V}_{s_1} = -\omega_s L_s \mathbf{I}_{s_1} - \omega_s M \mathbf{I}_{r_1} e^{j\alpha}. \qquad (7.4.6)$$

$$0 = j\omega_r M \mathbf{I}_{s_1} + (R_r + j\omega_r L_r)\mathbf{I}_{r_1} e^{j\alpha}. \qquad (7.4.7)$$

It is interesting to note that these two phasor equations can be solved simultaneously even though they are derived from circuits operating at different frequencies. This follows because all the terms in any one equation are at the same frequency, so all $e^{j\omega_s t}$ and $e^{j\omega_r t}$ terms cancel out. Physically, the turning rotor can be thought of as "boosting" the rotor frequency to be equal to the stator frequency, as far as its reflected effect on the stator is concerned.

At this point in the solution, the slip s (defined in Chapter 5) is introduced. By substituting $\omega_r = s\omega_s$ in Equation (7.4.7) and solving simultaneously with Equation (7.4.6), there results

$$\mathbf{I}_{s_1} = \frac{-j\mathbf{V}_{s_1}\left(\dfrac{R_r}{s} + j\omega_s L_r\right)}{\omega_s L_s\left[\dfrac{R_r}{s} + j\omega_s\left(\dfrac{L_s L_r - M^2}{L_s}\right)\right]}. \qquad (7.4.8)$$

It will be recalled from coupled-circuit theory that the coefficient of coupling is defined as $K = M/\sqrt{L_r L_s}$, so for perfect coupling $(K = 1)$, $L_s L_r = M^2$, and the large term in the denominator of Equation (7.4.8) will vanish. This assumption is not justified in this case, and will lead to incorrect results. However, the quantity $(L_s L_r - M^2)/L_s$ is indeed quite small, and in fact is the leakage inductance of the rotor circuit. This leakage inductance, designated here as L_{er}, is the inductance presented to the rotor current due to flux linking the rotor circuit only, exclusive of that which crosses the air gap and links the stator circuit. After this substitution is made, Equation (7.4.8) becomes

$$\mathbf{I}_{s_1} = \frac{-j\mathbf{V}_{s_1}\left(\dfrac{R_r}{s} + j\omega_s L_r\right)}{\omega_s L_s\left(\dfrac{R_r}{s} + j\omega_s L_{er}\right)}. \qquad (7.4.9)$$

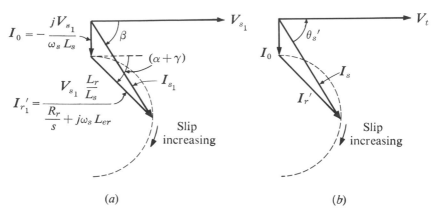

(a)   (b)

FIGURE 7.4. Comparison of induction motor phasor diagrams. (*a*) Diagram from circuit derivation. (*b*) Diagram from rotating field derivation, identical with Figure 5.6.1 except that V_t is placed in reference position.

This result can be separated into the sum of two components, one due to the stator and another to the rotor. The rotor has no effect when turning at synchronous speed, so setting $s = 0$, Equation (7.4.9) becomes

$$\mathbf{I_0} = -\frac{j\mathbf{V}_{s_1}}{\omega_s L_s}. \tag{7.4.10}$$

This expression fulfills the requirement of being entirely independent of rotor conditions, and represents the no-load stator current.

The remaining component of $\mathbf{I}_{s_1}$, to be designated $\mathbf{I}_{r_1}{}'$, is found by phasor subtraction to be

$$\mathbf{I}_{r_1}{}' = \mathbf{I}_{s_1} - \mathbf{I}_0 \cong \frac{\mathbf{V}_{s_1}\dfrac{L_r}{L_s}}{\dfrac{R_r}{s} + j\omega_s L_{er}}. \tag{7.4.11}$$

This expresses $\mathbf{I}_{r_1}$ in stator quantities, and is identical with the equation for $\mathbf{I}_r{}'$ in Section 5.6, giving the semicircular locus of Figure 7.4(*a*). For comparison, the diagram developed from field theory is repeated as Figure 7.4(*b*), identical to Figure 5.6.1 except that here the stator voltage phasor is shown in the reference position.

The torque expression is obtained, as in Section 7.3, by substitution into Equation (7.2.3), and after trigonometric reduction becomes

$$T = MI_s I_r \sin{(\alpha + \gamma - \beta)}. \tag{7.4.12}$$

Inspection of the phasor diagram of Figure 7.4(a) shows that the angle between $\mathbf{I}_{s_1}$ and $\mathbf{I}_{r_1}$ is indeed $(\alpha + \gamma - \beta)$. It should be noted that both β and $(\alpha + \gamma)$ are plotted as numerically negative in Figure 7.4(a), as they will be in any actual case involving motor action.

From this point on, the development of induction motor theory can be carried out in terms of an equivalent circuit, in the same manner as was done in Chapter 5. This equivalent is valid only in the steady state. However, electrical transients are normally short compared to mechanical transients. Thus, electrical transient solutions can usually be made with the assumption of constant speed, and performance during the relatively slow mechanical transients can be based on the steady-state torque-speed characteristics of the machine.

PROBLEM 7.4.1. Derive the induction motor equation for V_{s_2}, similar to Equation (7.4.4), starting with the Equations (7.2.2) for flux linkage.

PROBLEM 7.4.2. Derive Equation (7.4.5) for the induction motor rotor, starting with Equations (7.2.2) for flux linkage.

PROBLEM 7.4.3. Solve Equations (7.4.6) and (7.4.7) to obtain Equation (7.4.8).

PROBLEM 7.4.4. Show that Equation (7.4.10) is correct for zero slip, and use it to determine $\mathbf{I}_{r_1}'$ in Equation (7.4.11).

PROBLEM 7.4.5. Derive the induction motor torque Equation (7.4.12).

PROBLEM 7.4.6. Draw the induction motor equivalent circuit of Figure 5.6.2, labeling it with the quantities used in Section 7.4.

7.5   The Commutation of Generated Voltage

The magnitude and frequency of the voltages generated in the rotor windings are functions of rotor speed. When commutation is used, however, the commutated rotor voltage is a function of rotor speed in magnitude only; its frequency is determined by the difference between the speed of the stator field and the speed (if any) of the brushes. These characteristics of commutation were discussed in Chapter 6, and the problem here is to find an analytical representation of commutation.

Attention is first directed to the generalized machine of Figure 7.2(a) in operation at constant rotor speed, with the brushes fixed on the stator winding axes, and with steady direct currents in the two stator windings. The terminal conditions are then given by

$$i_{s_1} = I_{s_1}, \qquad i_{s_2} = I_{s_2},$$
$$i_{r_1} = i_{r_2} = 0,$$
$$\theta_r = \Omega t.$$

From the original linkage equations, Equation (7.2.2), after appropriate substitution and differentiation, these terminal conditions give

$$v_{r_1} = -\Omega M I_{s_1} \sin \Omega t + \Omega M I_{s_2} \cos \Omega t,$$
$$v_{r_2} = -\Omega M I_{s_1} \cos \Omega t - \Omega M I_{s_2} \sin \Omega t. \tag{7.5.1}$$

These are the voltages appearing at the rotor terminals marked v_{r_1} and v_{r_2} in Figure 7.2(a), and could be observed experimentally by the use of slip rings (sliding contacts).

The commutated voltages V_{rd} and V_{rq}, appearing at the direct and quadrature axis brushes,* can be related to v_{r_1} and v_{r_2} by consideration of one of the effects of commutation discussed in Chapter 6. This effect is that commutation renders the frequency of the brush voltages independent of rotor speed. In this example, the frequency is zero, since the brushes are stationary and the stator windings carry direct current. Further, the brush voltages are identical with the rotor voltages at certain rotor positions, so it is necessary only to evaluate v_{r_1} and v_{r_2} at these special positions to determine V_{rd} and V_{rq}.

From Figure 7.2(a) it is readily seen that $v_{r_1} = V_{rd}$ and $v_{r_2} = V_{rq}$ when $\theta_r = 0°$. Substitution of these conditions into Equation (7.5.1), with $\Omega t = \theta_r = 0°$, results in

$$v_{r_1}\big|_{\theta_r=0} = \Omega M I_{s_2} = V_{rd}$$
$$v_{r_2}\big|_{\theta_r=0} = -\Omega M I_{s_1} = V_{rq}. \tag{7.5.2}$$

Since V_{rd} and V_{rq} are direct voltages in this example, the above values hold for all rotor positions. These relationships illustrate the concept that commutated motional voltages appearing at brushes on one axis are due entirely to fields along the other axis.

The identities developed in Equation (7.5.2) may now be substituted back into Equation (7.5.1), giving

$$v_{r_1} = V_{rd} \cos \Omega t + V_{rq} \sin \Omega t,$$
$$v_{r_2} = -V_{rd} \sin \Omega t + V_{rq} \cos \Omega t. \tag{7.5.3}$$

By simultaneous solution of Equation (7.5.3) there also results

$$V_{rd} = v_{r_1} \cos \Omega t - v_{r_2} \sin \Omega t,$$
$$V_{rq} = v_{r_1} \sin \Omega t + v_{r_2} \cos \Omega t. \tag{7.5.4}$$

Equations (7.5.3) and (7.5.4) were derived for steady direct stator currents, but can be shown to hold for more general situations.

---

* The designations v_{rd} and v_{rq} correspond to those of Chapter 6 for v_{bd} and v_{bq} (later, $-v_a$), the "brush" voltages. It is semantically correct to refer to "direct-axis (or quadrature-axis) *rotor* voltage" because the voltage appears at the axis position whether or not there actually are brushes in that position on the commutator.

When Equation (7.5.3) is written in matrix form,

$$\begin{bmatrix} v_{r_1} \\ v_{r_2} \end{bmatrix} = \begin{bmatrix} \cos \Omega t & \sin \Omega t \\ -\sin \Omega t & \cos \Omega t \end{bmatrix} \cdot \begin{bmatrix} V_{rd} \\ V_{rq} \end{bmatrix}, \tag{7.5.5}$$

the central 2×2 matrix is recognized as the "rotation matrix" developed in Section 4.6 in connection with the d-q components used in synchronous machine analysis. In the present case, the rotation matrix relates the motionally-generated voltages in rotating windings to those appearing at stationary brushes. It is an example of a "transformation of variables" of the sort widely used in advanced rotating machine analysis. These transformations are of a class known as "orthogonal," which means that the transformation matrix has these two special (and inter-related) properties: (1) the inverse of the transformation matrix is the same as its transpose, and (2) the determinant of the transformation matrix is equal to unity. The formal treatment of transformation theory is introduced in Section 7.9, but its full development is left for a more advanced course of study.

PROBLEM 7.5.1. Obtain Equation (7.5.4) by inverting the matrix in Equation (7.5.5).

7.6   Circuit Equations for a Commutator Machine

The actual voltages appearing at the brushes of a commutator machine may contain a number of components in addition to those given by Equation (7.5.2), which is repeated here:

$$\begin{aligned} V_{rd} &= \Omega M I_{s_2}, \\ V_{rq} &= -\Omega M I_{s_1}. \end{aligned} \tag{7.5.2}$$

These additional components are considered separately below, and then combined to give the complete circuit equations for the commutator machine.

1. *Motional voltages between brush axes.* When current flows in the rotor brushes, each brush-axis current generates a motional voltage at the rotor brushes on the other axis. This may at first seem surprising, since the rotor axes are in quadrature and have zero mutual coupling. However, this is exactly the situation where motional voltages can be expected if a commutator is present, for a field along one axis produces motional voltage at the brushes along the other axis. For example, current flowing into the positive v_{rd} brush [Figure 7.2(a)] produces a field along the positive direct axis, in the same direction as current i_{s_1} in the direct-axis stator winding. Thus, by analogy with Equation (7.5.2), the motional voltages between brush axes are

$$\begin{aligned} V_{rd}' &= \Omega M_r I_{rq}, \\ V_{rq}' &= -\Omega M_r I_{rd}. \end{aligned} \tag{7.6.1}$$

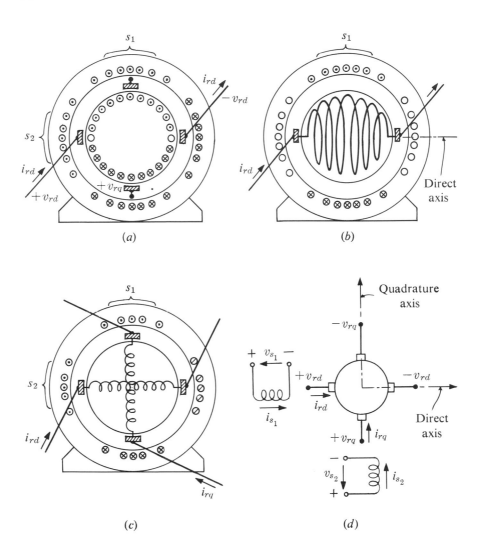

FIGURE 7.6. Mutual coupling in a commutated machine. (*a*) Rotor-conductor current configuration for current in direct-axis brushes only. (*b*) Equivalent coil representation of commutated rotor, for direct-axis brush current only. Equivalent coil is mutually coupled to stator winding s_1 but not to s_2. (*c*) Equivalent coil representation for both brush axes. Coil axes are fixed by brush positions. (*d*) Two-axis commutator machine showing complete reference polarity markings. Stator windings are shown as equivalent coils with axis along appropriate machine axis.

The constant M_r is termed a "motional inductance," and unlike the quantity M appearing in Equation (7.5.2) it cannot be measured experimentally as an ordinary mutual inductance. With the rotor driven by an external means, however, M_r can be measured by forcing a known direct current through one set of brushes and observing the voltage appearing at the other set of brushes.

2. *Voltages due to ordinary self- and mutual induction.* In addition to voltages generated by rotation, ordinary induced voltages may appear at the brushes if the rotor or stator currents are changing. This is illustrated in Figure 7.6, where the various current configurations are shown for a commutator machine.

The rotor currents, as injected by the brushes, produce the effect of an equivalent coil that is coupled with the stator windings. It is easily seen that r_d, the equivalent rotor coil on the direct axis, is coupled with s_1 but not with s_2. Also, r_q is coupled only with s_2. The coupling is at a maximum with the brushes in the position shown, and cannot be changed unless the brushes are shifted. Thus, changes in the current in a stator winding will induce voltage at the brushes along the same axis. These voltage components are

$$v_{rd}' = pMi_{s_1},$$
$$v_{rq}' = pMi_{s_2}. \tag{7.6.2}$$

The complete expressions for the brush voltages can be obtained by combining the various components in Equations (7.5.2), (7.6.1), and (7.6.2), and also including resistance (R_r) and self-inductance (L_r) voltages. The complete brush voltages are, then,

$$v_{rd} = (R_r + pL_r)i_{rd} + pMi_{s_1} + \Omega Mi_{s_2} + \Omega M_r i_{rq},$$
$$v_{rq} = (R_r + pL_r)i_{rq} + pMi_{s_2} - \Omega Mi_{s_1} - \Omega M_r i_{rd}. \tag{7.6.3}$$

The stator voltages take on a considerably simpler form, as long as the brushes are stationary on the stator coil axes. Since the rotor field axes are fixed with respect to the brushes, the rotor currents cannot induce motional voltages into the stator windings, although they can induce ordinary voltages of mutual induction. With the brushes stationary on the stator coil axes, the complete stator voltages are

$$v_{s_1} = (R_s + pL_s)i_{s_1} + pMi_{rd},$$
$$v_{s_2} = (R_s + pL_s)i_{s_2} + pMi_{rq}. \tag{7.6.4}$$

These four circuit equations, which describe the terminal behavior of the commutator machine as a circuit element, can be expressed in matrix form as $[V] = [Z] \cdot [I]$, which in full is

$$
\begin{bmatrix} v_{s_1} \\ v_{s_2} \\ v_{rd} \\ v_{rq} \end{bmatrix} = \begin{bmatrix} R_s + pL_s & 0 & pM & 0 \\ 0 & R_s + pL_s & 0 & pM \\ pM & \Omega M & R_r + pL_r & \Omega M_r \\ -\Omega M & pM & -\Omega M_r & R_r + pL_r \end{bmatrix} \cdot \begin{bmatrix} i_{s_1} \\ i_{s_2} \\ i_{rd} \\ i_{rq} \end{bmatrix}.
\qquad (7.6.5)
$$

The $[Z]$ term is called the *impedance matrix* of the commutator machine. In addition to terms of the form $(R + pL)$ and pM, which are customarily encountered in circuit theory, the impedance matrix also contains motional terms of the form ΩM and ΩM_r. Such terms are given the name *motional impedance*.

The circuit equations are not restricted to direct currents and voltages, but *are* restricted to a constant shaft speed. This latter limitation is not always a serious one, since electrical transients are often very short compared to mechanical transients, so that many problems can be solved as though the speed were constant. The result may then be used in conjunction with the torque equation, developed in the next section, to determine the (relatively slow) variation of speed with time.

PROBLEM 7.6.1. The stator of a commutator machine is excited by alternating currents, such that $i_{s_1} = I \cos(\omega_s t + \alpha)$ and $i_{s_2} = I \sin(\omega_s t + \alpha)$. The rotor is caused to turn at speed Ω. Find v_{rd} and v_{rq}. Interpret the result in terms of rotating field theory. *Answer:* $v_{rd} = MI(\Omega - \omega_s) \sin(\omega_s t + \alpha)$.

7.7 Torque in a Commutator Machine

The torque expression can be derived from a consideration of the energy balance. From Equation (2.2.1), where losses are ignored,

$$
dW_e + dW_m = dW_f,
\qquad (7.7.1)
$$

where dW_e is an increment of electric energy entering the system, dW_m is an increment of mechanical energy entering the system, and dW_f is the incremental increase in magnetic field energy. Equation (7.7.1) can be converted to a power balance by dividing both sides by dt. Then,

$$
P_e + P_m = P_f.
\qquad (7.7.2)
$$

The mechanical power input is given as

$$
P_m = T\Omega.
\qquad (7.7.3)
$$

The electrical power input is

$$
P_e = v_{s_1} i_{s_1} + v_{s_2} i_{s_2} + v_{rd} i_{rd} + v_{rq} i_{rq}.
\qquad (7.7.4)
$$

Upon substitution from Equation (7.6.5) and rearrangement, Equation (7.7.4) becomes

$$P_e = R_s i_{s_1}^2 + R_s i_{s_2}^2 + R_r i_{rd}^2 + R_r i_{rq}^2$$
$$+ L_s i_{s_1} p i_{s_1} + L_s i_{s_2} p i_{s_2} + L_r i_{rd} p i_{rd} + L_r i_{rq} p i_{rq}$$
$$+ M i_{s_1} p i_{rd} + M i_{s_2} p i_{rq} + M i_{rd} p i_{s_1} + M i_{rq} p i_{s_2}$$
$$- \Omega M i_{s_1} i_{rq} + \Omega M i_{s_2} i_{rd} - \Omega M_r i_{rd} i_{rq} + \Omega M_r i_{rq} i_{rd}. \qquad (7.7.5)$$

All of the terms in the first three lines of Equation (7.7.5) can be identified. The terms of the form Ri^2 are resistive power loss and are ignored in Equation (7.7.2). The terms in the second line are of the form $p(Li^2/2) = Lipi$, which represents power into self-inductive field storage. (Self-inductances are constant in the nonsalient-pole machine.) The terms in the third line are of the form $p(Mi_1 i_2) = Mi_1 p i_2 + Mi_2 p i_1$, which represents power into mutually-inductive field storage. Thus, the second and third lines of Equation (7.7.5) are identical with P_f. With these modifications, Equation (7.7.2) becomes

$$- \Omega M i_{s_1} i_{rq} + \Omega M i_{s_2} i_{rd} + T\Omega = 0,$$

or

$$T = M(i_{s_1} i_{rq} - i_{s_2} i_{rd}). \qquad (7.7.6)$$

For comparison, the torque equation developed from field theory in Chapter 6 is repeated below:

$$T = K_b(B_{s_1} B_{rq} - B_{s_2} B_{rd}). \qquad (6.6.5)$$

According to the load convention, the electromagnetically developed torque T is positive for generator action, for which the machine is a mechanical load. The negative term in Equation (7.7.6) arises because of the various electrical polarity conventions used, and has no particular significance. However, considerable care is necessary in interpreting the polarities that result from use of Equation (7.7.6).

Example 7.7.1. Determine the terminal characteristics of the separately-excited dc motor of Figure 7.7(a) and compare with the results from Chapter 6.
 The terminal conditions are

$$i_{s_1} = I_{s_1} \text{ (constant)}; \qquad i_{s_2} = i_{rd} = 0 \text{ (not used)}$$
$$v_{rq} = \text{voltage applied to rotor brushes}$$
$$i_{rq} = \text{current in rotor brushes.}$$

The direct-axis voltage v_{rd} is not needed in this problem because there are no brushes on the direct axis. However, v_{rd} exists and is not necessarily zero. The quadrature axis voltage, v_{rq}, is obtained from the commutator machine matrix, Equation (7.6.5), as

$$v_{rq} = - \Omega M I_{s_1} + (R_r + p L_r) i_{rq}. \qquad (7.7.7)$$

The rotor inductance in practical machines is small and can often be neglected; in any case it has no effect in the steady state. Thus Equation (7.7.7) has the same form as Equation (6.13.4), which is repeated here:

$$v_a = e_a + i_a R_a. \tag{6.13.4}$$

For Equations (7.7.7) and (6.13.4) to agree, it is necessary that

$$e_a = -\Omega M I_{s_1}. \tag{7.7.8}$$

Agreement can occur if I_{s_1} is reversed in direction, or if Ω is made negative. The situation may be better understood from Figure 7.7(b), where all quantities are shown in their positive reference directions. It can be seen that the field quantities $\mathbf{B}_r$ and $\mathbf{B}_s$ are directed in such a way that the rotor will tend to turn in the clockwise direction, so the machine cannot drive a passive mechanical load in the $+\Omega$ direction. Some quantity must be reversed; in the discussion of Chapter 6, rotor brush polarity was reversed (see Figure 6.8.2).

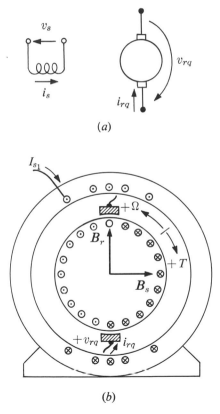

FIGURE 7.7. Separately-excited motor operation. (a) Connection diagram; (b) Internal field configuration.

When the torque is evaluated from Equation (7.7.6), there results

$$T = MI_{s_1}i_{rq}. \tag{7.7.9}$$

Except for the sign, this is of the same form as Equation (6.13.5), which is

$$T = -ki_f i_a. \tag{6.13.5}$$

As was the case for Equation (7.7.7), the sign difference can be corrected if I_{s_1} is made negative or if v_{rq} and i_{rq} are made negative. Or, if the rotor is allowed to rotate in the $-\Omega$ direction, no change in the sign of Equation (7.6.9) is necessary for motor action to take place.

These apparent dilemmas in the polarity conventions arise because of the original adoption of the load convention for representing conditions at both the electrical and the mechanical terminals. Obviously, a machine cannot be both motor and generator at the same time in the steady state. As one of two possible alternatives, a polarity convention could have been adopted that considered motor action to give positive conditions at both terminal-pairs, in which case the energy balance of Equation (2.2.1) would be written

$$dW_e = dW_m + dW_f.$$

This convention would cause the mechanical variables and the electrical variables all to be positive for motor action and all to be negative for generator action. The convention used in this text was adopted because it treats the electrical and mechanical terminals alike, and provides a correct analogy between electrical and mechanical quantities as presented in Chapter 1.

Of course it is not necessary to reverse anything to use expressions such as Equation (7.7.7) and Equation (7.7.9). If the calculations are carried out accurately, correct answers will result. The reversals suggested in connection with Figure 7.7 were for purposes of visualization. A simple numerical example will illustrate the situation.

Example 7.7.2. A certain separately-excited motor has the following parameters and operating conditions. Find the speed and torque.

$$M = 0.5 \text{ H} \qquad V_{rq} = 100 \text{ V}$$

$$R_r = 5.0 \text{ ohms} \qquad I_{rq} = +4 \text{ A}$$

$$I_{s_1} = +2 \text{ A}$$

Solution. From Equation (7.7.7), in the steady state,

$$\Omega = -\frac{V_{rq} - I_{rq}R_r}{MI_{s_1}} = -\frac{100 - (4)(5)}{(0.5)(2)} = -80 \text{ rad/s}.$$

From Equation (7.7.9),

$$T = MI_{s_1}I_{rq} = (0.5)(2)(4) = +4 \text{ N-m}.$$

The polarities of Ω and T show that the machine is indeed operating as a motor, but in the clockwise $(-\Omega)$ direction. The power balance is

$$
\begin{aligned}
\text{Electrical input} &= V_{rq}I_{rq} = (100)(4) &&= 400 \text{ W} \\
\text{Electrical loss} &= I_{rq}{}^2R_r = (4)^2(5) &&= -80 \text{ W} \\
\text{Net electrical power converted:} & && 320 \text{ W} \\
\text{Mechanical power} &= T\Omega = (4)(-80) &&= -320 \text{ W} \\
& && 0
\end{aligned}
$$

PROBLEM 7.7.1. Show that Equations (7.6.5) and (7.7.6) reduce to the expected form (see Chapter 6) for (*a*) a separately-excited dc generator; (*b*) a series-connected dc motor.

PROBLEM 7.7.2. A compound-wound dc machine has two dissimilar windings on the direct axis and none on the quadrature axis (see Figure 6.11.3). Modify Equations (7.6.5) to represent this situation.

7.8 The Amplidyne Generator

The amplidyne is a high-gain dynamic generator with the relatively short time constant of a few hundredths of a second. It provides an excellent and somewhat more complicated application of the commutator-machine theory developed in the preceding sections.

The amplidyne in its simplest form is illustrated in the upper part of Figure 7.8.1, where the interconnecting switch S is kept open. The significant features of the amplidyne are (1) the short circuit between the quadrature-axis brushes, and (2) the direct-axis compensating winding, connected so that its field opposes that of the rotor. This situation differs from that of the two-axis machine discussed in Section 7.6, for in the amplidyne both of the stator windings are on the direct axis and there is no stator winding on the quadrature axis. It is, therefore, necessary to revise the commutator machine matrix of Equation (7.6.5) to take these changes into account. It is not necessary to go through a formal derivation again, for with a little thought, it is possible to deduce the needed changes, as shown in Equation (7.8.1) and explained below.

$$
\begin{bmatrix} v_{sa} \\ v_{sb} \\ v_{rd} \\ v_{rq} \end{bmatrix} = \begin{bmatrix} R_a + pL_a & pM_{ab} & pM_{ad} & 0 \\ pM_{ab} & R_b + pL_b & pM_{bd} & 0 \\ pM_{ad} & pM_{bd} & R_r + pL_r & \Omega M_r \\ -\Omega M_{aq} & -\Omega M_{bq} & -\Omega M_r & R_r + pL_r \end{bmatrix} \cdot \begin{bmatrix} i_{sa} \\ i_{sb} \\ i_{rd} \\ i_{rq} \end{bmatrix}. \quad (7.8.1)
$$

Several comments about Equation (7.8.1) will prove helpful.
1. The subscripts *a* and *b* refer to the two direct-axis windings.

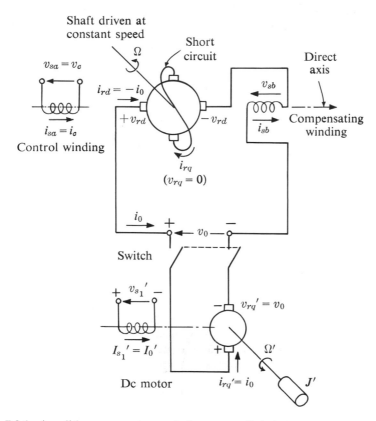

FIGURE 7.8.1. Amplidyne generator and dc motor. Switch is closed to connect motor.

2. Terms such as M_{ab} and M_{aq} refer to the mutual inductance between stator winding a and, respectively, the b stator winding and the quadrature brush axis.

3. The underlined term in the first row of the matrix, pM_{ab}, describes the voltage of mutual induction induced into stator winding a by changes of i_{sb}. A zero appears in the original matrix [Equation (7.6.5)] at this location because there is no second direct-axis winding.

4. The underlined term in the fourth row of the matrix, $-\Omega M_{bq}$, describes the motional-voltage component generated at the quadrature-axis brushes by current in the new stator winding, i_{sb}. This replaces a pM term in the original matrix. The negative sign was determined by inspection of the neighboring term $-\Omega M$ in the original matrix, which also refers to a direct-axis stator current.

The output terminal conditions for the amplidyne will now be derived. In view of the interconnections, new and somewhat simpler subscript designations are assigned on Figure 7.8.1. These are

$$
\begin{aligned}
\text{Output current,} && i_0 &= i_{sb} = -i_{rd}. \\
\text{Output voltage,} && v_0 &= v_{rd} - v_{sb}. \\
\text{Control voltage,} && v_c &= v_{sa}. \\
\text{Control current,} && i_c &= i_{sa}. \\
\text{Short-circuit voltage,} && v_{rq} &= 0.
\end{aligned}
\tag{7.8.2}
$$

Although methods exist for direct manipulation of Equation (7.8.1) in matrix form (see Sections 7.9–7.11), it is often just as satisfactory to write out the separate equations, which are

$$
v_c = (R_a + pL_a)i_c + \boxed{pM_{ab}i_0 - pM_{ad}i_0},
$$

$$
v_{sb} = pM_{ab}i_c + (R_b + pL_b)i_0 - pM_{bd}i_0,
\tag{7.8.3}
$$

$$
v_{rd} = pM_{ad}i_c + pM_{bd}i_0 - (R_r + pL_r)i_0 + \Omega M_r i_{rq},
$$

$$
0 = -\Omega M_{aq}i_c \boxed{-\Omega M_{bq}i_0 + \Omega M_r i_0} + (R_r + pL_r)i_{rq}.
$$

As a first attempt at simplification, let $M_{ab} = M_{ad}$ and $M_{bq} = M_r$. Then the boxed portions of Equation (7.8.3) vanish.

Several straightforward substitutions are now made. The last equation in Equation (7.8.3) is solved for i_{rq}, and the result substituted into the expansion of $v_0 = v_{rd} - v_{sb}$, giving

$$
v_0 = \frac{\Omega^2 M_{aq} M_r}{R_r + pL_r} i_c - [(R_r + R_{sb}) + p(L_{sb} + L_r - 2M_{bd})]i_0. \tag{7.8.4}
$$

This is of the same form as Equation (7.7.7) for the single-axis machine, which is repeated for comparison:

$$
v_{rq} = -\Omega M I_{s_1} + (R_r + pL_r)i_{rq}. \tag{7.7.7}
$$

The difference in signs occurs because v_0 and i_0 were assigned differently in the present case. The observation of major importance is that the first term on the right of Equation (7.8.4), the generated voltage term, is approximately the square of the first term in Equation (7.7.7). The amplidyne incorporates two stages of amplification in one machine by using both brush axes. Also of interest in Equation (7.8.4) is the term $(L_{sb} + L_r - 2M_{bd})$, which is recognized as the expression for the net inductance of two mutually-coupled coils connected in series bucking. All of these three inductances involve windings of relatively few turns and will be numerically small.

The over-all transfer function v_0/v_c cannot be evaluated unless the nature of the load connected to v_0 is known. In Figure 7.8.1 provision is made for connecting a separately-excited dc motor which, for simplicity, is to drive a pure inertia load. To minimize confusion, all motor parameters are primed. The motor equations, after switch S is closed, are

$$i_{s_1}' = I_0' \text{ (direct current)},$$
$$i_{rq}' = i_0,$$
$$v_{rq}' = v_0, \quad\quad\quad\quad (7.8.5)$$
$$T' + T_m' = 0 \text{ (torque balance)},$$
$$T' = M'I_0'i_0 \text{ [Equation (7.7.9)]},$$
$$T_m' = J'p\Omega'.$$

The system equations then become

Torque balance: $M'I_0'i_0 + J'p\Omega' = 0$

Motor voltage: $v_0 = -\Omega'M'I_0' + (R_r' + pL_r')i_0$ [Equation (7.7.7)]

Control voltage: $v_c = (R_a + pL_a)i_c$

Generator voltage: $v_0 = \dfrac{\Omega^2 M_{aq}M_r}{R_r + pL_r}i_c - (R_{eq} + pL_{eq})i_0$, [Equation (7.8.4)]

where $R_{eq} = R_r + R_{sb}$ and $L_{eq} = L_{sb} + L_r - 2M_{bd}$. When these three equations are solved simultaneously, there results, after some algebra,

$$\frac{\Omega'}{v_c} = -\frac{\Omega^2 M_{aq}M_r M'I_0'}{(R_r + pL_r)(R_a + pL_a)(p^2 J'L_T + pJ'R_T + M'^2 I_0'^2)}, \quad (7.8.6)$$

where $R_T = R_{eq} + R_r'$ and $L_T = L_{eq} + L_r'$, all in series around the loop connecting the two rotors.

Several comments apply to Equation (7.8.6).

1. The transfer function relates the motor speed Ω' to the amplidyne control voltage. The negative sign arises out of the polarity conventions discussed at length in Section 7.7; the motor must actually turn in the $-\Omega'$ direction if I_0' and v_c are positive.

2. Of the several time constants involved in the response, that due to the quadrature rotor term $(R_r + pL_r)$ is likely to be very short.

3. The control winding must have many turns to make M_{aq} large and give a high gain, so the response due to $(R_a + pL_a)$ will be longer.

4. The time constant of the mechanical response will probably predominate. The possibility of oscillations should not be overlooked. However, one would normally find $R_T \gg L_T$, so the $p^2 J'L_T$ term might have negligible effect and the whole mechanical term would produce only one significant response mode.

PROBLEM 7.8.1. (*a*) Redraw the amplidyne of Figure 7.8.1 so that the short circuit is between the direct-axis brushes and the other windings are on the quadrature axis. (*b*) For this revised condition, rewrite the matrix equation (7.8.1).

PROBLEM 7.8.2. For the amplidyne-motor combination of Section 7.8, calculate the transfer function i_0/v_c. *Answer:*

$$pJ'\Omega^2 M_{aq}M_r M'I_0'/(R_r + pL_r)(R_a + pL_a)(p^2 J'L_T + pJ'R_T + M'^2 I_0'^2).$$

It is now possible to present a physical interpretation of the "rotation matrix" or *d-q* transformation as applied to voltages on the *synchronous* machine, and originally discussed in Section 4.6. Figure 7.8.2 illustrates a salient-pole synchronous machine whose stator windings have been replaced with a re-entrant commutated winding, and with a set of four brushes that are rotated mechanically in synchronism with the rotor. These brushes commutate the stator winding, an impractical arrangement that is useful only as a conceptual aid.

If direct currents are injected into these rotating brushes, the resulting field is caused to rotate in exactly the same manner as does the field produced by alternating currents in polyphase stator windings. In this conceptual model, the brushes are always caused to turn in synchronism with the rotor, but the angular position of their rotating field can be changed by adjusting the relative amounts of direct and quadrature brush current. Thus, this model provides

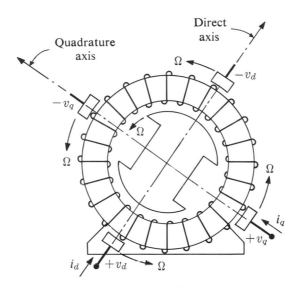

FIGURE 7.8.2. Visualization of *d-q* transformation. Equivalent commutated stator, and brushes that rotate with the rotor, can represent actual polyphase stator. Direct currents and voltages at rotating brushes produce same fields within machine as alternating currents and voltages applied to actual stator phase windings.

a method of visualizing the effect of the *d-q* transformation on currents, showing how equivalent direct currents could produce the same fields as do the actual alternating currents.

This model also provides an interpretation of the effect of the *d-q* transformation on voltages. When the transformation is applied to the polyphase voltages at the actual stator terminals of a synchronous machine, the result proves to be identical with the voltages at the rotating brushes in the model of Figure 7.8.2. Steady-state alternating voltages at the stator terminals transform into steady direct voltages at the rotating brushes.

From the discussion in the previous sections, it can be seen that current through the direct-axis brushes produces motional voltage at the quadrature-axis brushes. In fact, all of the relationships of the two-axis commutator machine matrix apply to the model of Figure 7.8.2, and through it, to the analysis of alternating-current machines.*

7.9   The Connection Matrix†

When a large system is assembled from a number of components, the interconnection can be represented in matrix form. As a first illustration, Figure 7.9.1(*a*) shows a network made up of seven active components lettered *A* through *G*. The voltage reference directions across the elements were assigned arbitrarily, and the current reference direction for each element was then assigned according to the load convention.

In Figure 7.9.1(*b*) a single component is shown in detail. It is seen that the component contains an operational impedance $Z_n(p)$ and a source $e_n(t)$, both labeled according to the load convention. Each such component can thus represent the Thevenin's equivalent of a more complex circuit. The properties of the various individual components can be displayed in matrix form as $[v_n] = [e_n] + [Z_n][i_n]$, which when expanded gives (for this example)

$$
\begin{bmatrix} v_a \\ v_b \\ v_c \\ v_d \\ v_e \\ v_f \\ v_g \end{bmatrix} = \begin{bmatrix} e_a \\ e_b \\ e_c \\ e_d \\ e_e \\ e_f \\ e_g \end{bmatrix} + \begin{bmatrix} Z_a & 0 & 0 & 0 & 0 & 0 & 0 \\ 0 & Z_b & 0 & 0 & 0 & 0 & 0 \\ 0 & 0 & Z_c & 0 & 0 & 0 & 0 \\ 0 & 0 & 0 & Z_d & 0 & 0 & 0 \\ 0 & 0 & 0 & 0 & Z_e & 0 & 0 \\ 0 & 0 & 0 & 0 & 0 & Z_f & 0 \\ 0 & 0 & 0 & 0 & 0 & 0 & Z_g \end{bmatrix} \cdot \begin{bmatrix} i_a \\ i_b \\ i_c \\ i_d \\ i_e \\ i_f \\ i_g \end{bmatrix}. \quad (7.9.1)
$$

* This model describes v_d and v_q using Park's notation, Reference 4.4. See explanatory footnote in Section 4.5.
† The remainder of this chapter uses elementary matrix algebra, including the addition, multiplication, transposition, and inversion of matrices.

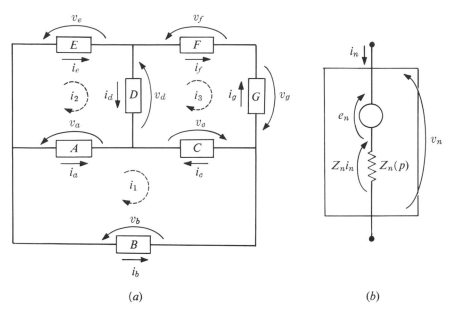

(a)   (b)

FIGURE 7.9.1. (a) Assembly of two-terminal components. (b) Detail of individual component.

It is unlikely that in any actual problem there would be a source in every component, so that some of the members of the $[e_n]$ matrix would be zero. The $[Z_n]$ matrix, on the other hand, is less general than it might be, for the presence of mutual coupling between components would produce symmetrical entries in some of the off-diagonal positions. It is noted that the component matrix equation of Equation (7.9.1) gives no indication of how the individual components are interconnected.

Upon returning to the interconnected system of Figure 7.9.1(a), it is obvious that only three independent currents are required to describe the system. If these are chosen as the mesh currents i_1, i_2, and i_3, a set of equations can be written to describe the individual element currents, as follows:

$$
\begin{aligned}
i_a &= i_1 - i_2 \\
i_b &= -i_1 \\
i_c &= -i_1 + i_3 \\
i_d &= i_2 - i_3 \\
i_e &= i_2 \\
i_f &= i_3 \\
i_g &= -i_3.
\end{aligned}
\tag{7.9.2}
$$

In matrix form, Equation (7.9.2) is

$$
\begin{bmatrix} i_a \\ i_b \\ i_c \\ i_d \\ i_e \\ i_f \\ i_g \end{bmatrix}
=
\begin{bmatrix}
1 & -1 & 0 \\
-1 & 0 & 0 \\
-1 & 0 & 1 \\
0 & 1 & -1 \\
0 & 1 & 0 \\
0 & 0 & 1 \\
0 & 0 & -1
\end{bmatrix}
\cdot
\begin{bmatrix} i_1 \\ i_2 \\ i_3 \end{bmatrix}.
\tag{7.9.3}
$$

The central 7×3 matrix is designated as $[C]$, the connection matrix, for it describes the way in which the seven individual elements are connected into three meshes. From $[C]$ it is possible to reconstruct the network in every detail except for the order in which series-connected elements such as F and G are connected. The connection matrix $[C]$ may alternatively be thought of as performing a change of variables, eliminating four of the original seven variables. It is noted that the connection matrix is not square, and therefore has no inverse.

If voltage summations are taken around the three chosen meshes in Figure 7.9.1(a), a rather surprising development follows. The voltage equations are

$$
\begin{aligned}
\text{Mesh 1:} \quad & v_a - v_b - v_c && = 0 \\
\text{Mesh 2:} \quad & -v_a && + v_d + v_e && = 0 \\
\text{Mesh 3:} \quad & v_c - v_d && + v_f - v_g = 0.
\end{aligned}
\tag{7.9.4}
$$

In matrix form, Equation (7.9.4) is

$$
\begin{bmatrix}
1 & -1 & -1 & 0 & 0 & 0 & 0 \\
-1 & 0 & 0 & 1 & 1 & 0 & 0 \\
0 & 0 & 1 & -1 & 0 & 1 & -1
\end{bmatrix}
\cdot
\begin{bmatrix} v_a \\ v_b \\ v_c \\ v_d \\ v_e \\ v_f \\ v_g \end{bmatrix}
= 0.
\tag{7.9.5}
$$

It is seen that the leading 3×7 matrix is the transpose of $[C]$, or $[C]_t$. This result is not accidental, but follows from conservation of energy, as is shown in the next section.

To summarize the results to this point, there have been developed equations containing the component matrix, the connection matrix, and the transpose of the connection matrix, as follows:

$$[v_n] = [e_n] + [Z_n][i_n]. \tag{7.9.1a}$$

$$[i_n] = [C][i_\eta]. \tag{7.9.3a}$$

$$0 = [C]_t[v_n]. \tag{7.9.5a}$$

The subscript n represents the original components ($n = a, b, c, \ldots, g$) and the subscript η (eta) represents the new variables, in this case mesh currents ($\eta = 1, 2, 3$). The formal derivation of Equation (7.9.5a), as well as of several other important relationships, now follows.

PROBLEM 7.9.1. Rewrite the connection matrix $[C]$ for the network of Figure 7.9.1, but with the currents $[i_\eta]$ as shown in Figure P7.9.1.

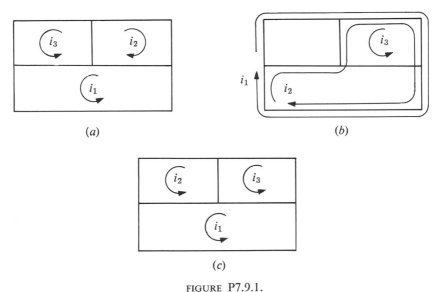

(a)   (b)

(c)

FIGURE P7.9.1.

PROBLEM 7.9.2. For each part of Problem 7.9.1, write the voltage summation around the chosen loops as in Equation (7.9.5), and show that the resulting matrix is the transpose of that in Problem 7.9.1.

7.10 Formal Development of Matrix Transformations

The purpose of a transformation of variables is to simplify an analytical solution and to make it more orderly. In the preceding section new currents,

$[i_n]$, were assigned to take the place of the larger number of currents, $[i_n]$, that appeared in the original statement of the example. It is now necessary to introduce a new set of voltages, $[v_n]$, and a new set of component imped-ances, $[Z_n]$, that are related to $[v_n]$ and $[Z_n]$ by appropriate transformations yet to be developed.

The required transformations are developed from two basic concepts, termed *invariancy of form* and *invariancy of power*.* Invariancy of form requires that the mathematical relationship between the transformed variables remain of the same form as the mathematical relationship between the original variables. Invariancy of power requires that the total power of the system remain unchanged by the transformation.

The original component matrix of Section 7.9 has the form

$$[v_n] = [e_n] + [Z_n][i_n], \qquad (7.10.1)$$

so the new variables are bound, by the requirement of invariancy of form, to appear in the same sort of relationship, or

$$[v_\eta] = [e_\eta] + [Z_\eta][i_\eta]. \qquad (7.10.2)$$

Except for $[i_\eta]$, the quantities in Equation (7.10.2) remain to be derived.

In the original network of Section 7.9, the total power (in the absence of radiation) is zero. That is,

$$i_a v_a + i_b v_b + \cdots + i_g v_g = 0.$$

This can be expressed in matrix form as

$$[i_n]_t [v_n] = 0, \qquad (7.10.3)$$

where the transpose of the column matrix $[i_n]$ is

$$[i_n]_t = [i_a \; i_b \; i_c \; i_d \; i_e \; i_f \; i_g],$$

and $[v_n]$ is as given in Equation (7.9.1).

Invariancy of power then requires that the instantaneous power remain zero after the transformation, or

$$[i_\eta]_t [v_\eta] = 0. \qquad (7.10.4)$$

The original equation defining the connection matrix, Equation (7.9.3a),

* This development is a modification of that originally introduced by Gabriel Kron. See Reference 7.1.

which is $[i_n] = [C][i_\eta]$, can be written in transposed form as

$$[i_n]_t = [i_\eta]_t[C]_t, \qquad (7.10.5)$$

which may be substituted in Equation (7.10.3) to give

$$[i_\eta]_t[C]_t[v_n] = 0. \qquad (7.10.6)$$

Comparison of Equations (7.10.4) and (7.10.6) shows that equivalence will result if

$$[v_\eta] = [C]_t[v_n]. \qquad (7.10.7)$$

Comparison of Equation (7.10.7) with Equation (7.9.5a) shows that in the example of Section 7.9, $[v_\eta] = 0$. This is not unexpected, since Equation (7.9.5a) was derived by taking voltage summations around closed paths.

Equation (7.10.7), when written in more detail, becomes

$$[e_\eta] + [Z_\eta][i_\eta] = [C]_t\{[e_n] + [Z_n][i_n]\}. \qquad (7.10.8)$$

The matrices $[e_n]$ and $[e_\eta]$ represent ideal voltage sources, whose values are unchanged by changes in currents or impedances. That is, the same $[e_\eta]$ matrix must result from a given $[e_n]$ matrix regardless of the values of $[i]$ and $[Z]$. This requirement is met in Equation (7.10.8) if $[C]_t$ is considered to operate separately on $[e_n]$ and $[Z_n][i_n]$, with no mixing between the terms. Then it follows that

$$[e_\eta] = [C]_t[e_n], \qquad (7.10.9)$$

and

$$[Z_\eta][i_\eta] = [C]_t[Z_n][i_n]. \qquad (7.10.10)$$

Equation (7.9.3a), which is $[i_n] = [C][i_\eta]$, is now substituted into Equation (7.10.10) to give

$$[Z_\eta][i_\eta] = [C]_t[Z_n][C][i_\eta]. \qquad (7.10.11)$$

This equality is satisfied if

$$[Z_\eta] = [C]_t[Z_n][C], \qquad (7.10.12)$$

which defines the transformation from $[Z_n]$ to $[Z_\eta]$.

The new variables have now been defined. In a typical problem, the given quantities are $[e_n]$, $[Z_n]$, and $[C]$ and it is desired to find $[i_n]$. The first step in the solution is to transform the variables according to

$$[e_\eta] = [C]_t[e_n], \qquad (7.10.9)$$

$$[Z_\eta] = [C]_t[Z_n][C]. \qquad (7.10.12)$$

Then, since $[v_\eta] = 0$ in problems of the type discussed here, the equation $[v_\eta] = [e_\eta] + [Z_\eta][i_\eta]$ can be solved to give

$$[i_\eta] = -[Z_\eta]^{-1}[e_\eta], \tag{7.10.13}$$

and finally,

$$[i_n] = [C][i_\eta]. \tag{7.9.3a}$$

The step of Equation (7.10.13) contains the inversion of a matrix and is usually the most difficult and time-consuming part of the entire solution. It corresponds to the simultaneous solution of the entire set of (usually differential) equations.

PROBLEM 7.10.1. The power summation of Equation (7.10.3) can also be written as $[v_n]_t[i_n] = 0$, and that of Equation (7.10.4) as $[v_\eta]_t[i_\eta] = 0$. Carry out the entire derivation of Section 7.10 with this change.

7.11 Examples of Large System Analysis by Matrix Methods

In this section, several illustrative examples are used to show the application of the procedures described in the previous section. In outline form, the procedure is as follows.

1. *Component matrix equation.* The terminal properties of all of the individual components are assembled into a single component matrix equation of the form

$$[v_n] = [e_n] + [Z_n][i_n]. \tag{7.11.1}$$

2. *Connection matrix equation.* A new set of currents, adequate to define all of the interconnections, is defined in the form

$$[i_n] = [C][i_\eta]. \tag{7.11.2}$$

Various topological rules, not discussed here, may be useful in determining the minimum number of new currents required.

3. *Transformation of variables.* The new variables are determined according to

$$[e_\eta] = [C]_t[e_n]. \tag{7.11.3}$$

$$[Z_\eta] = [C]_t[Z_n][C]. \tag{7.11.4}$$

4. *Solution of transformed equation.* The $[Z_\eta]$ matrix is inverted to find

$$[i_\eta] = -[Z_\eta]^{-1}[e_\eta]. \tag{7.11.5}$$

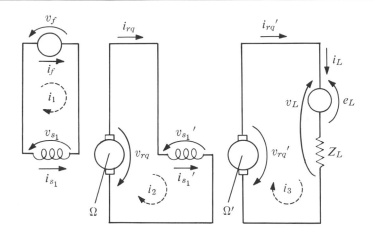

FIGURE 7.11.1. Interconnected generators for Example 7.11.1.

5. *Evaluation of original variables.* When desired, the original variables $[v_n]$ and $[i_n]$ are found by applying the equations already given in steps 1 and 2 above, or

$$[v_n] = [e_n] + [Z_n][i_n], \tag{7.11.6}$$

$$[i_n] = [C][i_n]. \tag{7.11.7}$$

Example 7.11.1. Two dc generators are connected as shown in Figure 7.11.1. The input to the stator field of the first generator is a voltage source, and the output of the second generator is connected to an element containing an impedance and a voltage source (possibly a storage battery being charged). The two shafts are driven at constant speeds. All quantities associated with the second generator are primed for clarity.

As a preparatory step, the terminal relationships for the various components are written separately. From the commutator machine matrix of Equation (7.8.1), with unused rows and columns removed, there can be written for the first machine

$$\begin{bmatrix} v_{s1} \\ v_{rq} \end{bmatrix} = \begin{bmatrix} R_s + pL_s & 0 \\ -\Omega M & R_r + pL_r \end{bmatrix} \cdot \begin{bmatrix} i_{s1} \\ i_{rq} \end{bmatrix}. \tag{7.11.8}$$

A second equation, identical except for the prime designation, describes the second machine:

$$\begin{bmatrix} v_{s1}' \\ v_{rq}' \end{bmatrix} = \begin{bmatrix} R_s' + pL_s' & 0 \\ -\Omega'M' & R_r' + pL_r' \end{bmatrix} \cdot \begin{bmatrix} i_{s1}' \\ i_{rq}' \end{bmatrix}. \tag{7.11.9}$$

The source v_f is considered ideal and is described by the single equation

$$v_f = e_f + Z_f i_f, \qquad (7.11.10)$$

where

$$Z_f = 0.$$

The load is also described by a single equation,

$$v_L = e_L + Z_L i_L. \qquad (7.11.11)$$

The components are now all assembled (step 1) into a single component matrix equation of the form

$$[v_n] = [e_n] + [Z_n][i_n],$$

which in detail is

$$
\begin{bmatrix} v_f \\ v_{s1} \\ v_{rq} \\ v_{s1}' \\ v_{rq}' \\ v_L \end{bmatrix}
=
\begin{bmatrix} e_f \\ 0 \\ 0 \\ 0 \\ 0 \\ e_L \end{bmatrix}
+
\begin{bmatrix}
Z_f & 0 & 0 & 0 & 0 & 0 \\
0 & Z_s & 0 & 0 & 0 & 0 \\
0 & -\Omega M & Z_r & 0 & 0 & 0 \\
0 & 0 & 0 & Z_s' & 0 & 0 \\
0 & 0 & 0 & -\Omega' M' & Z_r' & 0 \\
0 & 0 & 0 & 0 & 0 & Z_L
\end{bmatrix}
\cdot
\begin{bmatrix} i_f \\ i_{s1} \\ i_{rq} \\ i_{s1}' \\ i_{rq}' \\ i_L \end{bmatrix}. \qquad (7.11.12)
$$

The known quantities are e_f, e_L, and all of the Z's. For compactness, the substitutions $Z_s = R_s + pL_s$, etc., have been made. No operations have been performed as yet, and expansion of the component matrix equation as it stands will yield only the individual equations from which it was assembled.

The connection matrix equation $[i_n] = [C][i_n]$ is now written (step 2) from inspection of the interconnected system, using the mesh currents $[i_n]$ as shown, and in full is

$$
\begin{bmatrix} i_f \\ i_{s1} \\ i_{rq} \\ i_{s1}' \\ i_{rq}' \\ i_L \end{bmatrix}
=
\begin{bmatrix}
1 & 0 & 0 \\
-1 & 0 & 0 \\
0 & 1 & 0 \\
0 & 1 & 0 \\
0 & 0 & 1 \\
0 & 0 & 1
\end{bmatrix}
\cdot
\begin{bmatrix} i_1 \\ i_2 \\ i_3 \end{bmatrix}. \qquad (7.11.13)
$$

Step 3, which is $[e_n] = [C]_t[e_n]$, then gives

$$
\begin{bmatrix} e_1 \\ e_2 \\ e_3 \end{bmatrix}
=
\begin{bmatrix}
1 & -1 & 0 & 0 & 0 & 0 \\
0 & 0 & 1 & 1 & 0 & 0 \\
0 & 0 & 0 & 0 & 1 & 1
\end{bmatrix}
\cdot
\begin{bmatrix} e_f \\ 0 \\ 0 \\ 0 \\ 0 \\ e_L \end{bmatrix}
=
\begin{bmatrix} e_f \\ 0 \\ e_L \end{bmatrix}. \qquad (7.11.14)
$$

The new or transformed impedance, $[Z_\eta] = [C]_t[Z][C]$, is found by performing the indicated matrix multiplications consecutively, as follows:

$$[Z_\eta] = \begin{bmatrix} 1 & -1 & 0 & 0 & 0 & 0 \\ 0 & 0 & 1 & 1 & 0 & 0 \\ 0 & 0 & 0 & 0 & 1 & 1 \end{bmatrix} \cdot$$

$$\begin{bmatrix} 0 & 0 & 0 & 0 & 0 & 0 \\ 0 & Z_s & 0 & 0 & 0 & 0 \\ 0 & -\Omega M & Z_r & 0 & 0 & 0 \\ 0 & 0 & 0 & Z_s' & 0 & 0 \\ 0 & 0 & 0 & -\Omega' M' & Z_r' & 0 \\ 0 & 0 & 0 & 0 & 0 & Z_L \end{bmatrix} \cdot [C]$$

$$[Z_\eta] = \begin{bmatrix} 0 & -Z_s & 0 & 0 & 0 & 0 \\ 0 & -\Omega M & Z_r & Z_s' & 0 & 0 \\ 0 & 0 & 0 & -\Omega' M' & Z_r' & Z_L \end{bmatrix} \cdot \begin{bmatrix} 1 & 0 & 0 \\ -1 & 0 & 0 \\ 0 & 1 & 0 \\ 0 & 1 & 0 \\ 0 & 0 & 1 \\ 0 & 0 & 1 \end{bmatrix}$$

$$[Z_\eta] = \begin{bmatrix} Z_s & 0 & 0 \\ \Omega M & Z_r + Z_s' & 0 \\ 0 & -\Omega' M' & Z_r' + Z_L \end{bmatrix}. \tag{7.11.15}$$

It is now seen that the various elements in the $[Z_\eta]$ matrix are the self-impedances around the circuit meshes and the mutual (in this case motional) impedances between them.

Step 4 calls for the inversion of the $[Z_\eta]$ matrix. A good procedure for doing this is as follows:

1. Write the transpose (for nonsymmetrical matrices).
2. Substitute for each element in the transpose its cofactor.
3. Alternate signs according to the rule for determinants.
4. Divide each cofactor element by the determinant of the transpose.

Because of the many zeros, this example is fairly simple and yields

$$[Z_\eta]^{-1} = \frac{1}{\Delta} \begin{bmatrix} (Z_r + Z_s')(Z_r' + Z_L) & 0 & 0 \\ -\Omega M(Z_r' + Z_L) & Z_s(Z_r' + Z_L) & 0 \\ -\Omega M \Omega' M' & \Omega' M' Z_s & Z_s(Z_r + Z_s') \end{bmatrix} \tag{7.11.16}$$

where $\Delta = Z_s(Z_r + Z_s')(Z_{r'} + Z_L)$, or

$$[Z_\eta]^{-1} = \begin{bmatrix} \dfrac{1}{Z_s} & 0 & 0 \\[2ex] \dfrac{-\Omega M}{Z_s(Z_r + Z_s')} & \dfrac{1}{(Z_r + Z_s')} & 0 \\[2ex] \dfrac{-\Omega M \Omega' M'}{Z_s(Z_r + Z_s')(Z_{r'} + Z_L)} & \dfrac{\Omega' M'}{(Z_r + Z_s')(Z_{r'} + Z_L)} & \dfrac{1}{(Z_{r'} + Z_L)} \end{bmatrix}. \quad (7.11.17)$$

It is noted that each element in $[Z_\eta]^{-1}$ is an admittance, so the matrix may be written

$$[Z_\eta]^{-1} = \begin{bmatrix} Y_{11} & 0 & 0 \\ Y_{21} & Y_{22} & 0 \\ Y_{31} & Y_{32} & Y_{33} \end{bmatrix} = [Y]. \quad (7.11.18)$$

Once the matrix is inverted, the transformed currents are found from $[i_\eta] = -[Z_\eta]^{-1}[e_\eta]$, or

$$\begin{bmatrix} i_1 \\ i_2 \\ i_3 \end{bmatrix} = - \begin{bmatrix} Y_{11} & 0 & 0 \\ Y_{21} & Y_{22} & 0 \\ Y_{31} & Y_{32} & Y_{33} \end{bmatrix} \cdot \begin{bmatrix} e_f \\ 0 \\ e_L \end{bmatrix} = - \begin{bmatrix} Y_{11}e_f \\ Y_{21}e_f \\ Y_{31}e_f + Y_{33}e_L \end{bmatrix}. \quad (7.11.19)$$

Then finally (step 5), the original currents are $[i_n] = [C][i_\eta]$, or

$$\begin{bmatrix} i_f \\ i_{s1} \\ i_{rq} \\ i_{s1}' \\ i_{rq}' \\ i_L \end{bmatrix} = \begin{bmatrix} 1 & 0 & 0 \\ -1 & 0 & 0 \\ 0 & 1 & 0 \\ 0 & 1 & 0 \\ 0 & 0 & 1 \\ 0 & 0 & 1 \end{bmatrix} \cdot \begin{bmatrix} i_1 \\ i_2 \\ i_3 \end{bmatrix} = \begin{bmatrix} i_1 \\ -i_1 \\ i_2 \\ i_2 \\ i_3 \\ i_3 \end{bmatrix}. \quad (7.11.20)$$

If desired, the component voltages $[v_n] = [e_n] + [Z_n][i_n]$ can also be determined. The values for i_1, i_2, and i_3 in Equation (7.11.19) work out to be

$$i_1 = -\frac{e_f}{Z_s}$$

$$i_2 = \frac{e_f \Omega M}{Z_s(Z_r + Z_s')}$$

$$i_3 = \frac{e_f \Omega M \Omega' M'}{Z_s(Z_r + Z_s')(Z_{r'} + Z_L)} - \frac{e_L}{(Z_{r'} + Z_L)}. \quad (7.11.21)$$

The results of this example could have been obtained much more readily, without any matrix inversion, by direct substitution into the original machine equations as given at the beginning of the example. It is usually the case that systems of sufficient complexity for generalized methods to be of value are very tedious to solve without machine computation, whereas systems that are simple enough for "textbook examples" can be solved more easily without using the generalized methods. Thus, the student should accept this as an illustration of a powerful method rather than as a practical application of it.

It is to be noted that use was made of the previously-developed terminal equations for the commutator machine, without the need to develop them all over again. The interconnection was represented by the connection matrix and from that point on, the manipulations became routine.

PROBLEM 7.11.1. Carry out the missing steps in the development of Example 7.11.1.

PROBLEM 7.11.2. Write the component matrix equation and the connection matrix for the interconnected machines of (*a*) Figure P7.12; (*b*) Figure P7.14. The illustrations are in the advanced problem set at the end of the chapter.

Example 7.11.2. In this example an unbalanced bridge problem is solved numerically, using only resistors and batteries so that the calculations will be relatively simple. The circuit is shown in Figure 7.11.2. The reference directions for $[v_n]$ were chosen at random.

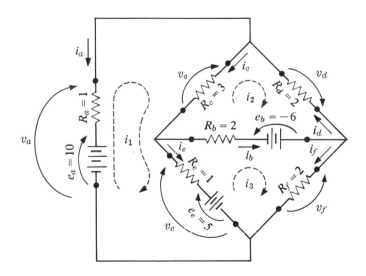

FIGURE 7.11.2 Bridge circuit for Example 7.11.2.

The component matrix equation is

$$
\begin{bmatrix} v_a \\ v_b \\ v_c \\ v_d \\ v_e \\ v_f \end{bmatrix} = \begin{bmatrix} 10 \\ -6 \\ 0 \\ 0 \\ 5 \\ 0 \end{bmatrix} + \begin{bmatrix} 1 & 0 & 0 & 0 & 0 & 0 \\ 0 & 2 & 0 & 0 & 0 & 0 \\ 0 & 0 & 3 & 0 & 0 & 0 \\ 0 & 0 & 0 & 2 & 0 & 0 \\ 0 & 0 & 0 & 0 & 1 & 0 \\ 0 & 0 & 0 & 0 & 0 & 2 \end{bmatrix} \cdot \begin{bmatrix} i_a \\ i_b \\ i_c \\ i_d \\ i_e \\ i_f \end{bmatrix}.
\tag{7.11.22}
$$

The connection matrix equation is

$$
\begin{bmatrix} i_a \\ i_b \\ i_c \\ i_d \\ i_e \\ i_f \end{bmatrix} = \begin{bmatrix} -1 & 0 & 0 \\ 0 & -1 & 1 \\ 1 & -1 & 0 \\ 0 & -1 & 0 \\ 1 & 0 & -1 \\ 0 & 0 & 1 \end{bmatrix} \cdot \begin{bmatrix} i_1 \\ i_2 \\ i_3 \end{bmatrix}.
\tag{7.11.23}
$$

The $[e_\eta]$ matrix equation is

$$
\begin{bmatrix} e_1 \\ e_2 \\ e_3 \end{bmatrix} = \begin{bmatrix} -1 & 0 & 1 & 0 & 1 & 0 \\ 0 & -1 & -1 & -1 & 0 & 0 \\ 0 & 1 & 0 & 0 & -1 & 1 \end{bmatrix} \cdot \begin{bmatrix} 10 \\ -6 \\ 0 \\ 0 \\ 5 \\ 0 \end{bmatrix} = \begin{bmatrix} -5 \\ 6 \\ -11 \end{bmatrix}.
\tag{7.11.24}
$$

These three voltages are seen to be the sums of the battery voltages taken around each of the three loops. The $[Z_\eta]$ matrix, from $[C]_t[Z_n][C]$, is

$$
[Z_\eta] = \begin{bmatrix} 5 & -3 & -1 \\ -3 & 7 & -2 \\ -1 & -2 & 5 \end{bmatrix}.
\tag{7.11.25}
$$

The elements in the $[Z_\eta]$ matrix are recognized as the self- and mutual resistances around the three meshes, and could have been obtained by inspection. Upon inverting,

$$
[Z_\eta]^{-1} = \frac{1}{91} \begin{bmatrix} 31 & 17 & 13 \\ 17 & 24 & 13 \\ 13 & 13 & 26 \end{bmatrix}.
\tag{7.11.26}
$$

Then $[i_\eta] = -[Z_\eta]^{-1}[e_\eta]$, or

$$
\begin{bmatrix} i_1 \\ i_2 \\ i_3 \end{bmatrix} = -\frac{1}{91} \begin{bmatrix} 31 & 17 & 13 \\ 17 & 24 & 13 \\ 13 & 13 & 26 \end{bmatrix} \cdot \begin{bmatrix} -5 \\ 6 \\ -11 \end{bmatrix} = \frac{1}{91} \begin{bmatrix} 196 \\ 84 \\ 273 \end{bmatrix} = \begin{bmatrix} 2.15 \\ 0.92 \\ 3.00 \end{bmatrix}. \quad (7.11.27)
$$

Finally, $[i_n] = [C][i_\eta]$, or

$$
\begin{bmatrix} i_a \\ i_b \\ i_c \\ i_d \\ i_e \\ i_f \end{bmatrix} = \begin{bmatrix} -1 & 0 & 0 \\ 0 & -1 & 1 \\ 1 & -1 & 0 \\ 0 & -1 & 0 \\ 1 & 0 & -1 \\ 0 & 0 & 1 \end{bmatrix} \cdot \begin{bmatrix} 2.15 \\ 0.92 \\ 3.00 \end{bmatrix} = \begin{bmatrix} -2.15 \\ +2.08 \\ +1.23 \\ -0.92 \\ -0.85 \\ +3.00 \end{bmatrix}, \quad (7.11.28a)
$$

and $[v_n] = [e_n] + [Z_n][i_n]$, or

$$
\begin{bmatrix} v_a \\ v_b \\ v_c \\ v_d \\ v_e \\ v_f \end{bmatrix} = \begin{bmatrix} 10 \\ -6 \\ 0 \\ 0 \\ 5 \\ 0 \end{bmatrix} + \begin{bmatrix} 1 & 0 & 0 & 0 & 0 & 0 \\ 0 & 2 & 0 & 0 & 0 & 0 \\ 0 & 0 & 3 & 0 & 0 & 0 \\ 0 & 0 & 0 & 2 & 0 & 0 \\ 0 & 0 & 0 & 0 & 1 & 0 \\ 0 & 0 & 0 & 0 & 0 & 2 \end{bmatrix} \cdot \begin{bmatrix} -2.15 \\ +2.08 \\ +1.23 \\ -0.92 \\ -0.85 \\ +3.00 \end{bmatrix} = \begin{bmatrix} +7.85 \\ -1.84 \\ +3.69 \\ -1.84 \\ +4.15 \\ +6.00 \end{bmatrix}. \quad (7.11.28b)
$$

As a check on the numerical work, the values in Equation (7.11.28) can be substituted into $[v_\eta] = 0$ or $[i_n]_t[v_n] = 0$.

PROBLEM 7.11.3. Carry out the numerical work leading to Equations (7.11.25) and (7.11.28). Also perform the numerical check indicated at the end of Example 7.11.2.

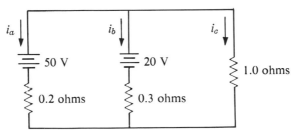

FIGURE P7.11.4.

PROBLEM 7.11.4. Figure P7.11.4 shows two storage batteries, each with internal resistance, connected to a resistive load. Solve for the three currents and the load voltage by using the five formal steps of Section 7.11. *Answer:* $i_a = -80.3$; $i_b = 46.4$; $i_c = 33.9$; $v_c = 33.9$.

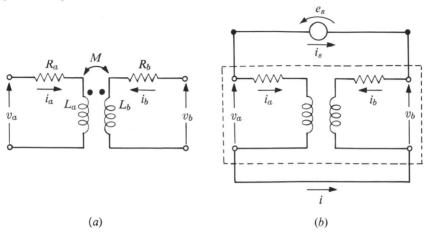

(a)   (b)

FIGURE 7.11.3. Interconnection of magnetically-coupled coils, for Example 7.11.3. (a) Magnetically-coupled coils. (b) Interconnection for Example 7.11.3.

Example 7.11.3. Magnetic coupling. The pair of magnetically-coupled coils shown in Figure 7.11.3(a) are represented at their terminals by the equations

$$\begin{bmatrix} v_a \\ v_b \end{bmatrix} = \begin{bmatrix} R_a + pL_a & pM \\ pM & R_b + pL_b \end{bmatrix} \cdot \begin{bmatrix} i_a \\ i_b \end{bmatrix}. \qquad (7.11.29)$$

It is of interest to compare these equations with those for the single-axis dc machine:

$$\begin{bmatrix} v_{s_1} \\ v_{rq} \end{bmatrix} = \begin{bmatrix} R_s + pL_s & 0 \\ -\Omega M & R_r + pL_r \end{bmatrix} \cdot \begin{bmatrix} i_{s_1} \\ i_{rq} \end{bmatrix}. \qquad (7.11.8)$$

The noteworthy difference is the lack of symmetry in the impedance matrix for the machine, which is not bilateral. A disturbance in the rotor circuit does not affect the stator circuit, whereas for the magnetically-coupled coils, the secondary and primary interact equally. Diagonal symmetry will always be found in the impedance matrix for stationary networks made up of linear, bilateral, passive elements, whereas energy conversion devices are characterized by a nonsymmetric (but not necessarily unilateral) impedance matrix.

With the coils connected as in Figure 7.13.3(b), the connection matrix is

$$\begin{bmatrix} i_a \\ i_b \\ i_s \end{bmatrix} = \begin{bmatrix} 1 \\ -1 \\ -1 \end{bmatrix} \cdot [i]. \qquad (7.11.30)$$

The $[i_n]$ matrix contains only a single entry, i, which is the current in the interconnected series circuit. It is tempting to assign no new current at all, since $i_a = i$; however, such a short-cut will lead to confusion in all but the simplest of systems.

The external source is considered as a component having $Z_s = 0$, and its equation is written as

$$V_s = e_s + Z_s i_s = e_s + 0. \tag{7.11.31}$$

Thus the component matrix equation appears as

$$\begin{bmatrix} v_a \\ v_b \\ v_s \end{bmatrix} = \begin{bmatrix} 0 \\ 0 \\ e_s \end{bmatrix} + \begin{bmatrix} Z_a & pM & 0 \\ pM & Z_b & 0 \\ 0 & 0 & 0 \end{bmatrix} \cdot \begin{bmatrix} i_a \\ i_b \\ i_s \end{bmatrix}, \tag{7.11.32}$$

where $Z_a = R_a + pL_a$ and $Z_b = R_b + pL_b$.

The presence of the entire row and column of zeros in the impedance matrix is not a cause for alarm, as these will disappear during the manipulation and before inversion is called for.

Upon carrying out the five successive steps of Equations (7.11.1) through (7.11.6),

$$[e_\eta] = \begin{bmatrix} 1 & -1 & -1 \end{bmatrix} \cdot \begin{bmatrix} 0 \\ 0 \\ e_s \end{bmatrix} = -e_s. \tag{7.11.33}$$

$$[Z_\eta] = \begin{bmatrix} 1 & -1 & -1 \end{bmatrix} \cdot \begin{bmatrix} Z_a & pM & 0 \\ pM & Z_b & 0 \\ 0 & 0 & 0 \end{bmatrix} \cdot \begin{bmatrix} 1 \\ -1 \\ -1 \end{bmatrix}$$

$$= (R_a + R_b) + p(L_a - 2M + L_b). \tag{7.11.34}$$

This is recognized as the expression for the impedance of two coupled coils connected in series bucking. Since $[Z_\eta]$ is a 1×1 matrix, inversion is simple algebraic inversion and

$$[i_\eta] = i = -e_s/[(R_a + R_b) + p(L_a - 2M + L_b). \tag{7.11.35}$$

If the voltages v_a and v_b are desired, two additional steps are required. These are

$$[i_n] = \begin{bmatrix} i_a \\ i_b \\ i_s \end{bmatrix} = \begin{bmatrix} 1 \\ -1 \\ 1 \end{bmatrix} \cdot [i], \tag{7.11.36}$$

and

$$[v_n] = [e_n] + [Z_n][i_n]. \tag{7.11.37}$$

If $[C]$ is square and (therefore) has an inverse, this final result can be found by $[v_n] = [C]^{-1}[v_\eta]$, a procedure that is not usually possible because $[C]$ is generally not square. The use of square matrices is illustrated in Problem 7.16.

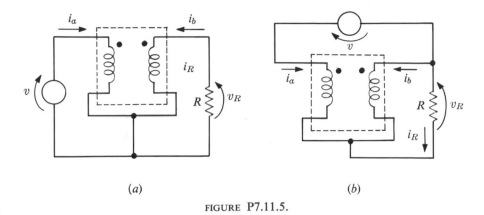

(a)   (b)

FIGURE P7.11.5.

PROBLEM 7.11.5. Repeat the analysis of Example 7.11.3, when the coupled coils are connected as in (a) Figure P7.11.5(a); (b) Figure P7.11.5(b).

Example 7.11.4. Parallel connection of compound dc generators. The compound-wound dc generator (Section 6.11) has two stator windings, both on the same axis. One winding carries a steady direct current, and the other is connected in series with the armature brushes so that its magnetic field aids that of the first winding. Such a machine can produce a terminal voltage that rises as the load (armature) current increases, and when two such generators are connected in parallel to a common load there results an unstable condition in which one of the machines tends to take on all of the load and will even drive the other as a motor.

Two compound generators are shown in Figure 7.11.4, connected in parallel to a common resistive load R_L. The currents for one machine are marked with primes to distinguish them from those for the other machine. The machine parameters and speeds are assumed identical, although this has no basic effect on the problem.

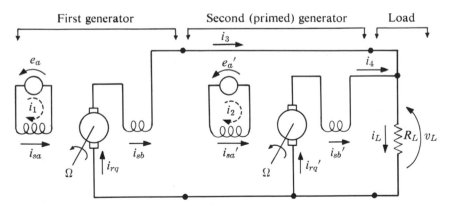

FIGURE 7.11.4. Parallel compound dc generators for Example 7.11.4.

The component matrix equation is

$$
\begin{bmatrix} v_{sa} \\ v_{sb} \\ v_{rq} \\ v_{sa}' \\ v_{sb}' \\ v_{rq}' \\ v_L \end{bmatrix}
=
\begin{bmatrix} e_a \\ 0 \\ 0 \\ e_a' \\ 0 \\ 0 \\ 0 \end{bmatrix}
+
\begin{bmatrix}
Z_{sa} & pM_{ab} & 0 & 0 & 0 & 0 & 0 \\
pM_{ab} & Z_{sb} & 0 & 0 & 0 & 0 & 0 \\
-\Omega M_{aq} & -\Omega M_{bq} & Z_r & 0 & 0 & 0 & 0 \\
0 & 0 & 0 & Z_{sa} & pM_{ab} & 0 & 0 \\
0 & 0 & 0 & pM_{ab} & Z_{sb} & 0 & 0 \\
0 & 0 & 0 & -\Omega M_{aq} & -\Omega M_{bq} & Z_r & 0 \\
0 & 0 & 0 & 0 & 0 & 0 & R_L
\end{bmatrix}
\begin{bmatrix} i_{sa} \\ i_{sb} \\ i_{rq} \\ i_{sa}' \\ i_{sb}' \\ i_{rq}' \\ i_L \end{bmatrix}
$$

$$(7.11.38)$$

The voltages e_a and e_a' have been handled in a manner slightly different from that used previously in that they are included as source voltages in the stator winding elements rather than as separate components. This eliminates two zero rows and columns from the $[Z_n]$ matrix, but has no effect on the results.

The connection matrix equation is

$$
\begin{bmatrix} i_{sa} \\ i_{sb} \\ i_{rq} \\ i_{sa}' \\ i_{sb}' \\ i_{rq}' \\ i_L \end{bmatrix}
=
\begin{bmatrix}
-1 & 0 & 0 & 0 \\
0 & 0 & 1 & 0 \\
0 & 0 & 1 & 0 \\
0 & -1 & 0 & 0 \\
0 & 0 & 0 & 1 \\
0 & 0 & 0 & 1 \\
0 & 0 & 1 & 1
\end{bmatrix}
\cdot
\begin{bmatrix} i_1 \\ i_2 \\ i_3 \\ i_4 \end{bmatrix}.
$$

$$(7.11.39)$$

The $[i_\eta]$ currents were selected as shown in Figure 7.11.4, and in this case are not mesh currents.

From Equation (7.11.39), the $[C]_t$ matrix is

$$
[C]_t =
\begin{bmatrix}
-1 & 0 & 0 & 0 & 0 & 0 & 0 \\
0 & 0 & 0 & -1 & 0 & 0 & 0 \\
0 & 1 & 1 & 0 & 0 & 0 & 1 \\
0 & 0 & 0 & 0 & 1 & 1 & 1
\end{bmatrix}.
$$

$$(7.11.40)$$

Then, $[Z_\eta] = [C]_t[Z_n][C]$, which when worked out gives

$$
[Z_\eta] =
\begin{bmatrix}
Z_{sa} & 0 & -pM_{ab} & 0 \\
0 & Z_{sa} & 0 & -pM_{ab} \\
-pM_{ab} + \Omega M_{aq} & 0 & Z_{sb} - \Omega M_{bq} + Z_r + Z_L & R_L \\
0 & -pM_{ab} + \Omega M_{aq} & R_L & Z_{sb} - \Omega M_{bq} + Z_r + Z_L
\end{bmatrix}.
$$

$$(7.11.41)$$

Similarly,

$$[e_\eta] = [C]_t[e_n] = \begin{bmatrix} -e_a \\ -e_a{}' \\ 0 \\ 0 \end{bmatrix}.$$

(7.11.42)

Before proceeding further, it is desirable to investigate the stability of the system (especially in view of the opening remarks of this example warning of instability). The matrix $[Z_\eta]$ appears in a set of differential equations of the form

$$-[Z_\eta][i_\eta] = [e_\eta].$$

(7.11.43)

To obtain the currents, this set must be solved simultaneously, and in the course of doing this by Cramer's rule there arises a denominator *determinant* $|Z_\eta|$ which when set equal to zero gives the natural (source-free) modes of response of the system. This denominator can then be examined for poles in the right half of the complex-frequency plane (s-plane), which if present are a positive indication of instability.

As a simplifying approximation, it is assumed that L_{sa} and $L_{sa}{}'$ are sufficiently large that i_{sa} and $i_{sa}{}'$ remain substantially constant during any transient phenomena. This is equivalent to supplying the two stator field windings from current sources. Then the terms pM_{ab} and pL_{sa} will have no effect on the rotor currents and can be set equal to zero. With this simplification, $[Z_\eta]$ becomes

$$[Z_\eta] = \begin{bmatrix} R_{sa} & 0 & 0 & 0 \\ 0 & R_{sa} & 0 & 0 \\ \Omega M_{aq} & 0 & Z_{sb} - \Omega M_{bq} + Z_r + Z_L & R_L \\ 0 & \Omega M_{aq} & R_L & Z_{sb} - \Omega M_{bq} + Z_r + Z_L \end{bmatrix}.$$

(7.11.44)

Setting the determinant $|Z_\eta| = 0$ for the stability investigation gives

$$|Z_\eta| = R_{sa}{}^2\{[(R_{sb} + R_b + R_L - \Omega M_{bq} + p(L_{sb} + L_r)]^2 - R_L{}^2\} = 0.$$ (7.11.45)

It is normal to have $R_L \gg (R_{sb} + R_r)$, and writing $(L_{sb} + L_r) = L$, the characteristic equation reduces to the approximate form

$$s^2L^2 + 2sL(R_L - \Omega M) + \Omega M(\Omega M - 2R_L) = 0.$$

(7.11.46)

Examination of the bracketed terms in Equation (7.11.46) shows that it is impossible to adjust the values of R_L and ΩM to avoid negative signs in the equation. Negative signs in the characteristic equation assure poles in the right half s-plane, with consequent instability, although an absence of negative signs does not insure stability. Therefore, this system is indeed unstable and a modification is required. Such a modification is shown in Figure 7.11.5, where the series windings sb and sb' have been interchanged with each other. The analysis of the revised system is left as an exercise, but (with the same assumptions and approximations as used

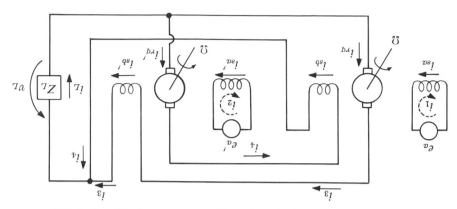

FIGURE 7.11.5. Parallel dc generators with series windings interchanged to provide stability.

above) the result is that the characteristic equation for the revised system has no negative terms if $R_L > \frac{1}{2}\Omega M_{bq}$, and the system can be shown by further analysis (such as factoring) to be stable.

This result is subject to a physical interpretation. If (in the revised system) a disturbance causes the armature current in one machine to increase, this increasing current now flows in the series winding of the other machine, boosting the other machine's motionally-generated voltage and thereby causing its armature current also to increase. If R_L is made too small, a negative sign may still appear in the characteristic equation and instability will arise in the form of increasing oscillations of current. If $R_L > \frac{1}{2}\Omega M_{bq}$, however, the oscillations will die out and the two machines will settle back until each again supplies half of the load.

PROBLEM 7.11.6. Carry out the stability investigation, as described in Example 7.11.4, for the connections of Figure 7.11.5. Use the same simplifying assumptions.

PROBLEM 7.11.7. Determine the steady-state currents I_3 and I_4, and the voltage V_L, for the system of Figure 7.11.5 using matrix methods.

This section has served to introduce the student to formal methods of large system analysis. The examples used have been simple and limited to electrical interconnections using mesh analysis. The procedure can be extended readily to include nodal methods, but these are less useful for machine analysis, since rotating machines ordinarily operate as voltage sources rather than as current sources. More complicated systems, involving mechanical as well as electrical interconnections, require additional topological concepts that are not treated here.*

---

* A good recent undergraduate text is Reference 7.2.

The serious student of electromechanical energy conversion quickly finds himself engaged with advanced analytical concepts, including Lagrangian and Hamiltonian functions, dyadic and tensor analysis, state-variable analysis, non-Riemannian dynamics, and diakoptics, a "tearing" procedure based on the partitioning of determinants. Successive attempts to "unify" the field have produced, instead, parallel treatments that complement each other and increase the complexity of the field.* The study of any one of the major approaches to electromechanical energy conversion systems is a challenging undertaking, and it is an important objective of this textbook to provide a background from which such advanced study can proceed.

Problems

7.1 The synchronous machine of Section 7.3 is undergoing a small oscillation in shaft speed, such that $\Omega = \Omega_s + \Omega_1 \cos \omega t$, where $\omega \ll \Omega_s$ and $\Omega_1 \ll \Omega_0$. Stator and rotor are supplied by current sources. Find the approximate voltage appearing at the rotor terminals.

7.2 The generalized machine is connected so that stator winding s_1 is in series with rotor winding r_2, and also s_2 is in series with r_1. Then a balanced polyphase current source is applied such that:

$$i_1 = I \cos \omega_s t = i_{s_1} = i_{r_2}$$

$$i_2 = I \sin \omega_s t = i_{s_2} = i_{r_1}.$$

Find torque and voltage at the source terminals for a constant speed Ω. What value must Ω have to produce a nonzero average torque? Let $\theta_r = \Omega t + \alpha$.

7.3 Repeat problem 7.2, except with the connections changed so that s_1 and r_1 are in series, and s_2 and r_2 are in series.

7.4 The generalized machine is connected so that a steady direct current I_s flows in s_1, while s_2, r_1, and r_2 are open circuited. The rotor is driven at a constant speed Ω. Determine v_{s_2}, v_{r_1}, and v_{r_2}.

7.5 The generalized machine is operating as an induction motor at a speed Ω when the supply is disconnected and a steady direct current is caused to flow in s_1. That is, $i_{s_1} = I$, $v_{r_1} = v_{r_2} = 0$, $i_{s_2} = 0$, $\omega_s = 0$, and $\theta_r = \Omega t$. (a) Show that $I_{r_1} = -(j\Omega MI)/(R_r + j\Omega L_r)$. (b) Show that $T = MII_r \cos \theta_r'$, where θ_r' is the rotor power factor angle. Start with Equation (7.2.3). (c) Sketch an approximate curve of torque vs. speed, based on the result of part (a) and an analysis similar to that of Section 5.2.

7.6 Solve the linkage matrix found in Problem 7.2.2 for the voltages and arrange the results in matrix form. Do this for two cases: (a) When expressed in terms of

* For a survey, see Reference 7.3.

θ_r, where θ_r is an unspecified function of time. (b) When the substitution $\theta_r = \omega t + \alpha$ is made. Note that the matrix equation is in the form $[v] = [Z] \cdot [i]$, where $[Z]$ is called the "impedance matrix."

7.7   The transformation matrix below is useful in a case when the brushes of a commutator machine are being driven at a speed Ω_b, as can be done with the Westinghouse generalized machine.

$$\begin{bmatrix} \cos(\Omega_r - \Omega_b)t & \sin(\Omega_r - \Omega_b)t \\ -\sin(\Omega_r - \Omega_b)t & \cos(\Omega_r - \Omega_b)t \end{bmatrix}$$

(a) If the stator currents are constant at I_{s_1} and I_{s_2}, and the rotor speed is Ω_r, show that the transformation gives the expected brush voltages when $\Omega_r = \Omega_b$ (identical with the use of slip rings). There is zero brush current. (b) What voltages result when $\Omega_b = 0.2\Omega_r$?

7.8   Most dc machines have salient poles on the direct axis, so that inductances along the two axes are not the same. Which of the various L's and M's in Equation (7.6.5) are changed in a salient pole machine? Are they made larger or smaller? Write the revised impedance matrix using as symbols M_d, M_q, etc.

7.9   Devise a series of experimental tests to be performed in the laboratory, for the determination of the generalized machine constants M, M_r, R_s, R_r, L_s, and L_r.

7.10   A dc generator without compensating winding supplies a load current i_{rq}. Show by use of the dc machine matrix that this has no effect on the voltage generated at the quadrature axis brushes, but does change the voltage generated at the direct axis brush position. Compare with the results predicted from Figure 6.9.1.

7.11   A dc generator has a compensating winding. Show the effect of this in terms of the dc machine matrix. What quantities must be made equal for perfect compensation to exist? How would this be done?

7.12   Figure P7.12 shows a control generator C whose output energizes the stator field of a second, larger generator B. Both are driven at constant Ω. Find the

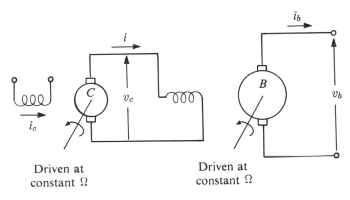

Driven at
constant Ω

Driven at
constant Ω

FIGURE P7.12.

transfer function v_b/i_c (a) with $i_b = 0$; (b) with a separately-excited shunt motor connected at v_b in the manner of Figure 7.8.

7.13 An amplidyne with no compensating winding is known as a Rosenberg generator. (a) Modify the amplidyne matrix Equation (7.8.1) to show this change. (b) With a fixed resistor R_L connected at the v_0 terminals in Figure 7.8 in place of the motor, and with direct current in the control winding, use the results of (a) to find the operational expression for i_0 for the Rosenberg generator. (c) Show that in the steady state the Rosenberg generator delivers an approximately constant current regardless of direction of rotation, speed of rotation, or value of R_L. State the conditions necessary for this approximation to be valid.

7.14 The Ward-Leonard drive, shown in Figure P7.14, provides that the steady-state speed Ω_B is proportional to i_c, with considerable power amplification. Assume both machines have identical physical constants, and find $(\Omega_B/i_c)(p)$ and Ω_B/I_c in the steady state. Use the dc machine matrix.

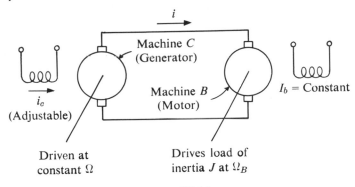

FIGURE P7.14.

7.15 Devise a rule or procedure for determining the paths of the currents $[i_n]$ in Figure 7.9.1(a) from inspection of $[C]$. The actual arrangement of the elements is assumed known.

7.16 For each part of Problem 7.9.1, let the designated new currents be represented as $[i_n']$. The results of Problem 7.9.1 are, then, of the form $[i_n] = [C'][i_n']$, where $[C']$ is the required new connection matrix. (a) Determine for each case (by inspection) another new connection matrix $[C'']$ such that $[i_n'] = [C''][i_n]$, where $[i_n]$ is defined in Equations (7.9.3) and (7.9.3a). (b) Show that in each case $[C'] \cdot [C''] = [C]$, the original matrix of Equation (7.9.3). Why should this be the case?

7.17 (a) Three identical resistors of R ohms each are connected in series. Determine the connection matrix $[C]$ and show by matrix methods that the equivalent resistance is $3R$. (Hint: Include a single dc voltage source, V, as a fourth element, and solve for its current. Then, $R_{eq} = V/I$.) (b) Three identical resistors of R ohms each are connected in parallel. Determine the connection matrix $[C]$ and show by matrix methods that the equivalent resistance is $R/3$.

7.18 In Figure 7.9.1, element D is replaced by an open circuit and element G is replaced by a short circuit. Rewrite Equations (7.9.1) and (7.9.3), keeping in mind that infinity cannot be substituted for Z_d.

7.19 In the network of Figure 7.9.1, all elements are inductances of 1.0 H except element D, which is an ideal voltage source having $v_d = 10 \cos t$. In addition, elements C and E have a positive mutual coupling of 0.5 H. (*a*) Write the numerical forms of the component matrix equation and the connection matrix. (*b*) Carry out the complete steady-state solution by matrix methods, and include a check.

7.20 For the amplidyne and motor combination of Figure 7.8, (*a*) Write the component matrix equation and the connection matrix. (*b*) Carry out the solution of the text example using matrix methods.

7.21 Many practical amplidyne generators have an additional quadrature-axis compensating winding connected in series with the short circuit as shown in Figure P7.21. (*a*) Modify the amplidyne Equations (7.8.1) to include this additional winding. (*b*) Write the component matrix equation and the connection matrix when the modified amplidyne is connected to a pure resistive load R_L. (*c*) Determine the behavior of the modified amplidyne analytically, and deduce the function of the additional winding.

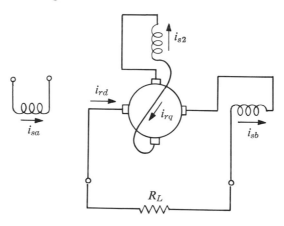

FIGURE P7.21.

REFERENCES

7.1 GABRIEL KRON. *Tensors for Circuits.* New York: Dover Publications, 1959.
7.2 H. E. KOENIG and W. A. BLACKWELL. *Electromechanical System Theory.* New York: McGraw-Hill, 1961.
7.3 American Institute of Electrical Engineers, *Electromechanical Energy Conversion*, special publication S-128, April, 1961, I.E.E.E., New York.

Appendix

A.1 Constrained Magnetic Circuits

The magnetic field configuration in the vicinity of a current-carrying coil of wire is continuously variable and difficult to compute. Such a configuration is suggested in Figure A.1.1, where a tangent to one of the continuous "flux lines" indicates the direction of the B-field at that point, and the spacing between adjacent flux lines indicates the density of the B-field.

If a closed path of material of high magnetic permeability (such as iron) is inserted into the coil, two changes take place:

1. The flux density within the highly permeable material increases many-fold, so that the (relatively unchanged) field outside the material is only a few per cent of the total and may often be ignored.

2. If the highly permeable material is properly shaped, the magnetic field is constrained to follow a definite path of controlled cross-section.

These two changes reduce greatly the complexity of magnetic calculations.

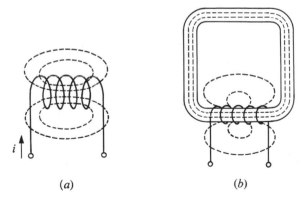

(a)   (b)

FIGURE A.1.1. Magnetic fields in air and in a ferromagnetic material.

237

Example 1. The steel rectangle of Figure A.1.2 has a relative permeability μ_r and is dimensioned as shown. A winding of N turns carries i amperes. Calculate the linkages with the winding. Disregard distortion of the field at the corners.

Solution: Ampere's law states that $\oint_l \mathbf{H} \cdot d\mathbf{l} = i$; where i is the current enclosed by a closed path of integration. As a result of the uniform cross-sectional area A, the B-field within the iron has the same value regardless of where the area A is located. Since $\mathbf{B} = \mu_0 \mu_r \mathbf{H}$, the H-field must also be the same everywhere. If the path of integration is chosen around the mean perimeter of the rectangle, $\mathbf{H}$ and $d\mathbf{L}$ are always colinear, and the closed integral becomes simply Hl, where $l = 2h + 2b$.

The "current enclosed" in this example consists of the same current (i) passing through the enclosure N times, and is thus equal to the product Ni. This product is ordinarily called the "magnetomotive force" (mmf) in units of "ampere-turns," although dimensionally it is in amperes.

Amperes' law for the constrained magnetic path becomes

$$Hl = Ni,$$

and from the relationship

$$B = \mu_r \mu_0 H$$

there results

$$B = \mu_r \mu_0 NI/l.$$

The total flux in the steel path may also be calculated from

$$\phi = \int \mathbf{B} \cdot d\mathbf{A}.$$

In this case, B is normal to dA, so $\phi = BA$. The linkage with the electric winding is $\lambda = N\phi = NBA = \mu_r \mu_0 N^2 Ai/l$. The inductance is $L = \lambda/i = \mu_r \mu_0 N^2 A/l$.

Example 2. A ring is assembled of two materials as shown in Figure A.1.3. Find the total flux produced by a current i flowing in N turns. Use the mean lengths marked on the sketch.

Solution. First it is recognized that the total flux is the same in all parts of the ring, if the field external to the ring is ignored (because $\nabla \cdot \mathbf{B} = 0$). The B (or H) values in the two parts will, however, be different. Integration along the two

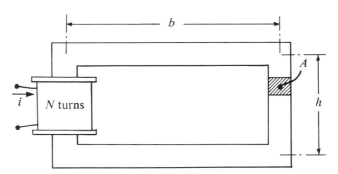

FIGURE A.1.2. Magnetic circuit for Example 1.

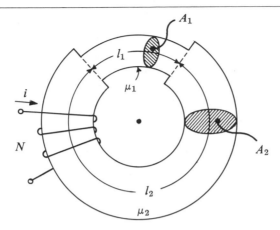

FIGURE A.1.3. Magnetic circuit for Example 2.

members, one at a time, gives,

$$H_1 l_1 + H_2 l_2 = Ni,$$

where Ni is the mmf from the coil.

A second equation arises from the continuity of flux:

$$B_1 A_1 = B_2 A_2.$$

These two equations may be solved simultaneously for B_1 and B_2 after the substitution of $B_1 = \mu_1 H_1$ and $B_2 = \mu_2 H_2$.

A.2   Analogous Magnetic and Electric Circuits

The constrained magnetic circuit has many similarities to an electric circuit, and the resulting analog, although not an exact one, is so commonly used that some of the magnetic quantities have derived their names from the analog. The analog is fairly obvious and is tabulated in Table A.2.1.

TABLE A.2.1

Electric and Magnetic Circuit Analogs

Magnetic Quantity	*Electric Analog*
ϕ, flux (Wb)	i, current (A)
mmf, magnetomotive force (amp-turns)	v, electromotive force (V)
mmf/$\phi = \mathscr{R}$, reluctance	$v/i = R$, resistance
$\mathscr{R} = l/\mu_0\mu_r A$	$R = l/\sigma A$ [σ = conductivity]
$1/\mathscr{R} = \mathscr{P}$, permeance	$1/R = G$, conductance
$\Sigma\, Hl$ = applied mmf	$\Sigma\, v = 0$ Kirchhoff's voltage law for series elements
$\Sigma\, \phi$'s = total flux	$\Sigma\, i = 0$ Kirchhoff's current law for parallel elements

The analogy becomes less useful in dealing with power and energy. For example, i^2R represents power whereas $\phi^2\mathcal{R}$ does not represent power, but instead (it turns out) represents potential energy stored in the field. This difficulty arises because "flux," although named from the Greek word meaning "flow," does not represent a continuous flow but is rather like a stress displacement, whereas current is a continuous transfer of charge. There is no magnetic quantity analogous to charge.

Example. A transformer core has one winding carrying current i, as shown in Figure A.2.1. All parts have the same cross-sectional area, A. Find the total flux in the coil.

Solution. An analogous electric circuit is sketched in Figure A.2.1, where the following are analogous:

Magnetic Quantity	Electric Quantity
Ni	V
$\mathcal{R}_1 = l_1/\mu A$	R_1
$\mathcal{R}_2 = l_2/\mu A$	R_2
ϕ	i

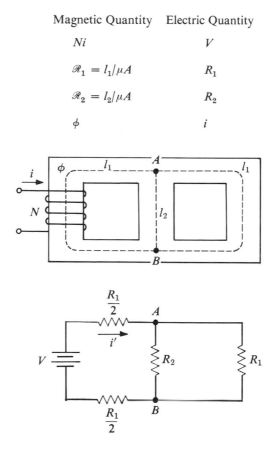

FIGURE A.2.1. Magnetic circuit and analogous electric circuit.

Solving the electric circuit, there results

$$i' = \frac{V}{R_1 + \dfrac{R_1 R_2}{R_1 + R_2}}.$$

The analogous solution for flux is

$$\phi = \frac{Ni}{\mathcal{R}_1 + \dfrac{\mathcal{R}_1 \mathcal{R}_2}{\mathcal{R}_1 + \mathcal{R}_2}}.$$

A.3   The Ideal Close-Coupled Transformer

If a varying voltage is applied to the winding N_1 of Figure A.3.1, with the secondary terminals open circuited, the flux and voltage are related by

$$v = d\lambda/dt = N_1 \, d\phi/dt,$$

or

$$\phi = \frac{1}{N_1} \int v \, dt.$$

The current that flows in the winding takes on whatever value is required to produce this flux. The current is to be thought of as a response variable in this case. If the reluctance is taken as zero in the idealized model, the self-inductance becomes infinite and $i = 0$.

If all of the flux is considered to go all of the way around the magnetic circuit (zero leakage), $d\phi/dt$ is the same throughout and the voltage per turn is the same for any wire encircling the core. Thus it follows that

$$\frac{v_1}{v_2} = \frac{N_1}{N_2}. \tag{A.3.1}$$

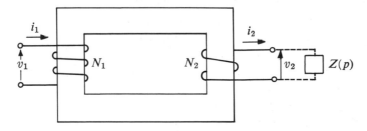

FIGURE A.3.1. Close-coupled transformer with iron core. In actual construction thousands of turns may be used, with primary and secondary winding layers interleaved to improve coupling.

If a current flows in one winding, a current must also flow in the other, for in the ideal model reluctance is zero and $N_1 i_1 = N_2 i_2$, or

$$\frac{i_1}{i_2} = \frac{N_2}{N_1}. \tag{A.3.2}$$

In Figure A.3.1 it is noted that the secondary winding is shown wound such that the mmf from a positive i_1 opposes that from a positive i_2. This numerical relationship will always occur in actual operation.

Equations (A.3.1) and (A.3.2) can be combined to give $v_1 i_1 = v_2 i_2$, showing that energy is conserved. It is noted that the primary polarities are marked according to the load convention and the secondary winding is marked according to the source convention.

The transformer can change the apparent impedance of a circuit element. In Figure A.3.1,

$$Z(p) = \frac{v_2}{i_2}.$$

But

$$v_2 = \frac{N_2}{N_1} v_1,$$

and

$$i_2 = \frac{N_1}{N_2} i_1.$$

Therefore,

$$\frac{v_1}{i_1} = \left(\frac{N_1}{N_2}\right)^2 Z(p).$$

Since v_1/i_1 is the equivalent impedance from the primary terminal, the transformer has changed the impedance level by a factor of $(N_1/N_2)^2$.

A.4   Practical Representation of the Transformer

The equivalent circuit of Figure A.4.1 can be shown to represent a practical close-coupled transformer.* R_1 and R_2 are the winding resistances. L_{e1} represents leakage inductance due to flux that links the turns of coil 1 but not of coil 2. L_m and R_m account for the small current that flows in the primary when the secondary is open-circuited, or vice versa. L_m is present because $\phi\mathcal{R} \neq 0$, and R_m is present to account for hysteresis and eddy-current loss in the iron core. What is L_{e2}?

The alternate equivalent of Figure A.4.2 is derived from the impedance-changing property of the ideal transformer.

* Chapter 18 of Reference 5.1, for example.

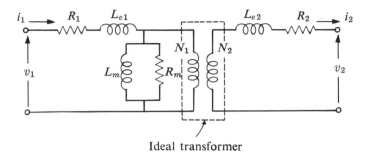

FIGURE A.4.1. Equivalent circuit for nonideal close-coupled transformer.

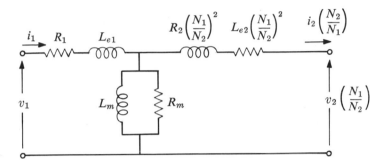

FIGURE A.4.2. Modified equivalent circuit for nonideal close-coupled transformer.

A.5   The *Blu* Rule

In Figure A.5.1 a wire is moving with a velocity $\mathbf{u}$ ($u = dx/dt$) through a magnetic field, $\mathbf{B}$, that is directed out of the paper. The flux linkage with the circuit, including the voltmeter, is $\lambda = N\phi = NBlx$, where $N = 1$. Therefore,

$$v = d\lambda/dt = NBl \, dx/dt = Blu. \tag{A.5.1}$$

This voltage can be thought of as being induced into the length l as it "cuts" the magnetic field. The same result follows if the field is moving with the wire held stationary. If $\mathbf{B}$ is also varying with time, the voltage is

$$v = \frac{d\lambda}{dt} = \frac{d(NBlx)}{dt} = NBl\frac{dx}{dt} + Nlx\frac{dB}{dt}$$

$$= Blu + \frac{\partial\phi}{\partial t}, \tag{A.5.2}$$

where the partial derivative indicates the time variation of flux due only to the variation of B, and not to the motion of the wire. Obviously, the *Blu* rule

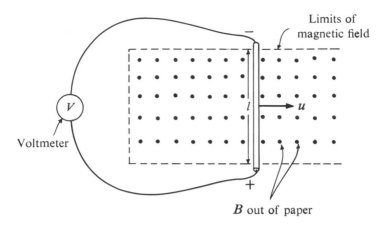

Voltmeter

B out of paper

FIGURE A.5.1. Illustration of *Blu* rule. Conductor moves normal to *B* field at velocity *u*.

holds only for non-time-varying fields, but even with this limitation it is a very useful concept in the analysis of a great variety of rotating machine problems. It can also be expressed more generally in vector notation as

$$v = \int \mathbf{E} \cdot d\mathbf{l} = \int (\mathbf{u} \times \mathbf{B}) \cdot d\mathbf{l}.$$

A.6   The *Bli* Rule

In Figure A.5.1, let a current *i* flow as a result of the motionally-generated voltage. Then, the power to the voltmeter (or any external electrical load) is *vi*, and (from conservation of energy) this must be equal in magnitude to the mechanical power required to move the conductor through the field. That is,

$$vi = uf,$$

where *f* is the force required to move the conductor at velocity *u*. Upon substituting *v = Blu*, there results

$$f = Bli.$$

This force must be applied to the right in Figure A.5.1; stated differently, the force developed on the current-carrying conductor by the field is to the left. As an aid in remembering the relative directions, the force developed on the conductor by the field can be expressed in vector notation as

$$\mathbf{f} = i\mathbf{l} \times \mathbf{B}, \tag{A.5.3}$$

where the positive direction of the current *i* establishes the direction of the vector length **l**.

This force can also be developed directly from field theory, and is expressed in more general form as

$$\mathbf{f} = \int i \, d\mathbf{l} \times \mathbf{B},$$ (A.5.4)

which for a straight conductor normal to a uniform field reduces to the *Bli* rule.

The *Bli* rule is often used for determining torques in dynamo machines having uniform *B* fields, but is less useful for machines having sinusoidally-distributed fields, and is not applicable to singly-excited devices of the type described in Chapter 2.

Still another form for the electromagnetic force can be derived by noting that as the conductor in Figure A.5.1 moves an incremental amount dx, the flux linkage with the circuit changes by $d\lambda = Bl \, dx$. Thus $d\lambda/dx = Bl$, and

$$f = Bli = i \frac{d\lambda}{dx}.$$ (A.5.5)

It is shown in Chapter 2 that under the proper constraints, $i \, d\lambda = dW_f$, the incremental change in stored field energy, and Equation (A.5.5) can be shown equivalent to the expression $f = \partial W_f/\partial x$. It provides an alternate and equally general approach to that of Chapter 2 for the determination of electromagnetic forces and torques.

Index